Flow charts for the

Engineering and Construction Contract

This contract should be used for the appointment of a contractor for engineering and construction work, including any level of design responsibility

An NEC document

April 2013

Construction Clients' Board endorsement of NEC3

The Construction Clients' Board recommends that public sector organisations use the NEC3 contracts when procuring construction. Standardising use of this comprehensive suite of contracts should help to deliver efficiencies across the public sector and promote behaviours in line with the principles of *Achieving Excellence in Construction.*

Cabinet Office UK

NEC is a division of Thomas Telford Ltd, which is a wholly owned subsidiary of the Institution of Civil Engineers (ICE), the owner and developer of the NEC.

The NEC is a family of standard contracts, each of which has these characteristics:

- Its use stimulates good management of the relationship between the two parties to the contract and, hence, of the work included in the contract.
- It can be used in a wide variety of commercial situations, for a wide variety of types of work and in any location.
- It is a clear and simple document – using language and a structure which are straightforward and easily understood.

NEC3 Engineering and Construction Contract is one of the NEC family and is consistent with all other NEC3 documents. Also available are the Engineering and Construction Contract Guidance Notes, Flow Charts and Options A, B, C, D, E and F.

ISBN (complete box set) 978 0 7277 5867 5
ISBN (this document) 978 0 7277 5905 4
ISBN (Engineering and Construction Contract) 978 0 7277 5865 1
ISBN (Option A: Priced contract with activity schedule) 978 0 7277 5869 9
ISBN (Option B: Priced contract with bill of quantities) 978 0 7277 5871 2
ISBN (Option C: Target contract with activity schedule) 978 0 7277 5873 6
ISBN (Option D: Target contract with bill of quantities) 978 0 7277 5875 0
ISBN (Option E: Cost reimbursable contract) 978 0 7277 5877 4
ISBN (Option F: Management contract) 978 0 7277 5879 8
ISBN (how to write the ECC Works Information) 978 0 7277 5907 8
ISBN (how to use the ECC communication forms) 978 0 7277 5909 2

Consultative edition 1991
First edition 1993
Second edition 1995
Reprinted 1996
Third edition June 2005
Reprinted with amendments 2007
Reprinted 2008, 2009, 2010 (twice), 2012
Reprinted with amendments 2013

British Library Cataloguing in Publication Data for this publication is available from the British Library.

Typeset by Academic + Technical, Bristol

Printed and bound in Great Britain by Bell & Bain Limited, Glasgow, UK

CONTENTS

The number of each flow chart is the same as the number of the clause in the NEC Engineering and Construction Contract to which it primarily relates.

Foreword				v
Preface				vii
Acknowledgements				ix
Amendments				x
Legend				1
Abbreviations				2
Flow charts	13	Communications	Sheets 1 to 3	3
	14	The *Project Manager* and the *Supervisor*		6
	15	Adding to the Working Areas		7
	16	Early warning		8
	17	Ambiguities and inconsistencies		9
	18	Illegal and impossible requirements		10
	19	Prevention		11
	20	Providing the Works	Sheets 1 and 2	12
	21	The *Contractor*'s design		14
	22	Using the *Contractor*'s design		15
	23	Design of Equipment		16
	24	People		17
	25	Working with the *Employer* and Others		18
	26	Subcontracting		19
	27	Other (*Contractor*) responsibilities		20
	30	Starting, Completion and Key Dates	Sheets 1 and 2	21
	31	The programme	Sheets 1 and 2	23
	32	Revising the programme		25
	33	Access to and use of the Site		26
	34	Instruction to stop or not to start work		27
	35	Take over	Sheets 1 and 2	28
	36	Acceleration		30
	40	Tests and inspections	Sheets 1 and 2	31
	41	Testing and inspection before delivery		33
	42	Searching for and notifying Defects		34
	43	Correcting Defects	Sheets 1 and 2	35
	44	Accepting Defects		37
	45	Uncorrected Defects		38
	50	Assessing the amount due	Sheets 1 to 7	39
	51	Payment	Sheets 1 and 2	46
	52	Defined Cost		48
	53	The *Contractor*'s share (Option C and D)	Sheets 1 and 2	49
	54	The Activity Schedule (Option A and C)		51
	55	The Bill of Quantities (Option B and D)		52
	60	Compensation events	Sheets 1 to 7	53
	61	Notifying compensation events	Sheets 1 to 4	60
	62	Quotations for compensation events	Sheets 1 and 2	64
	63	Assessing compensation events	Sheets 1 to 3	66
	64	The *Project Manager*'s assessments	Sheets 1 and 2	69
	65	Implementing compensation events		71
	70	The *Employer*'s title to Plant and Materials		72

71	Marking Equipment, Plant and Materials outside the Working Areas		73
72	Removing Equipment		74
73	Objects and materials within the Site		75
80	*Employer*'s risks	Sheets 1 to 3	76
81	*Contractor*'s risk		79
82	Repairs		80
83	Indemnity		81
84	Insurance cover		82
85	Insurance policies		83
86	If the *Contractor* does not insure		84
87	Insurance by the *Employer*		85
90	Termination		86
91	Reasons for termination	Sheets 1 to 5	87
92	Procedures on termination		92
93	Payment on termination		93
W1	Dispute resolution (used unless Option Y(UK)2 applies)	Sheets 1 to 4	94
W2	Dispute resolution (used when Option Y(UK)2 applies)	Sheets 1 to 5	98
X1	Price adjustment for inflation (used only with Options A, B, C and D)	Sheets 1 and 2	103
X2	Changes in the law		105
X3	Multiple currencies (used only with Options A and B)		106
X4	Parent company guarantee		107
X5	Sectional Completion		108
X6	Bonus for early Completion		109
X7	Delay damages		110
X12	Partnering	Sheets 1 to 3	111
X13	Performance bond		114
X14	Advanced payment to the *Contractor*		115
X15	Limitation of the *Contractor*'s liability for his design to reasonable skill and care		116
X16	Retention (not used with Option F)		117
X17	Low performance damages		118
X18	Limitation of liability		119
X20	Key Performance Indicators (not used with Option X12)		120
Y(UK)1	Project Bank Account	Sheets 1 to 3	121
Y(UK)2	The Housing Grants, Construction and Regeneration Act 1996		124
Y(UK)3	The Contracts (Rights of Third Parties) Act 1999		125

OREWORD

I was delighted to be asked to write the Foreword for the NEC3 Contracts.

I have followed the outstanding rise and success of NEC contracts for a number of years now, in particular during my tenure as the 146th President of the Institution of Civil Engineers, 2010/11.

In my position as UK Government's Chief Construction Adviser, I am working with Government and industry to ensure Britain's construction sector is equipped with the knowledge, skills and best practice it needs in its transition to a low carbon economy. I am promoting innovation in the sector, including in particular the use of Building Information Modelling (BIM) in public sector construction procurement; and the synergy and fit with the collaborative nature of NEC contracts is obvious. The Government's construction strategy is a very significant investment and NEC contracts will play an important role in setting high standards of contract preparation, management and the desirable behaviour of our industry.

In the UK, we are faced with having to deliver a 15–20 per cent reduction in the cost to the public sector of construction during the lifetime of this Parliament. Shifting mind-set, attitude and behaviour into best practice NEC processes will go a considerable way to achieving this.

Of course, NEC contracts are used successfully around the world in both public and private sector projects; this trend seems set to continue at an increasing pace. NEC contracts are, according to my good friend and NEC's creator Dr Martin Barnes CBE, about better management of projects. This is quite achievable and I encourage you to understand NEC contracts to the best you can and exploit the potential this offers us all.

Peter Hansford

UK Government's Chief Construction Adviser
Cabinet Office

PREFACE

The NEC contracts are the only suite of standard contracts designed to facilitate and encourage good management of the projects on which they are used. The experience of using NEC contracts around the world is that they really make a difference. Previously, standard contracts were written mainly as legal documents best left in the desk drawer until costly and delaying problems had occurred and there were lengthy arguments about who was to blame.

The language of NEC contracts is clear and simple, and the procedures set out are all designed to stimulate good management. Foresighted collaboration between all the contributors to the project is the aim. The contracts set out how the interfaces between all the organisations involved will be managed – from the client through the designers and main contractors to all the many subcontractors and suppliers.

Versions of the NEC contract are specific to the work of professional service providers such as project managers and designers, to main contractors, to subcontractors and to suppliers. The wide range of situations covered by the contracts means that they do not need to be altered to suit any particular situation.

The NEC contracts are the first to deal specifically and effectively with management of the inevitable risks and uncertainties which are encountered to some extent on all projects. Management of the expected is easy, effective management of the unexpected draws fully on the collaborative approach inherent in the NEC contracts.

Most people working on projects using the NEC contracts for the first time are hugely impressed by the difference between the confrontational characteristics of traditional contracts and the teamwork engendered by the NEC. The NEC does not include specific provisions for dispute avoidance. They are not necessary. Collaborative management itself is designed to avoid disputes and it really works.

It is common for the final account for the work on a project to be settled at the time when the work is finished. The traditional long period of expensive professional work after completion to settle final payments just is not needed.

The NEC contracts are truly a massive change for the better for the industries in which they are used.

Dr Martin Barnes CBE

Originator of the NEC contracts

CKNOWLEDGEMENTS

The NEC first edition was produced by the Institution of Civil Engineers through its NEC Working Group.

The original NEC was designed and drafted by Dr Martin Barnes then of Coopers and Lybrand with the assistance of Professor J. G. Perry then of the University of Birmingham, T. W. Weddell then of Travers Morgan Management, T. H. Nicholson, Consultant to the Institution of Civil Engineers, A. Norman then of the University of Manchester Institute of Science and Technology and P. A. Baird, then Corporate Contracts Consultant, Eskom, South Africa.

The second edition of the NEC documents for engineering and construction contracts was produced by the Institution of Civil Engineers through its NEC Panel.

The third edition of the NEC Engineering and Construction Contract was produced by the Institution of Civil Engineers through its NEC Panel. The Flow Charts were produced by John S. Gillespie with assistance from Tom Nicholson.

The members of the NEC Panel are:

P. Higgins, BSc, CEng, FICE, FCIArb (Chairman)
P. A. Baird, BSc, CEng, FICE, M(SA)ICE, MAPM
M. Barnes, BSc(Eng), PhD, FREng, FICE, FCIOB, CCMI, ACIArb, MBCS, FInstCES, FAPM
A. J. Bates, FRICS, MInstCES
A. J. M. Blackler, BA, LLB(Cantab), MCIArb
P. T. Cousins, BEng(Tech), DipArb, CEng, MICE, MCIArb, MCMI
L. T. Eames, BSc, FRICS, FCIOB
F. Forward, BA(Hons), DipArch, MSc(Const Law), RIBA, FCIArb
Professor J. G. Perry, MEng, PhD, CEng, FICE, MAPM
N. C. Shaw, FCIPS, CEng, MIMechE
T. W. Weddell, BSc, CEng, DIC, FICE, FIStructE, ACIArb

NEC Consultant:

R. A. Gerrard, BSc(Hons), MRICS, FCIArb, FCInstCES

Secretariat:

A. Cole, LLB, LLM, BL
J. M. Hawkins, BA(Hons), MSc
F. N. Vernon (Technical Adviser), BSc, CEng, MICE

The Institution of Civil Engineers acknowledges the help in preparing the third edition given by many other people, in particular, by:

J. C. Broome, BEng
A. Else, BSc, CEng, FICE
C. Flook, Esq.
R. Lewendon, FICE, MIHT, MCIArb, MAPM
T. H. Nicholson, BSc, FICE
R. Patterson, BA, MA(Cantab), MBA, CEng, MICE
C. Reed, CEng, MA, MSc, FICE
D. Weeks, FRICS
S. Zarka, FRICS

AMENDMENTS

Full details of all amendments are available on www.neccontract.com.

egend

CHART START

HEADINGS
Headings in caps provide guidance

STATEMENTS
If a clause is referenced, text is from the NEC

LOGIC LINKS
Links go to right and/or downward unless shown

QUESTION
Answer question to determine the route to follow

SUBROUTINE
Include another flow chart here

CONTINUATION
Link to matching point(s) on other chart sheets

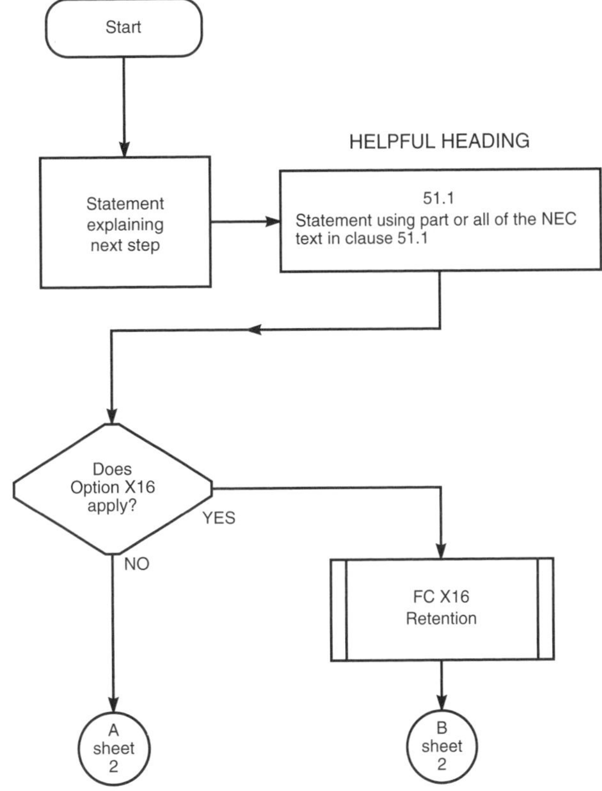

Start
HELPFUL HEADING
Statement explaining next step
51.1
Statement using part or all of the NEC text in clause 51.1
Does Option X16 apply?
YES
NO
FC X16 Retention
A sheet 2
B sheet 2

CHART TITLE
Chart number, title and sheet

Flow chart 51 Sheet 1 of 2
Payment

CONTINUATION

CHART FINISH

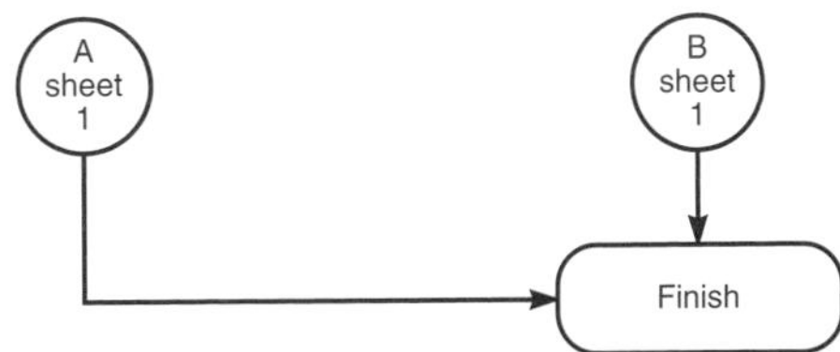

A sheet 1
B sheet 1
Finish

CHART TITLE

Flow chart 51 Sheet 2 of 2
Payment

ABBREVIATIONS USED IN THE FLOW CHART BOXES

FC 61	Flow chart for clause 61
FC X5	Flow chart for secondary Option X5
E	*Employer*
C	*Contractor*
PM	*Project Manager*
S	*Supervisor*
SC	Subcontractor
BOQ	Bill of quantities
CD	Contract Data
CE	Compensation event
DCP	*defect correction period*
PI	Partnering Information
P&M	Plant and Materials
PAF	Price Adjustment Factor
PWDD	Price for Work Done to Date
SCC	Schedule of Cost Components
SSCC	Shorter Schedule of Cost Components
SI	Site Information
WI	Works Information

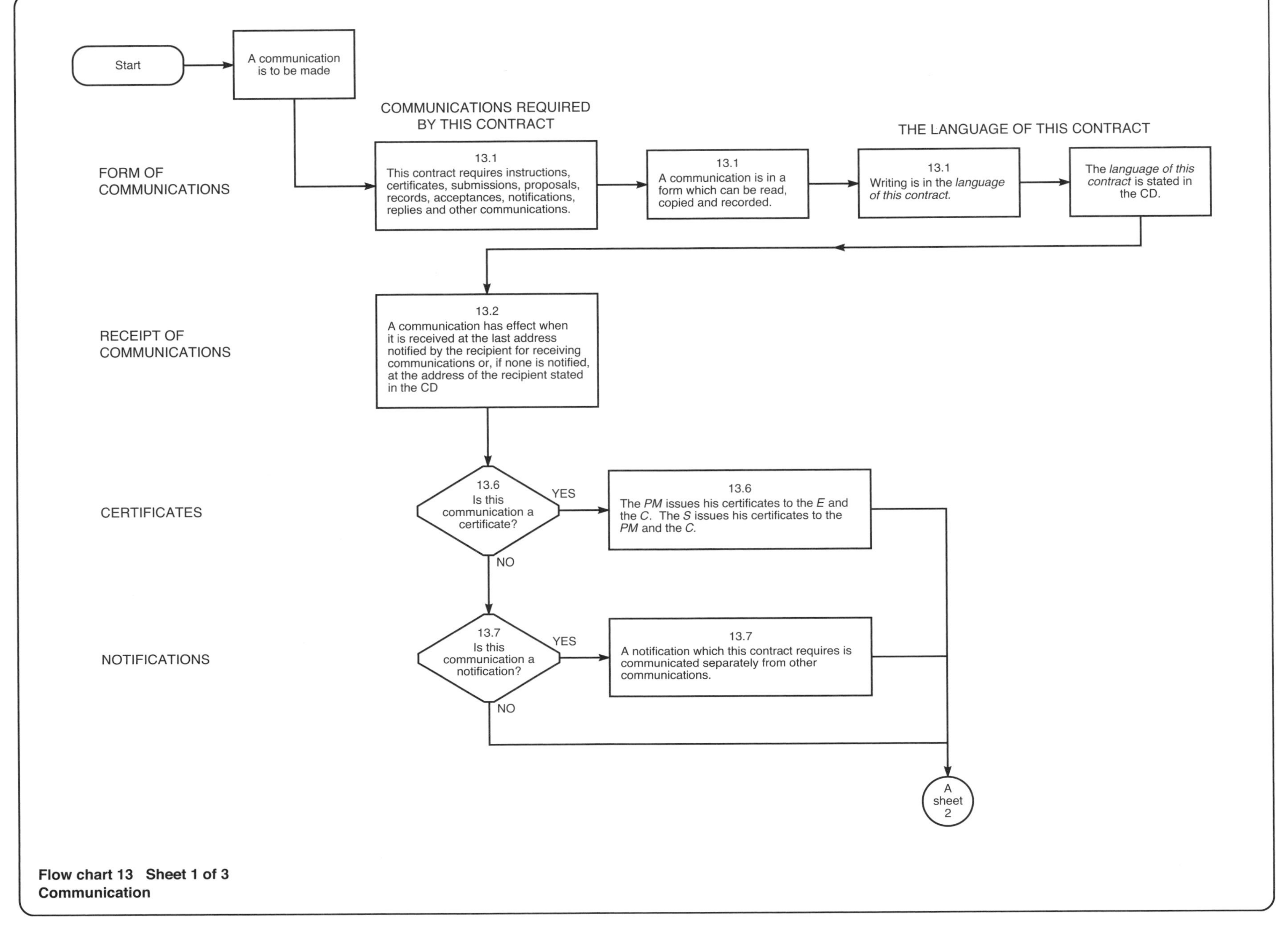
Start
A communication is to be made
COMMUNICATIONS REQUIRED BY THIS CONTRACT
THE LANGUAGE OF THIS CONTRACT
FORM OF COMMUNICATIONS
13.1 This contract requires instructions, certificates, submissions, proposals, records, acceptances, notifications, replies and other communications.
13.1 A communication is in a form which can be read, copied and recorded.
13.1 Writing is in the language of this contract.
The language of this contract is stated in the CD.
RECEIPT OF COMMUNICATIONS
13.2 A communication has effect when it is received at the last address notified by the recipient for receiving communications or, if none is notified, at the address of the recipient stated in the CD
CERTIFICATES
13.6 Is this communication a certificate?
YES
13.6 The PM issues his certificates to the E and the C. The S issues his certificates to the PM and the C.
NO
NOTIFICATIONS
13.7 Is this communication a notification?
YES
13.7 A notification which this contract requires is communicated separately from other communications.
NO
A sheet 2

Flow chart 13 Sheet 1 of 3
Communication

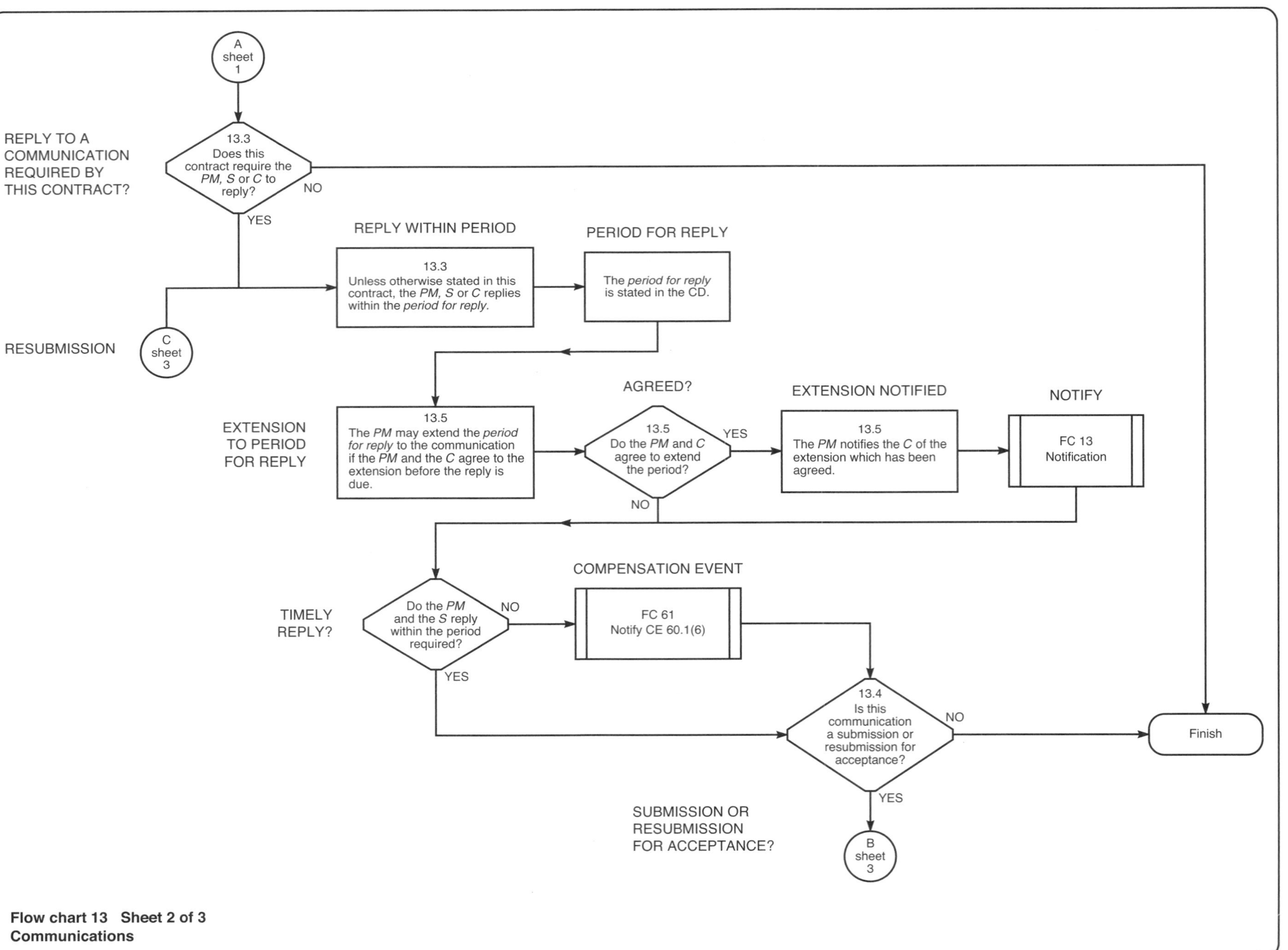
A sheet 1
REPLY TO A COMMUNICATION REQUIRED BY THIS CONTRACT?
13.3 Does this contract require the PM, S or C to reply?
NO
YES
REPLY WITHIN PERIOD
13.3 Unless otherwise stated in this contract, the PM, S or C replies within the period for reply.
PERIOD FOR REPLY
The period for reply is stated in the CD.
RESUBMISSION
C sheet 3
EXTENSION TO PERIOD FOR REPLY
13.5 The PM may extend the period for reply to the communication if the PM and the C agree to the extension before the reply is due.
AGREED?
13.5 Do the PM and C agree to extend the period?
YES
NO
EXTENSION NOTIFIED
13.5 The PM notifies the C of the extension which has been agreed.
NOTIFY
FC 13 Notification
TIMELY REPLY?
Do the PM and the S reply within the period required?
NO
YES
COMPENSATION EVENT
FC 61 Notify CE 60.1(6)
13.4 Is this communication a submission or resubmission for acceptance?
NO
YES
Finish
SUBMISSION OR RESUBMISSION FOR ACCEPTANCE?
B sheet 3

Flow chart 13 Sheet 2 of 3
Communications

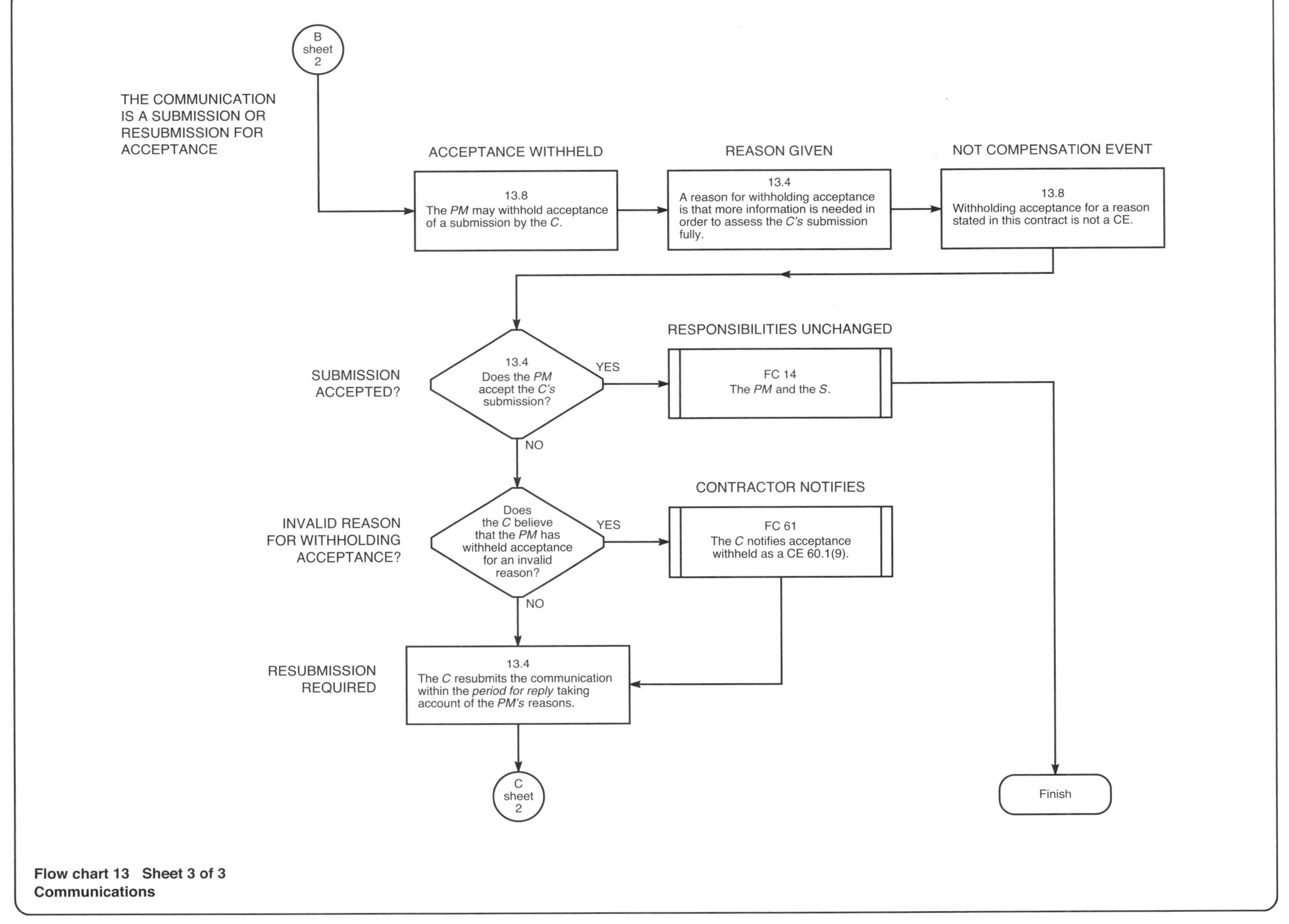
B sheet 2
THE COMMUNICATION IS A SUBMISSION OR RESUBMISSION FOR ACCEPTANCE
ACCEPTANCE WITHHELD
13.8 The PM may withhold acceptance of a submission by the C.
REASON GIVEN
13.4 A reason for withholding acceptance is that more information is needed in order to assess the C's submission fully.
NOT COMPENSATION EVENT
13.8 Withholding acceptance for a reason stated in this contract is not a CE.
SUBMISSION ACCEPTED?
13.4 Does the PM accept the C's submission?
YES
NO
RESPONSIBILITIES UNCHANGED
FC 14 The PM and the S.
INVALID REASON FOR WITHHOLDING ACCEPTANCE?
Does the C believe that the PM has withheld acceptance for an invalid reason?
YES
NO
CONTRACTOR NOTIFIES
FC 61 The C notifies acceptance withheld as a CE 60.1(9).
RESUBMISSION REQUIRED
13.4 The C resubmits the communication within the period for reply taking account of the PM's reasons.
C sheet 2
Finish

Flow chart 13 Sheet 3 of 3
Communications

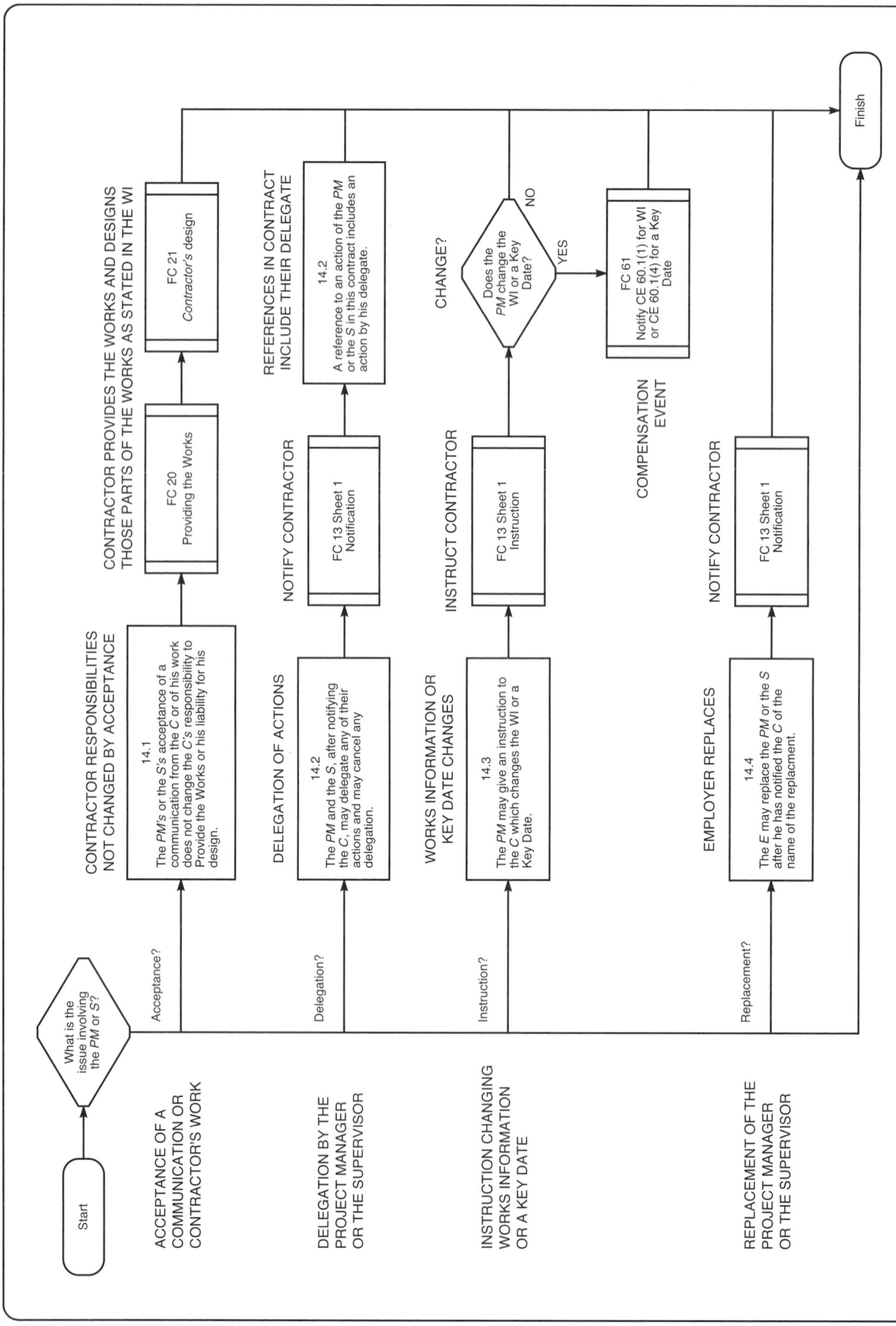

Start

What is the issue involving the *PM* or *S*?

ACCEPTANCE OF A COMMUNICATION OR CONTRACTOR'S WORK

Acceptance?

CONTRACTOR RESPONSIBILITIES NOT CHANGED BY ACCEPTANCE

14.1
The *PM's* or the *S's* acceptance of a communication from the *C* or of his work does not change the *C's* responsibility to Provide the Works or his liability for his design.

CONTRACTOR PROVIDES THE WORKS AND DESIGNS THOSE PARTS OF THE WORKS AS STATED IN THE WI

FC 20
Providing the Works

FC 21
Contractor's design

DELEGATION BY THE PROJECT MANAGER OR THE SUPERVISOR

Delegation?

DELEGATION OF ACTIONS

14.2
The *PM* and the *S*, after notifying the *C*, may delegate any of their actions and may cancel any delegation.

NOTIFY CONTRACTOR

FC 13 Sheet 1
Notification

REFERENCES IN CONTRACT INCLUDE THEIR DELEGATE

14.2
A reference to an action of the *PM* or the *S* in this contract includes an action by his delegate.

INSTRUCTION CHANGING WORKS INFORMATION OR A KEY DATE

Instruction?

WORKS INFORMATION OR KEY DATE CHANGES

14.3
The *PM* may give an instruction to the *C* which changes the WI or a Key Date.

INSTRUCT CONTRACTOR

FC 13 Sheet 1
Instruction

CHANGE?

Does the *PM* change the WI or a Key Date?

NO

YES

COMPENSATION EVENT

FC 61
Notify CE 60.1(1) for WI or CE 60.1(4) for a Key Date

REPLACEMENT OF THE PROJECT MANAGER OR THE SUPERVISOR

Replacement?

EMPLOYER REPLACES

14.4
The *E* may replace the *PM* or the *S* after he has notified the *C* of the name of the replacment.

NOTIFY CONTRACTOR

FC 13 Sheet 1
Notification

Finish

Flow chart 14
The *Project Manager* and the *Supervisor*

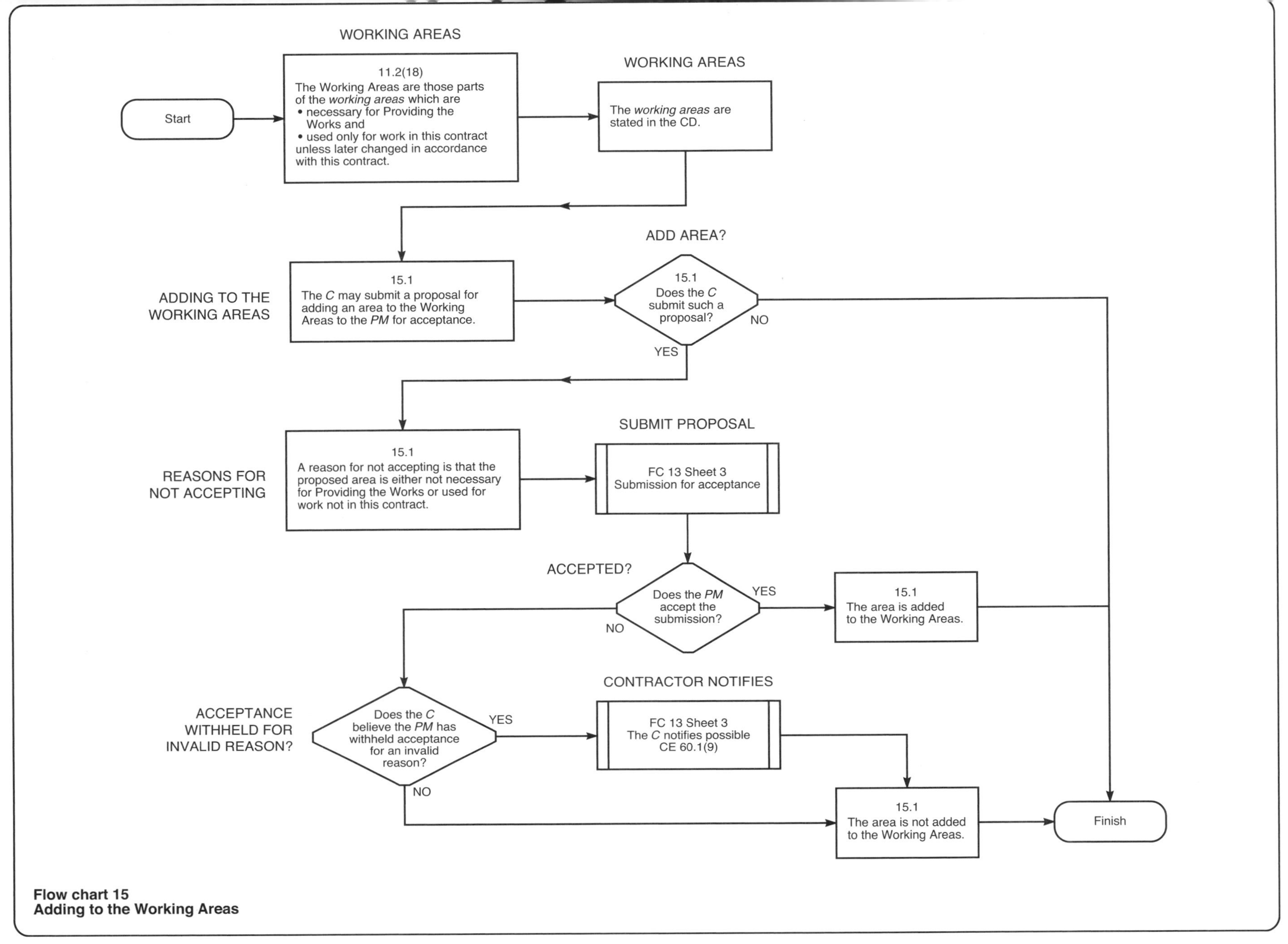
Start
WORKING AREAS
11.2(18)
The Working Areas are those parts of the *working areas* which are
• necessary for Providing the Works and
• used only for work in this contract unless later changed in accordance with this contract.
WORKING AREAS
The *working areas* are stated in the CD.
ADDING TO THE WORKING AREAS
15.1
The *C* may submit a proposal for adding an area to the Working Areas to the *PM* for acceptance.
ADD AREA?
15.1
Does the *C* submit such a proposal?
NO
YES
REASONS FOR NOT ACCEPTING
15.1
A reason for not accepting is that the proposed area is either not necessary for Providing the Works or used for work not in this contract.
SUBMIT PROPOSAL
FC 13 Sheet 3
Submission for acceptance
ACCEPTED?
Does the *PM* accept the submission?
YES
NO
15.1
The area is added to the Working Areas.
ACCEPTANCE WITHHELD FOR INVALID REASON?
Does the *C* believe the *PM* has withheld acceptance for an invalid reason?
YES
NO
CONTRACTOR NOTIFIES
FC 13 Sheet 3
The *C* notifies possible CE 60.1(9)
15.1
The area is not added to the Working Areas.
Finish

Flow chart 15
Adding to the Working Areas

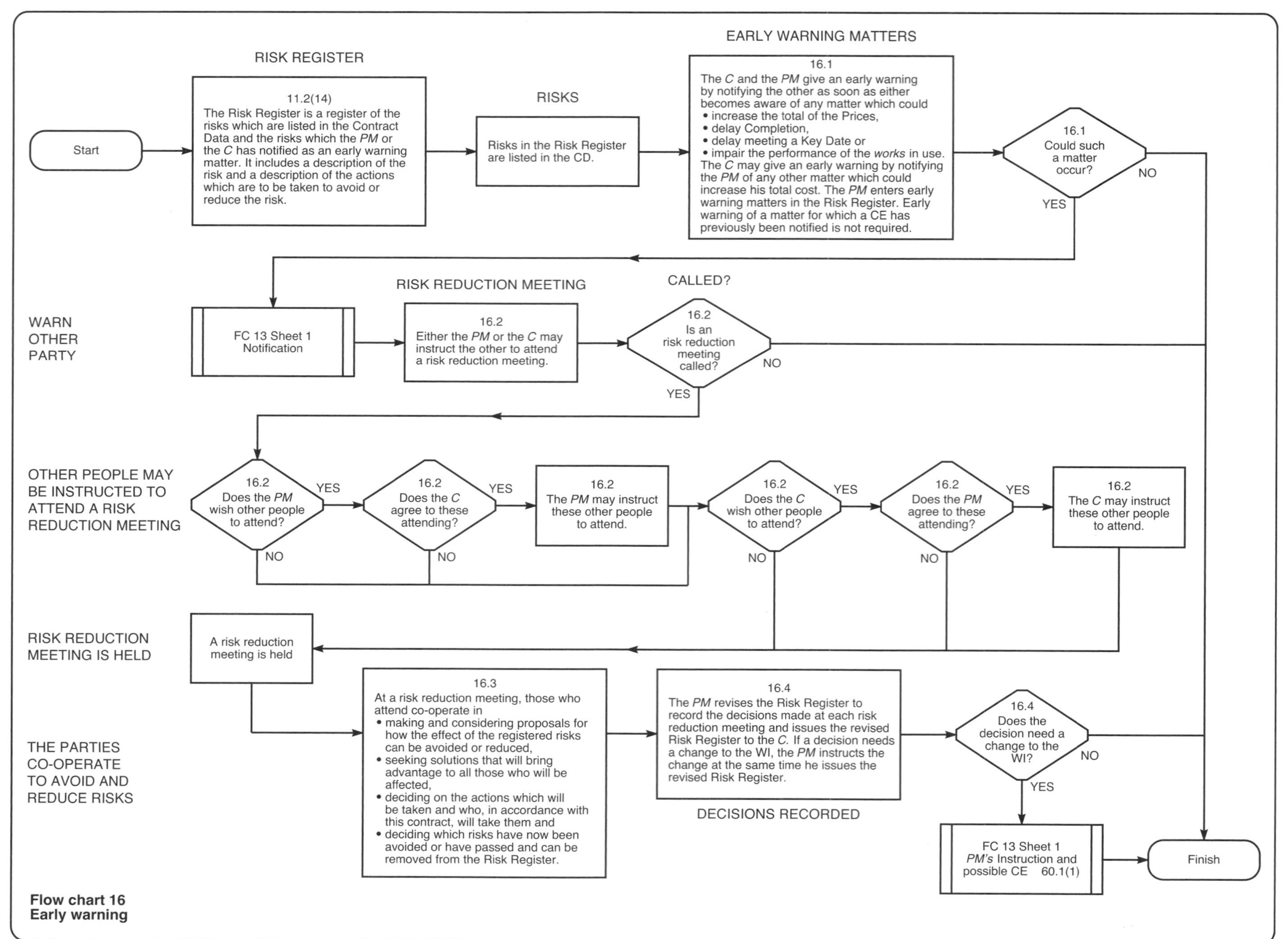

Start
RISK REGISTER
11.2(14)
The Risk Register is a register of the risks which are listed in the Contract Data and the risks which the PM or the C has notified as an early warning matter. It includes a description of the risk and a description of the actions which are to be taken to avoid or reduce the risk.
RISKS
Risks in the Risk Register are listed in the CD.
EARLY WARNING MATTERS
16.1
The C and the PM give an early warning by notifying the other as soon as either becomes aware of any matter which could
• increase the total of the Prices,
• delay Completion,
• delay meeting a Key Date or
• impair the performance of the works in use.
The C may give an early warning by notifying the PM of any other matter which could increase his total cost. The PM enters early warning matters in the Risk Register. Early warning of a matter for which a CE has previously been notified is not required.
16.1
Could such a matter occur?
YES
NO
WARN OTHER PARTY
FC 13 Sheet 1
Notification
RISK REDUCTION MEETING
16.2
Either the PM or the C may instruct the other to attend a risk reduction meeting.
CALLED?
16.2
Is an risk reduction meeting called?
YES
NO
OTHER PEOPLE MAY BE INSTRUCTED TO ATTEND A RISK REDUCTION MEETING
16.2
Does the PM wish other people to attend?
YES
NO
16.2
Does the C agree to these attending?
YES
NO
16.2
The PM may instruct these other people to attend.
16.2
Does the C wish other people to attend?
YES
NO
16.2
Does the PM agree to these attending?
YES
NO
16.2
The C may instruct these other people to attend.
RISK REDUCTION MEETING IS HELD
A risk reduction meeting is held
THE PARTIES CO-OPERATE TO AVOID AND REDUCE RISKS
16.3
At a risk reduction meeting, those who attend co-operate in
• making and considering proposals for how the effect of the registered risks can be avoided or reduced,
• seeking solutions that will bring advantage to all those who will be affected,
• deciding on the actions which will be taken and who, in accordance with this contract, will take them and
• deciding which risks have now been avoided or have passed and can be removed from the Risk Register.
16.4
The PM revises the Risk Register to record the decisions made at each risk reduction meeting and issues the revised Risk Register to the C. If a decision needs a change to the WI, the PM instructs the change at the same time he issues the revised Risk Register.
DECISIONS RECORDED
16.4
Does the decision need a change to the WI?
YES
NO
FC 13 Sheet 1
PM's Instruction and possible CE 60.1(1)
Finish
Flow chart 16
Early warning

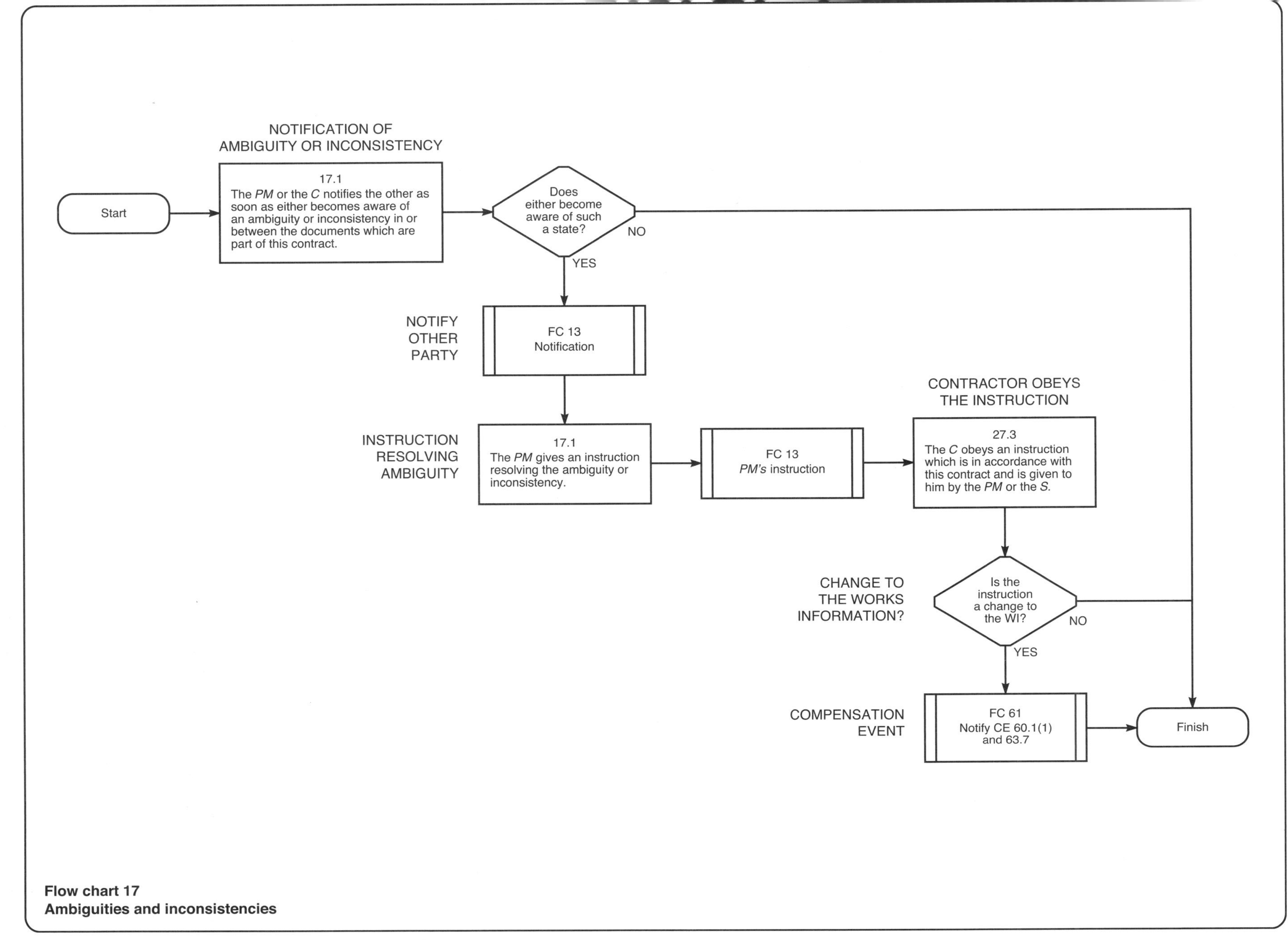
Start
NOTIFICATION OF AMBIGUITY OR INCONSISTENCY
17.1
The PM or the C notifies the other as soon as either becomes aware of an ambiguity or inconsistency in or between the documents which are part of this contract.
Does either become aware of such a state?
NO
YES
NOTIFY OTHER PARTY
FC 13
Notification
INSTRUCTION RESOLVING AMBIGUITY
17.1
The PM gives an instruction resolving the ambiguity or inconsistency.
FC 13
PM's instruction
CONTRACTOR OBEYS THE INSTRUCTION
27.3
The C obeys an instruction which is in accordance with this contract and is given to him by the PM or the S.
CHANGE TO THE WORKS INFORMATION?
Is the instruction a change to the WI?
NO
YES
COMPENSATION EVENT
FC 61
Notify CE 60.1(1) and 63.7
Finish

Flow chart 17
Ambiguities and inconsistencies

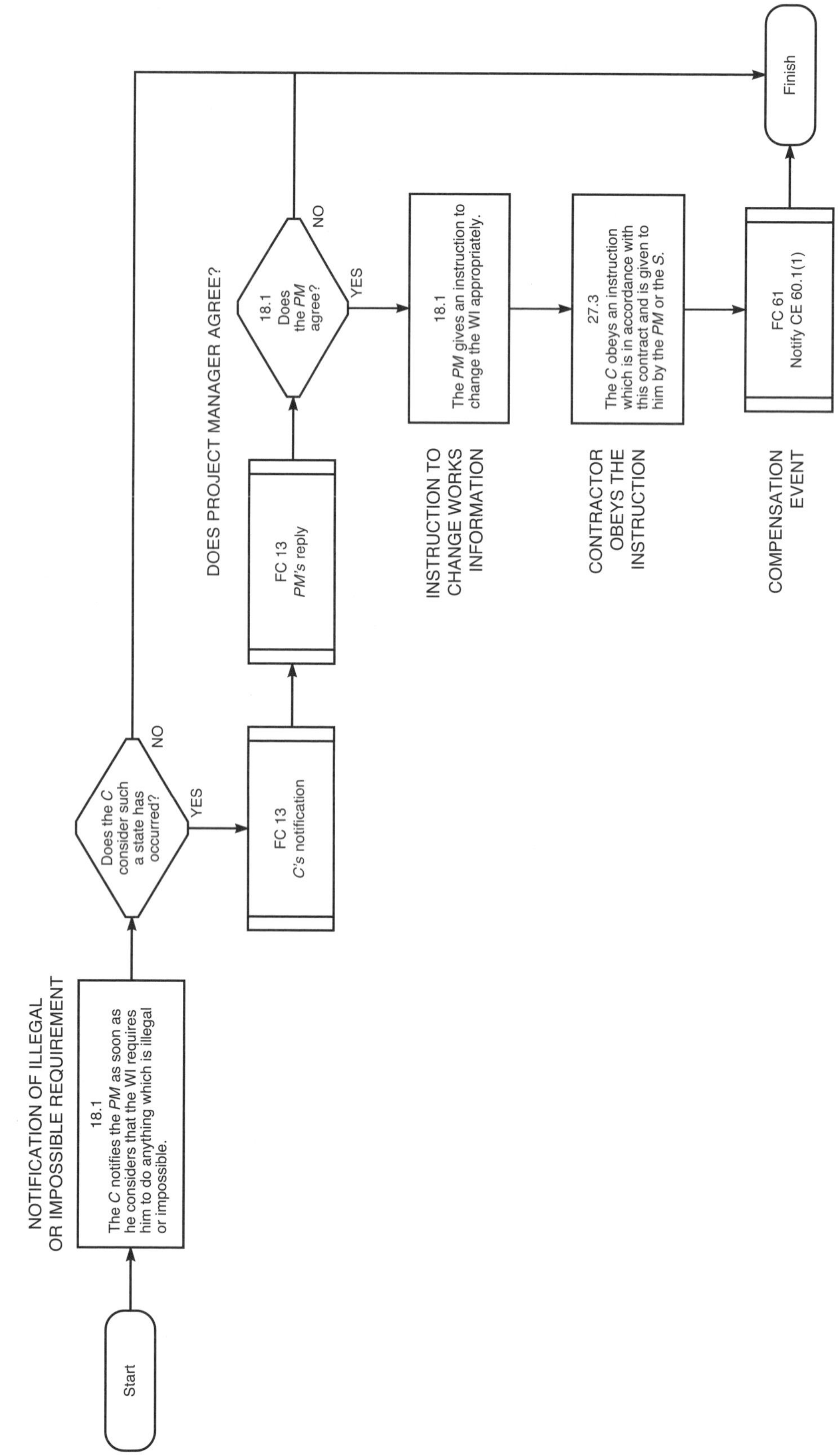

Flow chart 18
Illegal and impossible requirements

Start
NOTIFICATION OF ILLEGAL OR IMPOSSIBLE REQUIREMENT
18.1
The *C* notifies the *PM* as soon as he considers that the WI requires him to do anything which is illegal or impossible.
Does the *C* consider such a state has occurred?
NO
YES
FC 13
C's notification
DOES PROJECT MANAGER AGREE?
FC 13
PM's reply
18.1
Does the *PM* agree?
NO
YES
INSTRUCTION TO CHANGE WORKS INFORMATION
18.1
The *PM* gives an instruction to change the WI appropriately.
CONTRACTOR OBEYS THE INSTRUCTION
27.3
The *C* obeys an instruction which is in accordance with this contract and is given to him by the *PM* or the *S*.
COMPENSATION EVENT
FC 61
Notify CE 60.1(1)
Finish

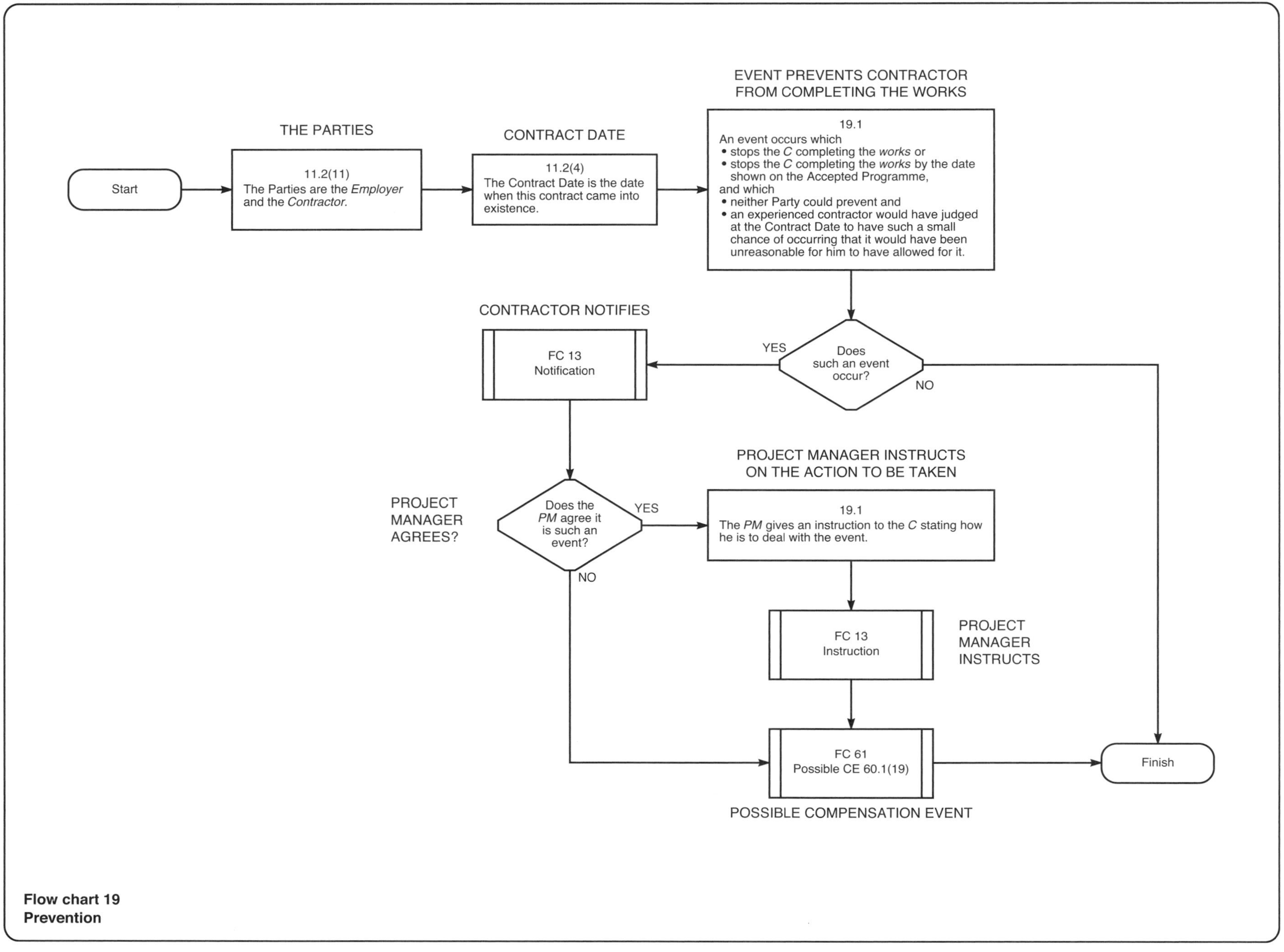

Start
THE PARTIES
11.2(11)
The Parties are the Employer and the Contractor.
CONTRACT DATE
11.2(4)
The Contract Date is the date when this contract came into existence.
EVENT PREVENTS CONTRACTOR FROM COMPLETING THE WORKS
19.1
An event occurs which
• stops the C completing the works or
• stops the C completing the works by the date shown on the Accepted Programme,
and which
• neither Party could prevent and
• an experienced contractor would have judged at the Contract Date to have such a small chance of occurring that it would have been unreasonable for him to have allowed for it.
Does such an event occur?
YES
NO
CONTRACTOR NOTIFIES
FC 13
Notification
PROJECT MANAGER AGREES?
Does the PM agree it is such an event?
YES
NO
PROJECT MANAGER INSTRUCTS ON THE ACTION TO BE TAKEN
19.1
The PM gives an instruction to the C stating how he is to deal with the event.
FC 13
Instruction
PROJECT MANAGER INSTRUCTS
FC 61
Possible CE 60.1(19)
POSSIBLE COMPENSATION EVENT
Finish
Flow chart 19
Prevention

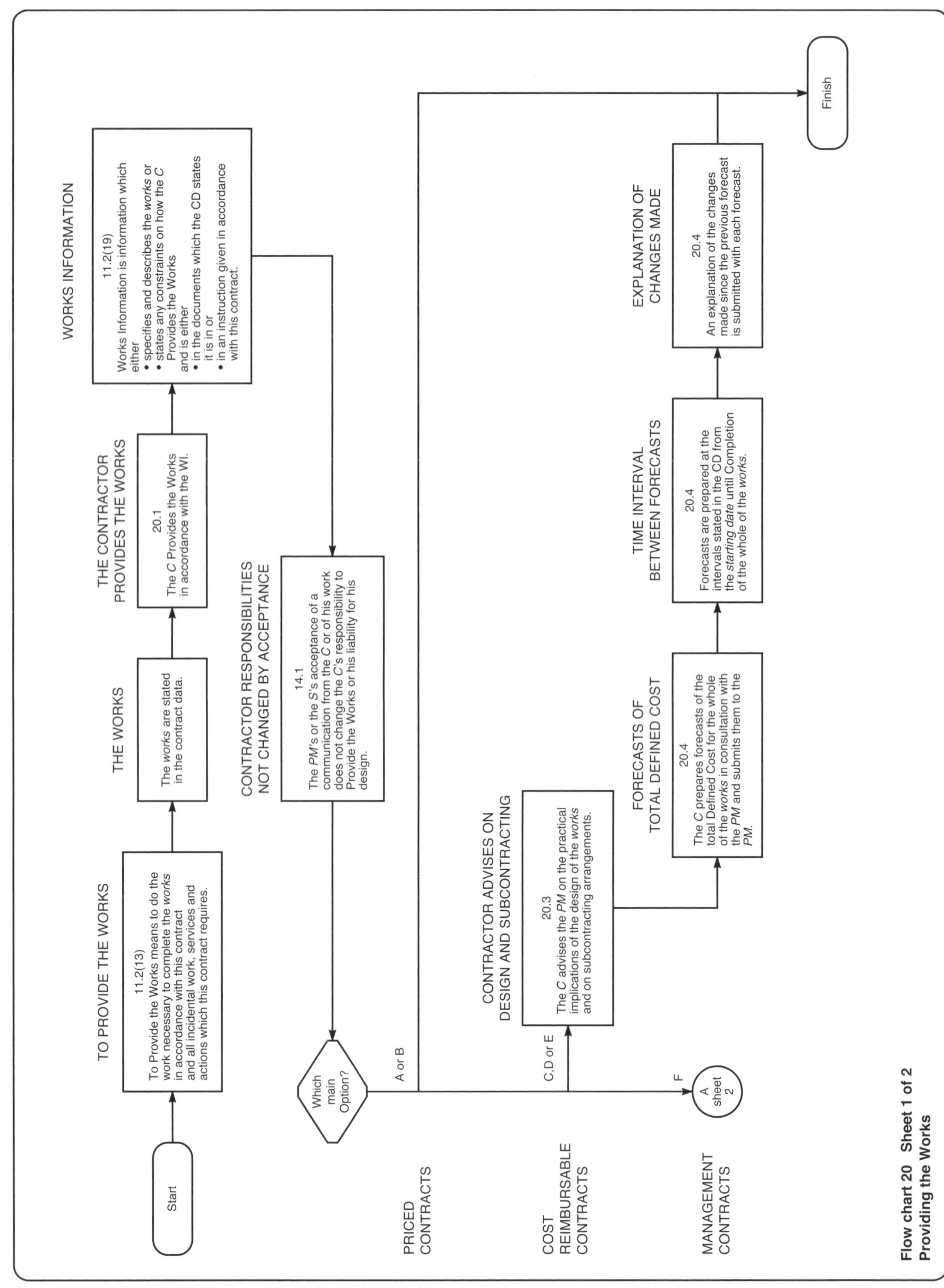

Start
TO PROVIDE THE WORKS
11.2(13)
To Provide the Works means to do the work necessary to complete the *works* in accordance with this contract and all incidental work, services and actions which this contract requires.
THE WORKS
The *works* are stated in the contract data.
THE CONTRACTOR PROVIDES THE WORKS
20.1
The *C* Provides the Works in accordance with the WI.
WORKS INFORMATION
11.2(19)
Works Information is information which either
• specifies and describes the *works* or
• states any constraints on how the *C* Provides the Works
and is either
• in the documents which the CD states it is in or
• in an instruction given in accordance with this contract.
CONTRACTOR RESPONSIBILITIES NOT CHANGED BY ACCEPTANCE
14.1
The *PM*'s or the *S*'s acceptance of a communication from the *C* or of his work does not change the *C*'s responsibility to Provide the Works or his liability for his design.
Which main Option?
PRICED CONTRACTS
A or B
COST REIMBURSABLE CONTRACTS
C,D or E
MANAGEMENT CONTRACTS
F
A sheet 2
CONTRACTOR ADVISES ON DESIGN AND SUBCONTRACTING
20.3
The *C* advises the *PM* on the practical implications of the design of the *works* and on subcontracting arrangements.
FORECASTS OF TOTAL DEFINED COST
20.4
The *C* prepares forecasts of the total Defined Cost for the whole of the *works* in consultation with the *PM* and submits them to the *PM*.
TIME INTERVAL BETWEEN FORECASTS
20.4
Forecasts are prepared at the intervals stated in the CD from the *starting date* until Completion of the whole of the *works*.
EXPLANATION OF CHANGES MADE
20.4
An explanation of the changes made since the previous forecast is submitted with each forecast.
Finish

Flow chart 20 Sheet 1 of 2
Providing the Works

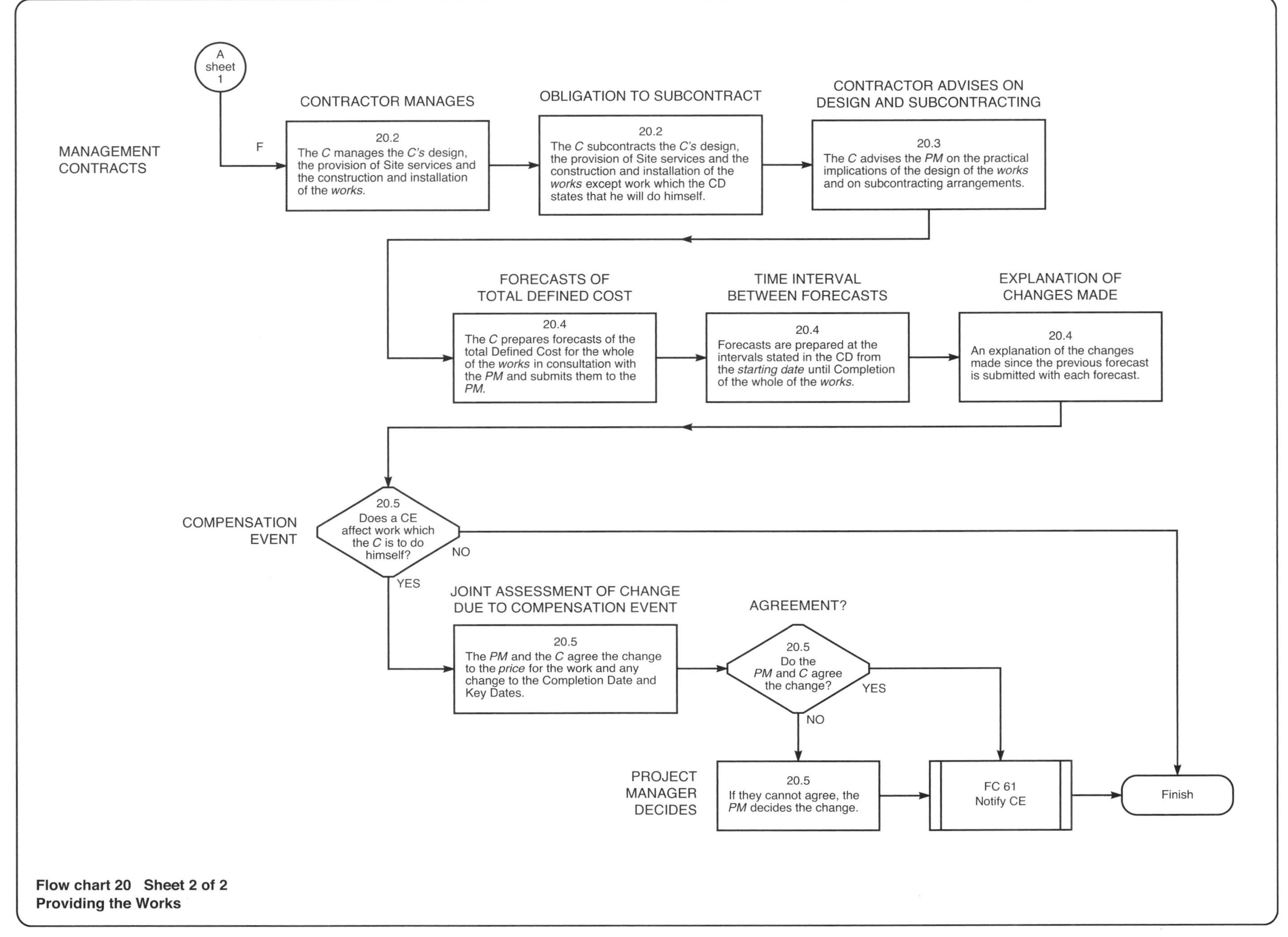
A sheet 1
MANAGEMENT CONTRACTS
F
CONTRACTOR MANAGES
20.2
The C manages the C's design, the provision of Site services and the construction and installation of the works.
OBLIGATION TO SUBCONTRACT
20.2
The C subcontracts the C's design, the provision of Site services and the construction and installation of the works except work which the CD states that he will do himself.
CONTRACTOR ADVISES ON DESIGN AND SUBCONTRACTING
20.3
The C advises the PM on the practical implications of the design of the works and on subcontracting arrangements.
FORECASTS OF TOTAL DEFINED COST
20.4
The C prepares forecasts of the total Defined Cost for the whole of the works in consultation with the PM and submits them to the PM.
TIME INTERVAL BETWEEN FORECASTS
20.4
Forecasts are prepared at the intervals stated in the CD from the starting date until Completion of the whole of the works.
EXPLANATION OF CHANGES MADE
20.4
An explanation of the changes made since the previous forecast is submitted with each forecast.
COMPENSATION EVENT
20.5
Does a CE affect work which the C is to do himself?
NO
YES
JOINT ASSESSMENT OF CHANGE DUE TO COMPENSATION EVENT
20.5
The PM and the C agree the change to the price for the work and any change to the Completion Date and Key Dates.
AGREEMENT?
20.5
Do the PM and C agree the change?
YES
NO
PROJECT MANAGER DECIDES
20.5
If they cannot agree, the PM decides the change.
FC 61
Notify CE
Finish
Flow chart 20 Sheet 2 of 2
Providing the Works

CONTRACTOR DESIGNS

21.1
The *C* designs the parts of the *works* which the WI states he is to design.

DESIGN ACCEPTANCE

21.2
The *C* submits the particulars of his design as the WI requires to the *PM* for acceptance.

SUBMIT DESIGN

FC 13
Submission for acceptance

Start

DESIGN TO BE SUBMITTED?

21.2
Does the WI require the *C* to submit his design?

YES

NO

SUBMISSION IN PARTS

21.3
The *C* may submit his design for acceptance in parts if the design of each part can be assessed fully.

REASON FOR NOT ACCEPTING

21.2
A reason for not accepting the *C's* design is that it does not comply with either the WI or the applicable law.

SUBMIT DESIGN

FC 13
Submission for acceptance

REVISE DESIGN

The *C* revises his design.

DESIGN ACCEPTED?

Does the *PM* accept the *C's* submission?

YES

NO

AWAIT ACCEPTANCE

21.2
The *C* does not proceed with the relevant work until the *PM* has accepted his design

CONTRACTOR PROVIDES THE WORKS

FC 20
Providing the Works

LIABILITY LIMITED TO REASONABLE SKILL AND CARE

Does Option X15 apply?

YES

NO

CONTRACTOR'S LIABILITY FOR HIS DESIGN

FC X15
Limitation of the *C's* liability for his design to reasonable skill and care

Finish

Flow chart 21
The *Contractor's* design

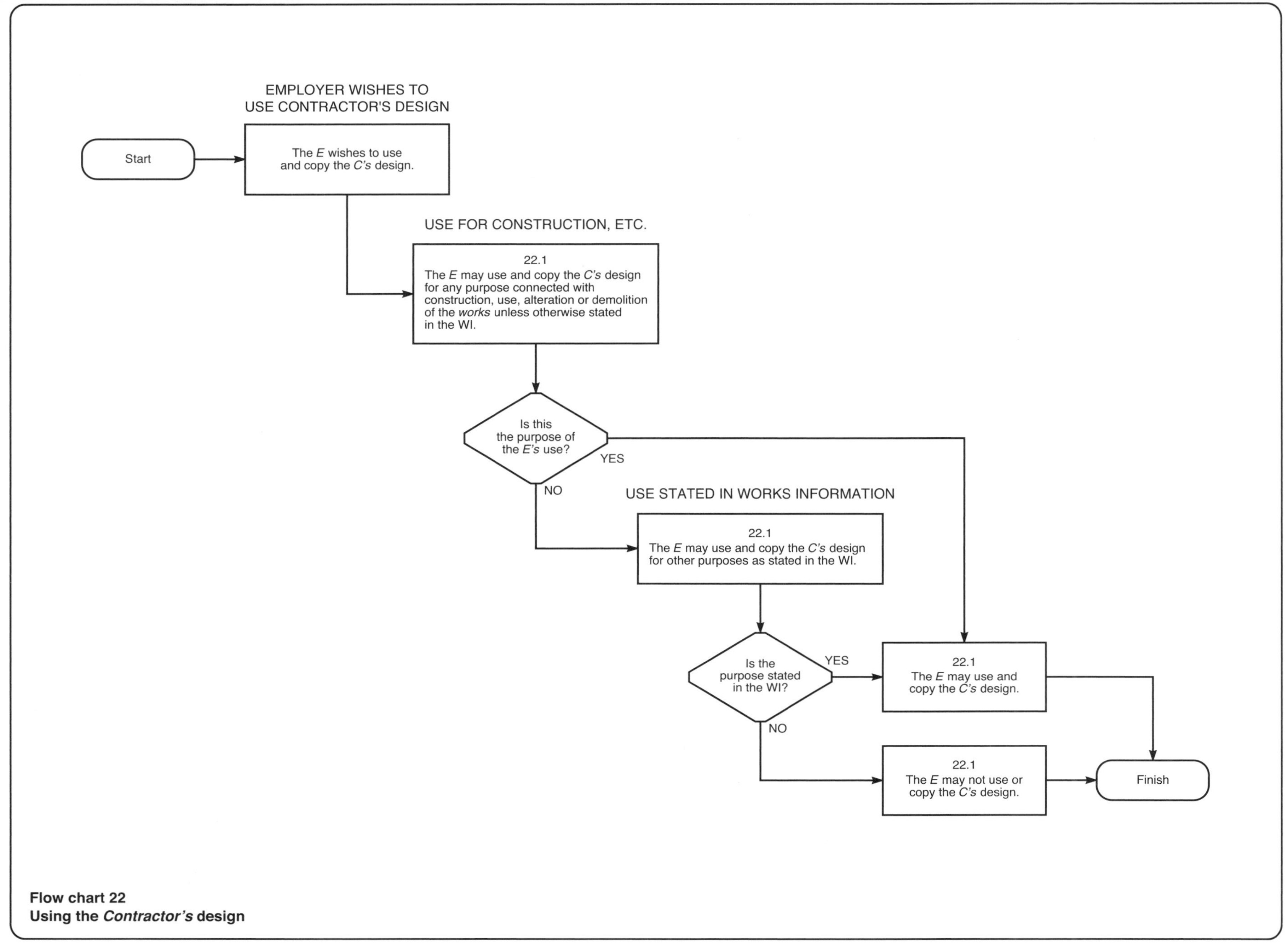
EMPLOYER WISHES TO
USE CONTRACTOR'S DESIGN
Start
The E wishes to use
and copy the C's design.
USE FOR CONSTRUCTION, ETC.
22.1
The E may use and copy the C's design
for any purpose connected with
construction, use, alteration or demolition
of the works unless otherwise stated
in the WI.
Is this
the purpose of
the E's use?
YES
NO
USE STATED IN WORKS INFORMATION
22.1
The E may use and copy the C's design
for other purposes as stated in the WI.
Is the
purpose stated
in the WI?
YES
NO
22.1
The E may use and
copy the C's design.
22.1
The E may not use or
copy the C's design.
Finish

Flow chart 22
Using the *Contractor's* design

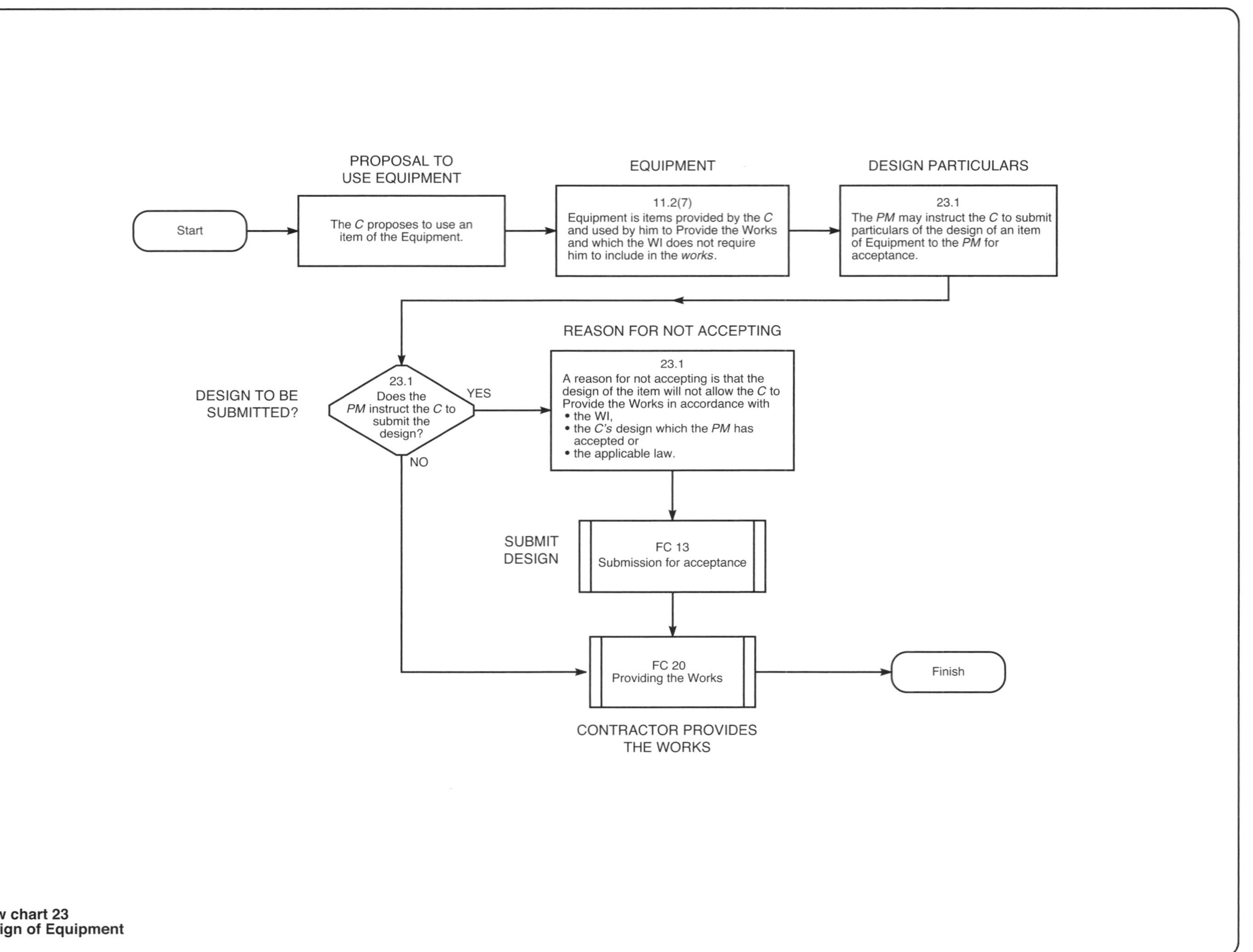
Start
PROPOSAL TO USE EQUIPMENT
The C proposes to use an item of the Equipment.
EQUIPMENT
11.2(7)
Equipment is items provided by the C and used by him to Provide the Works and which the WI does not require him to include in the works.
DESIGN PARTICULARS
23.1
The PM may instruct the C to submit particulars of the design of an item of Equipment to the PM for acceptance.
DESIGN TO BE SUBMITTED?
23.1
Does the PM instruct the C to submit the design?
YES
NO
REASON FOR NOT ACCEPTING
23.1
A reason for not accepting is that the design of the item will not allow the C to Provide the Works in accordance with
• the WI,
• the C's design which the PM has accepted or
• the applicable law.
SUBMIT DESIGN
FC 13
Submission for acceptance
CONTRACTOR PROVIDES THE WORKS
FC 20
Providing the Works
Finish
Flow chart 23
Design of Equipment

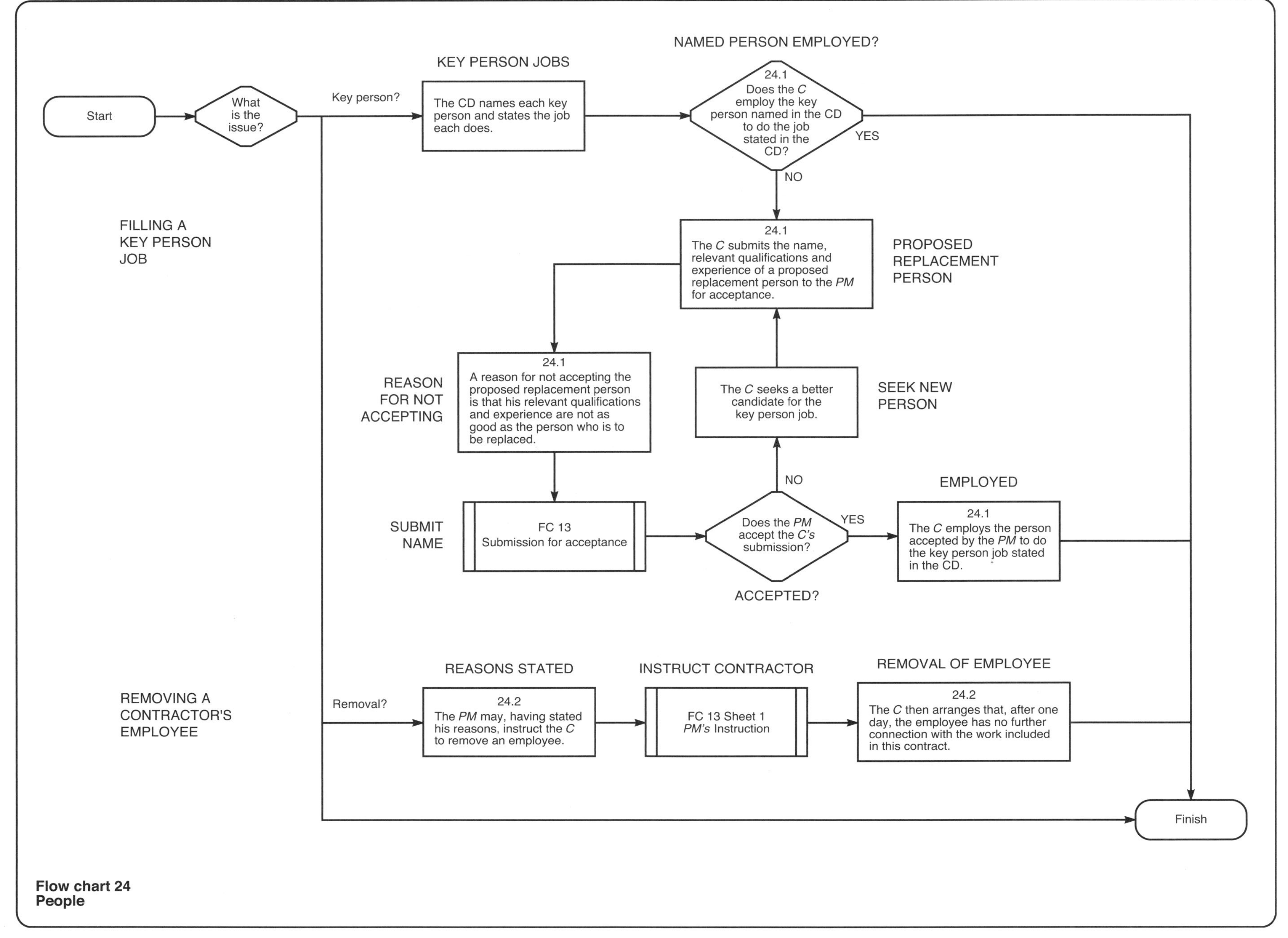
Start
What is the issue?
Key person?
KEY PERSON JOBS
The CD names each key person and states the job each does.
NAMED PERSON EMPLOYED?
24.1 Does the C employ the key person named in the CD to do the job stated in the CD?
YES
NO
FILLING A KEY PERSON JOB
24.1 The C submits the name, relevant qualifications and experience of a proposed replacement person to the PM for acceptance.
PROPOSED REPLACEMENT PERSON
REASON FOR NOT ACCEPTING
24.1 A reason for not accepting the proposed replacement person is that his relevant qualifications and experience are not as good as the person who is to be replaced.
The C seeks a better candidate for the key person job.
SEEK NEW PERSON
NO
EMPLOYED
SUBMIT NAME
FC 13 Submission for acceptance
Does the PM accept the C's submission?
YES
24.1 The C employs the person accepted by the PM to do the key person job stated in the CD.
ACCEPTED?
REASONS STATED
INSTRUCT CONTRACTOR
REMOVAL OF EMPLOYEE
REMOVING A CONTRACTOR'S EMPLOYEE
Removal?
24.2 The PM may, having stated his reasons, instruct the C to remove an employee.
FC 13 Sheet 1 PM's Instruction
24.2 The C then arranges that, after one day, the employee has no further connection with the work included in this contract.
Finish
Flow chart 24 People

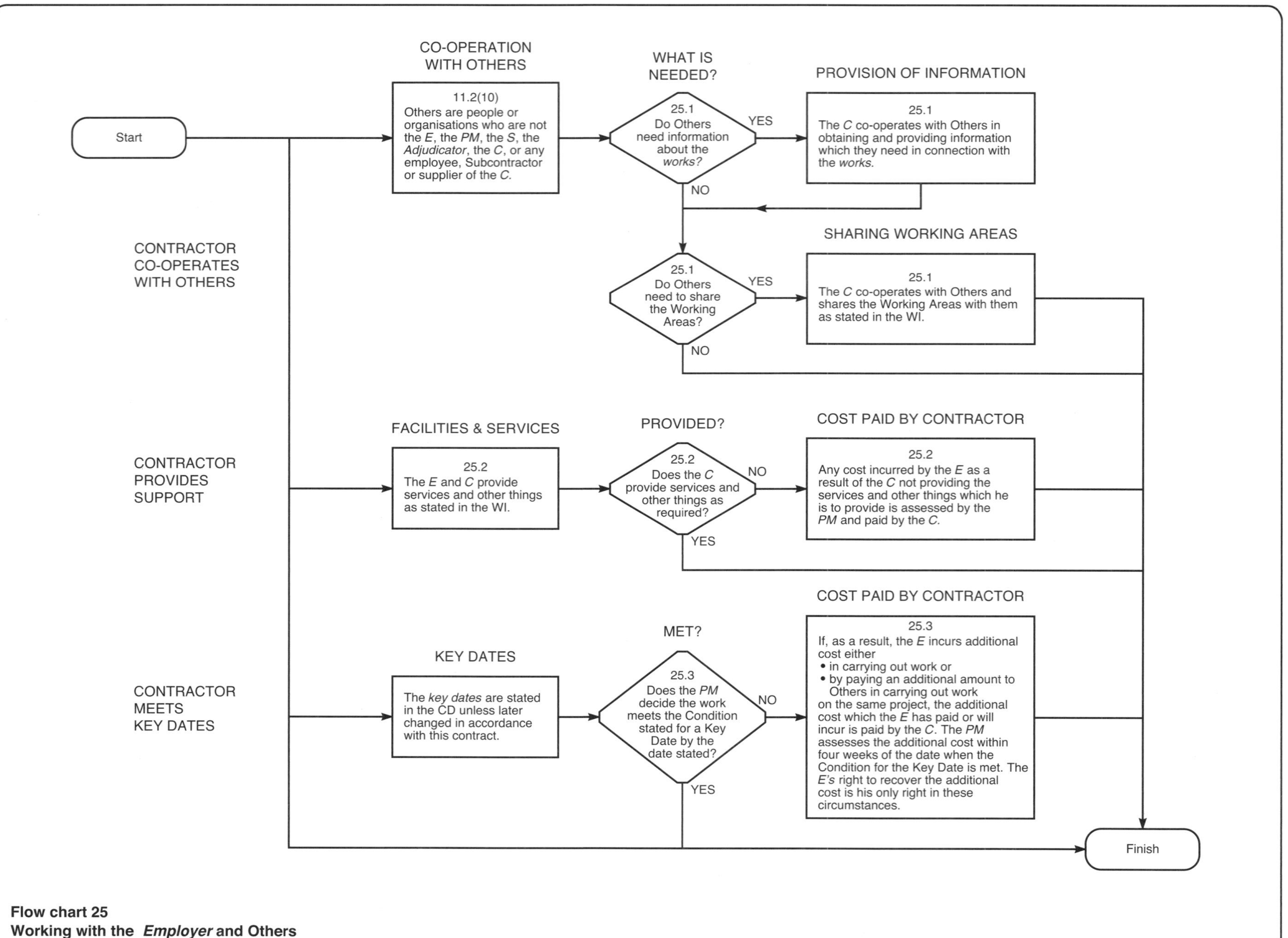
Start
CONTRACTOR CO-OPERATES WITH OTHERS
CONTRACTOR PROVIDES SUPPORT
CONTRACTOR MEETS KEY DATES
CO-OPERATION WITH OTHERS
11.2(10) Others are people or organisations who are not the *E*, the *PM*, the *S*, the *Adjudicator*, the *C*, or any employee, Subcontractor or supplier of the *C*.
WHAT IS NEEDED?
25.1 Do Others need information about the *works?*
YES
NO
PROVISION OF INFORMATION
25.1 The *C* co-operates with Others in obtaining and providing information which they need in connection with the *works.*
SHARING WORKING AREAS
25.1 Do Others need to share the Working Areas?
YES
NO
25.1 The *C* co-operates with Others and shares the Working Areas with them as stated in the WI.
FACILITIES & SERVICES
25.2 The *E* and *C* provide services and other things as stated in the WI.
PROVIDED?
25.2 Does the *C* provide services and other things as required?
NO
YES
COST PAID BY CONTRACTOR
25.2 Any cost incurred by the *E* as a result of the *C* not providing the services and other things which he is to provide is assessed by the *PM* and paid by the *C*.
KEY DATES
The *key dates* are stated in the CD unless later changed in accordance with this contract.
MET?
25.3 Does the *PM* decide the work meets the Condition stated for a Key Date by the date stated?
NO
YES
COST PAID BY CONTRACTOR
25.3 If, as a result, the *E* incurs additional cost either
• in carrying out work or
• by paying an additional amount to Others in carrying out work on the same project, the additional cost which the *E* has paid or will incur is paid by the *C*. The *PM* assesses the additional cost within four weeks of the date when the Condition for the Key Date is met. The *E's* right to recover the additional cost is his only right in these circumstances.
Finish

Flow chart 25
Working with the *Employer* and Others

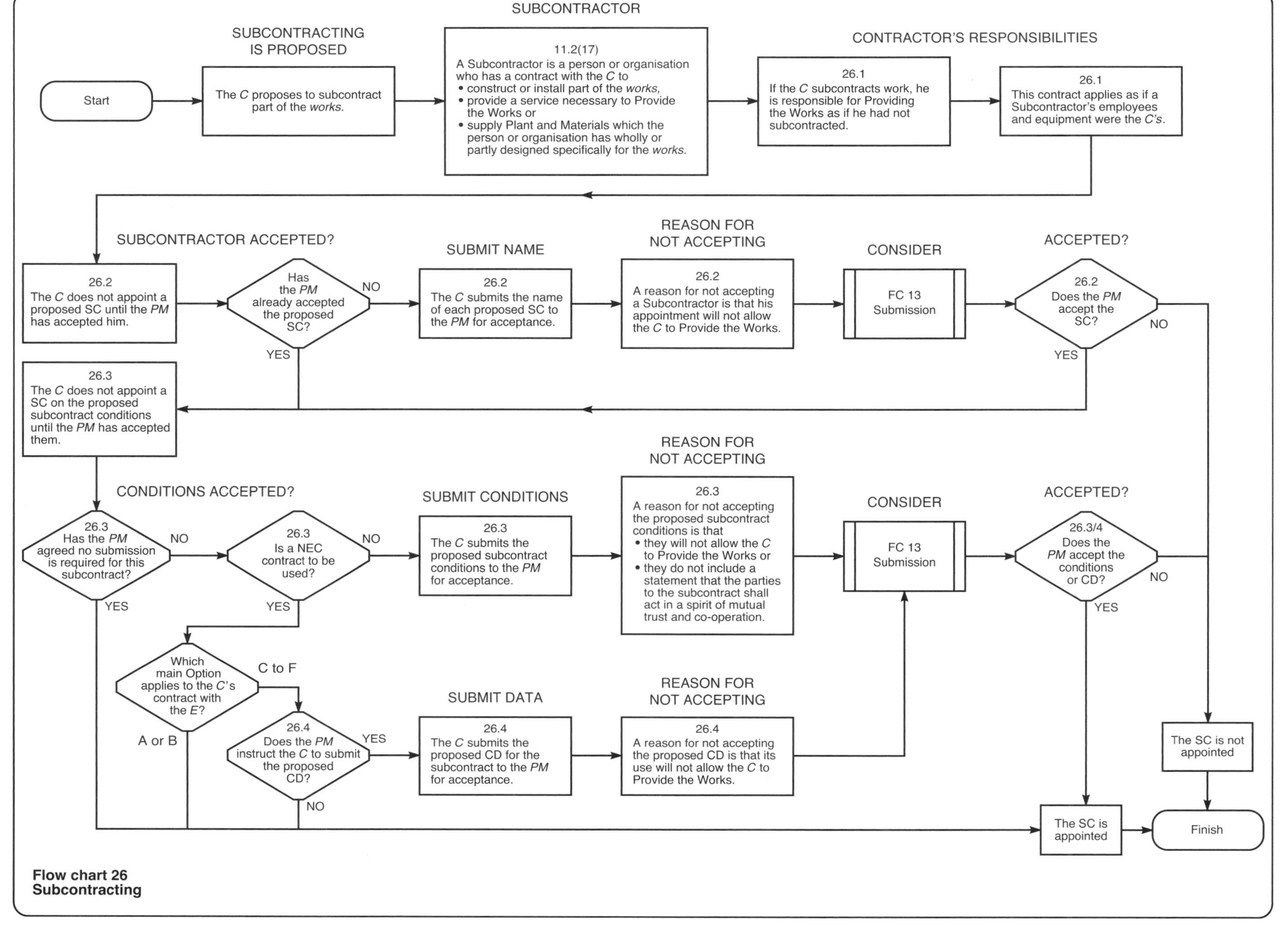
Start
SUBCONTRACTING IS PROPOSED
The C proposes to subcontract part of the works.
SUBCONTRACTOR
11.2(17)
A Subcontractor is a person or organisation who has a contract with the C to
• construct or install part of the works,
• provide a service necessary to Provide the Works or
• supply Plant and Materials which the person or organisation has wholly or partly designed specifically for the works.
CONTRACTOR'S RESPONSIBILITIES
26.1
If the C subcontracts work, he is responsible for Providing the Works as if he had not subcontracted.
26.1
This contract applies as if a Subcontractor's employees and equipment were the C's.
SUBCONTRACTOR ACCEPTED?
26.2
The C does not appoint a proposed SC until the PM has accepted him.
Has the PM already accepted the proposed SC?
NO
YES
SUBMIT NAME
26.2
The C submits the name of each proposed SC to the PM for acceptance.
REASON FOR NOT ACCEPTING
26.2
A reason for not accepting a Subcontractor is that his appointment will not allow the C to Provide the Works.
CONSIDER
FC 13 Submission
ACCEPTED?
26.2
Does the PM accept the SC?
NO
YES
26.3
The C does not appoint a SC on the proposed subcontract conditions until the PM has accepted them.
CONDITIONS ACCEPTED?
26.3
Has the PM agreed no submission is required for this subcontract?
NO
YES
26.3
Is a NEC contract to be used?
NO
YES
SUBMIT CONDITIONS
26.3
The C submits the proposed subcontract conditions to the PM for acceptance.
REASON FOR NOT ACCEPTING
26.3
A reason for not accepting the proposed subcontract conditions is that
• they will not allow the C to Provide the Works or
• they do not include a statement that the parties to the subcontract shall act in a spirit of mutual trust and co-operation.
CONSIDER
FC 13 Submission
ACCEPTED?
26.3/4
Does the PM accept the conditions or CD?
NO
YES
Which main Option applies to the C's contract with the E?
C to F
A or B
26.4
Does the PM instruct the C to submit the proposed CD?
YES
NO
SUBMIT DATA
26.4
The C submits the proposed CD for the subcontract to the PM for acceptance.
REASON FOR NOT ACCEPTING
26.4
A reason for not accepting the proposed CD is that its use will not allow the C to Provide the Works.
The SC is not appointed
The SC is appointed
Finish

Flow chart 26
Subcontracting

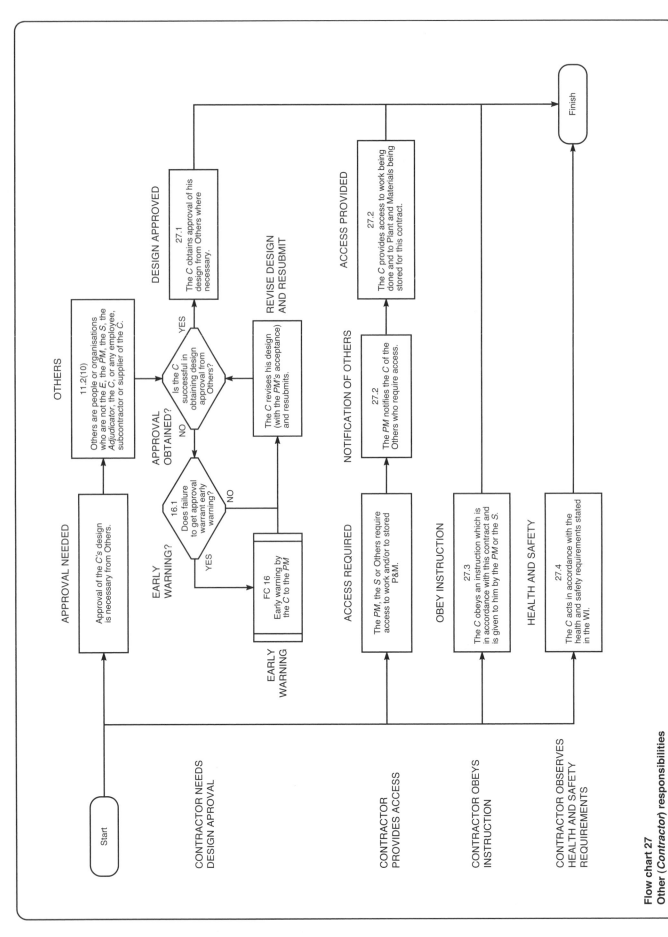

Flow chart 27
Other (*Contractor*) responsibilities

Start

CONTRACTOR NEEDS DESIGN APROVAL

APPROVAL NEEDED

Approval of the *C's* design is necessary from Others.

OTHERS

11.2(10)
Others are people or organisations who are not the *E*, the *PM*, the *S*, the *Adjudicator*, the *C*, or any employee, subcontractor or supplier of the *C*.

APPROVAL OBTAINED?

Is the *C* successful in obtaining design approval from Others?

YES

DESIGN APPROVED

27.1
The *C* obtains approval of his design from Others where necessary.

NO

EARLY WARNING?

16.1
Does failure to get approval warrant early warning?

YES

EARLY WARNING

FC 16
Early warning by the *C* to the *PM*

NO

REVISE DESIGN AND RESUBMIT

The *C* revises his design (with the *PM's* acceptance) and resubmits.

CONTRACTOR PROVIDES ACCESS

ACCESS REQUIRED

The *PM*, the *S* or Others require access to work and/or to stored P&M.

NOTIFICATION OF OTHERS

27.2
The *PM* notifies the *C* of the Others who require access.

ACCESS PROVIDED

27.2
The *C* provides access to work being done and to Plant and Materials being stored for this contract.

CONTRACTOR OBEYS INSTRUCTION

OBEY INSTRUCTION

27.3
The *C* obeys an instruction which is in accordance with this contract and is given to him by the *PM* or the *S*.

CONTRACTOR OBSERVES HEALTH AND SAFETY REQUIREMENTS

HEALTH AND SAFETY

27.4
The *C* acts in accordance with the health and safety requirements stated in the WI.

Finish

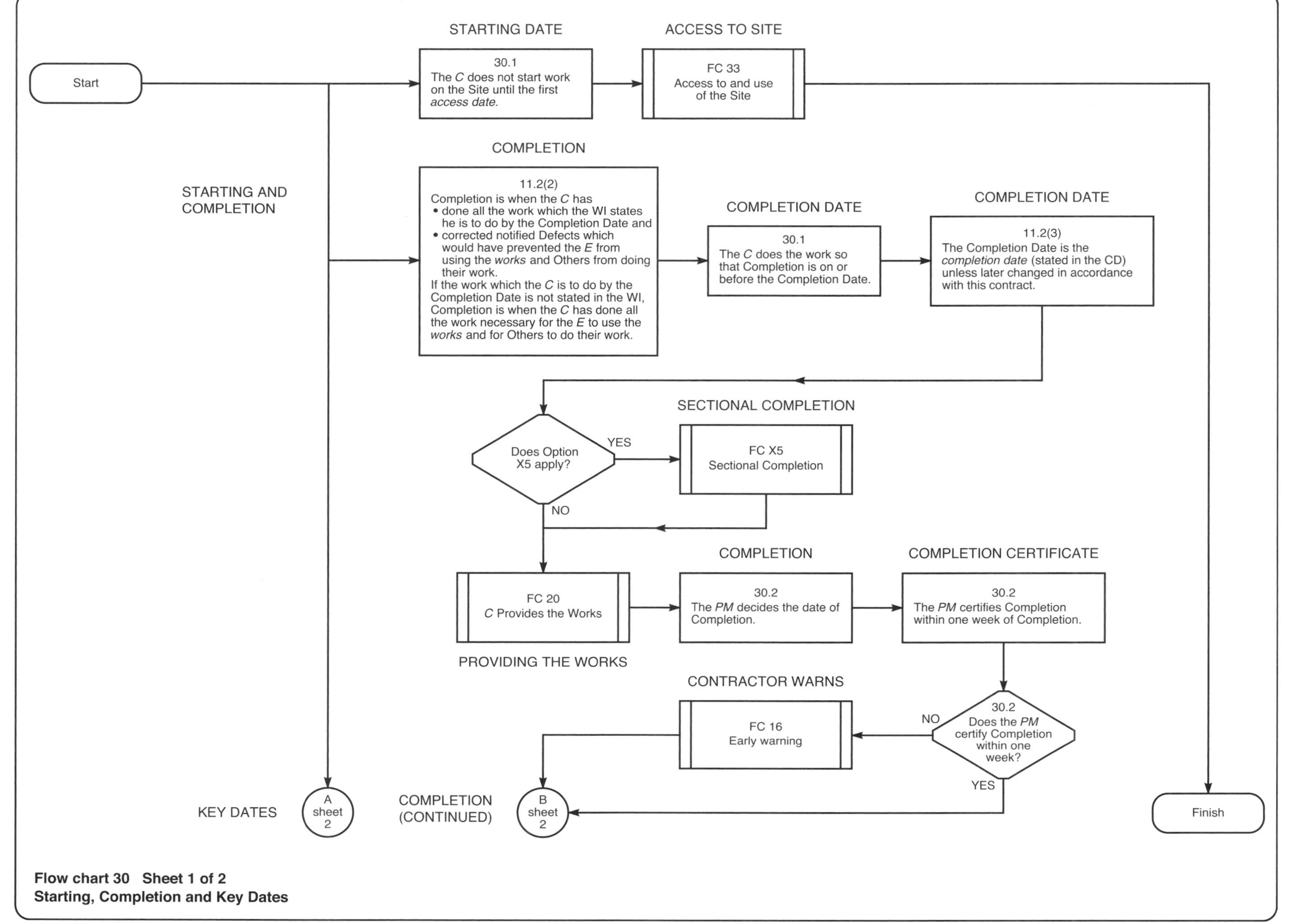
Start
STARTING DATE
30.1
The C does not start work on the Site until the first access date.
ACCESS TO SITE
FC 33
Access to and use of the Site
STARTING AND COMPLETION
COMPLETION
11.2(2)
Completion is when the C has
• done all the work which the WI states he is to do by the Completion Date and
• corrected notified Defects which would have prevented the E from using the works and Others from doing their work.
If the work which the C is to do by the Completion Date is not stated in the WI, Completion is when the C has done all the work necessary for the E to use the works and for Others to do their work.
COMPLETION DATE
30.1
The C does the work so that Completion is on or before the Completion Date.
COMPLETION DATE
11.2(3)
The Completion Date is the completion date (stated in the CD) unless later changed in accordance with this contract.
SECTIONAL COMPLETION
Does Option X5 apply?
YES
FC X5
Sectional Completion
NO
FC 20
C Provides the Works
PROVIDING THE WORKS
COMPLETION
30.2
The PM decides the date of Completion.
COMPLETION CERTIFICATE
30.2
The PM certifies Completion within one week of Completion.
CONTRACTOR WARNS
FC 16
Early warning
30.2
Does the PM certify Completion within one week?
NO
YES
KEY DATES
A sheet 2
COMPLETION (CONTINUED)
B sheet 2
Finish

Flow chart 30 Sheet 1 of 2
Starting, Completion and Key Dates

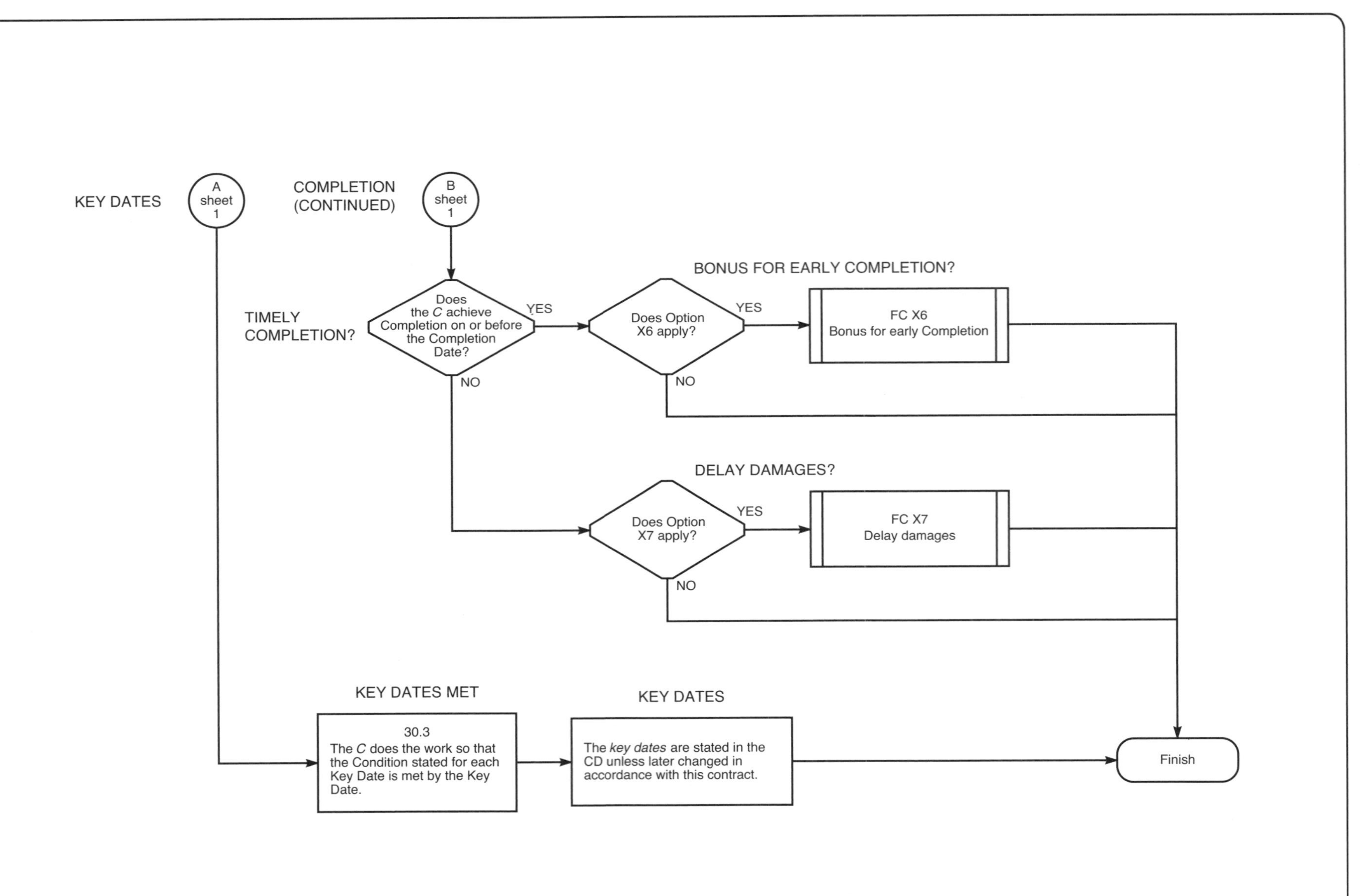
KEY DATES
A sheet 1
COMPLETION (CONTINUED)
B sheet 1
TIMELY COMPLETION?
Does the C achieve Completion on or before the Completion Date?
YES
NO
BONUS FOR EARLY COMPLETION?
Does Option X6 apply?
YES
NO
FC X6 Bonus for early Completion
DELAY DAMAGES?
Does Option X7 apply?
YES
NO
FC X7 Delay damages
KEY DATES MET
30.3 The C does the work so that the Condition stated for each Key Date is met by the Key Date.
KEY DATES
The key dates are stated in the CD unless later changed in accordance with this contract.
Finish

Flow chart 30 Sheet 2 of 2
Starting, Completion and Key Dates

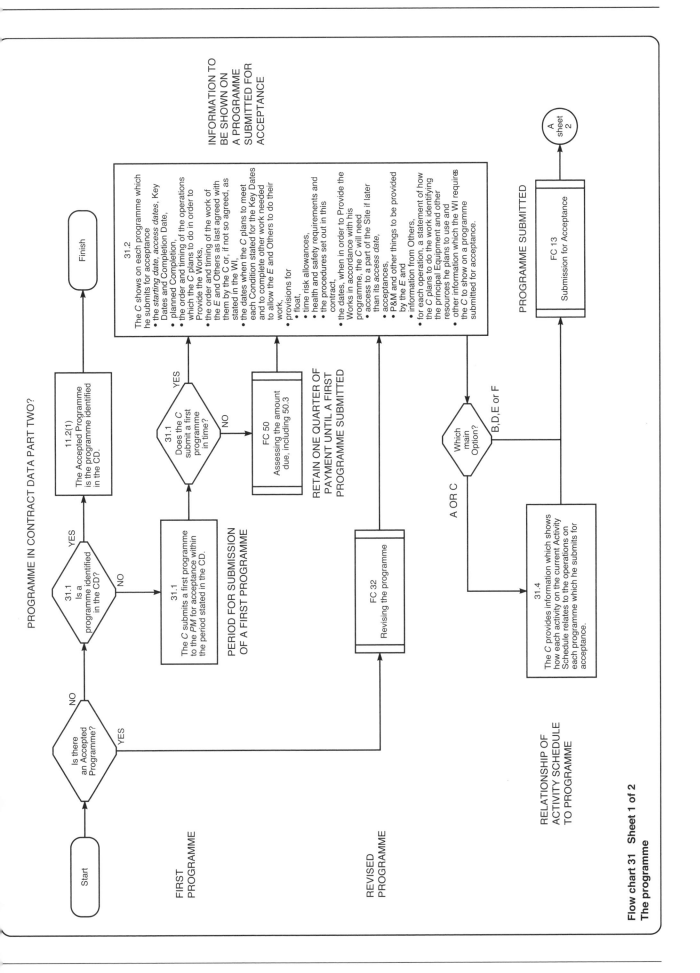

PROGRAMME IN CONTRACT DATA PART TWO?

Start

Is there an Accepted Programme?

NO

31.1
Is a programme identified in the CD?

YES

11.2(1)
The Accepted Programme is the programme identified in the CD.

Finish

YES

NO

FIRST PROGRAMME

31.1
The *C* submits a first programme to the *PM* for acceptance within the period stated in the CD.

PERIOD FOR SUBMISSION OF A FIRST PROGRAMME

31.1
Does the *C* submit a first programme in time?

YES

NO

FC 50
Assessing the amount due, including 50.3

RETAIN ONE QUARTER OF PAYMENT UNTIL A FIRST PROGRAMME SUBMITTED

31.2
The *C* shows on each programme which he submits for acceptance

- the *starting date, access dates*, Key Dates and Completion Date,
- planned Completion,
- the order and timing of the operations which the *C* plans to do in order to Provide the Works,
- the order and timing of the work of the *E* and Others as last agreed with them by the C or, if not so agreed, as stated in the WI,
- the dates when the *C* plans to meet each Condition stated for the Key Dates and to complete other work needed to allow the *E* and Others to do their work,
- provisions for
  - float,
  - time risk allowances,
  - health and safety requirements and
  - the procedures set out in this contract,
- the dates, when in order to Provide the Works in accordance with his programme, the *C* will need
  - access to a part of the Site if later than its *access date,*
  - acceptances,
  - P&M and other things to be provided by the *E* and
  - information from Others,
- for each operation, a statement of how the *C* plans to do the work identifying the principal Equipment and other resources he plans to use and
- other information which the WI requires the *C* to show on a programme submitted for acceptance.

INFORMATION TO BE SHOWN ON A PROGRAMME SUBMITTED FOR ACCEPTANCE

REVISED PROGRAMME

FC 32
Revising the programme

Which main Option?

A OR C

B,D,E or F

RELATIONSHIP OF ACTIVITY SCHEDULE TO PROGRAMME

31.4
The *C* provides information which shows how each activity on the current Activity Schedule relates to the operations on each programme which he submits for acceptance.

PROGRAMME SUBMITTED

FC 13
Submission for Acceptance

A sheet 2

Flow chart 31 Sheet 1 of 2
The programme

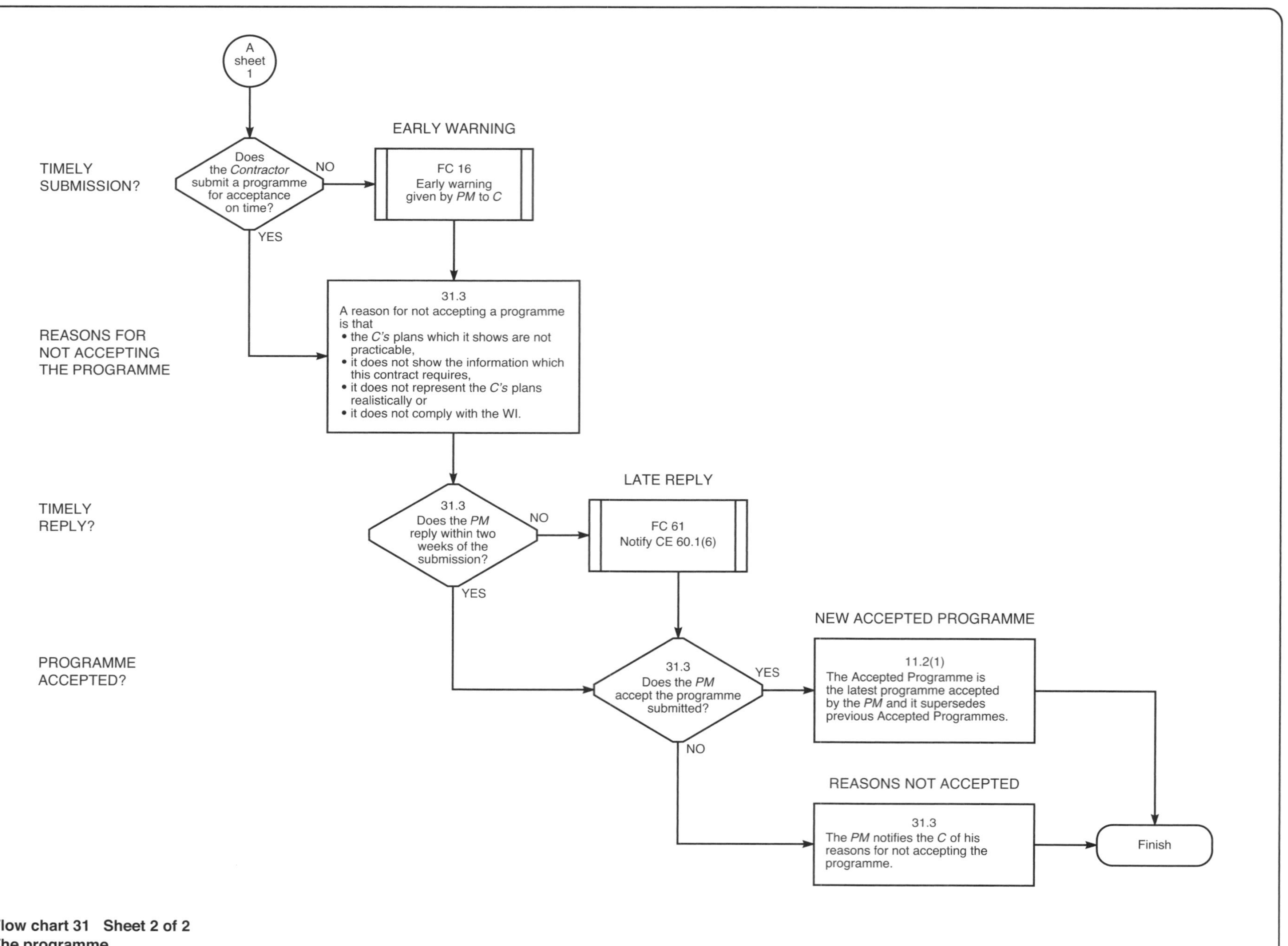
A sheet 1
TIMELY SUBMISSION?
Does the *Contractor* submit a programme for acceptance on time?
NO
YES
EARLY WARNING
FC 16 Early warning given by *PM* to *C*
REASONS FOR NOT ACCEPTING THE PROGRAMME
31.3
A reason for not accepting a programme is that
• the *C's* plans which it shows are not practicable,
• it does not show the information which this contract requires,
• it does not represent the *C's* plans realistically or
• it does not comply with the WI.
TIMELY REPLY?
31.3 Does the *PM* reply within two weeks of the submission?
NO
YES
LATE REPLY
FC 61 Notify CE 60.1(6)
PROGRAMME ACCEPTED?
31.3 Does the *PM* accept the programme submitted?
YES
NO
NEW ACCEPTED PROGRAMME
11.2(1)
The Accepted Programme is the latest programme accepted by the *PM* and it supersedes previous Accepted Programmes.
REASONS NOT ACCEPTED
31.3
The *PM* notifies the *C* of his reasons for not accepting the programme.
Finish

Flow chart 31 Sheet 2 of 2
The programme

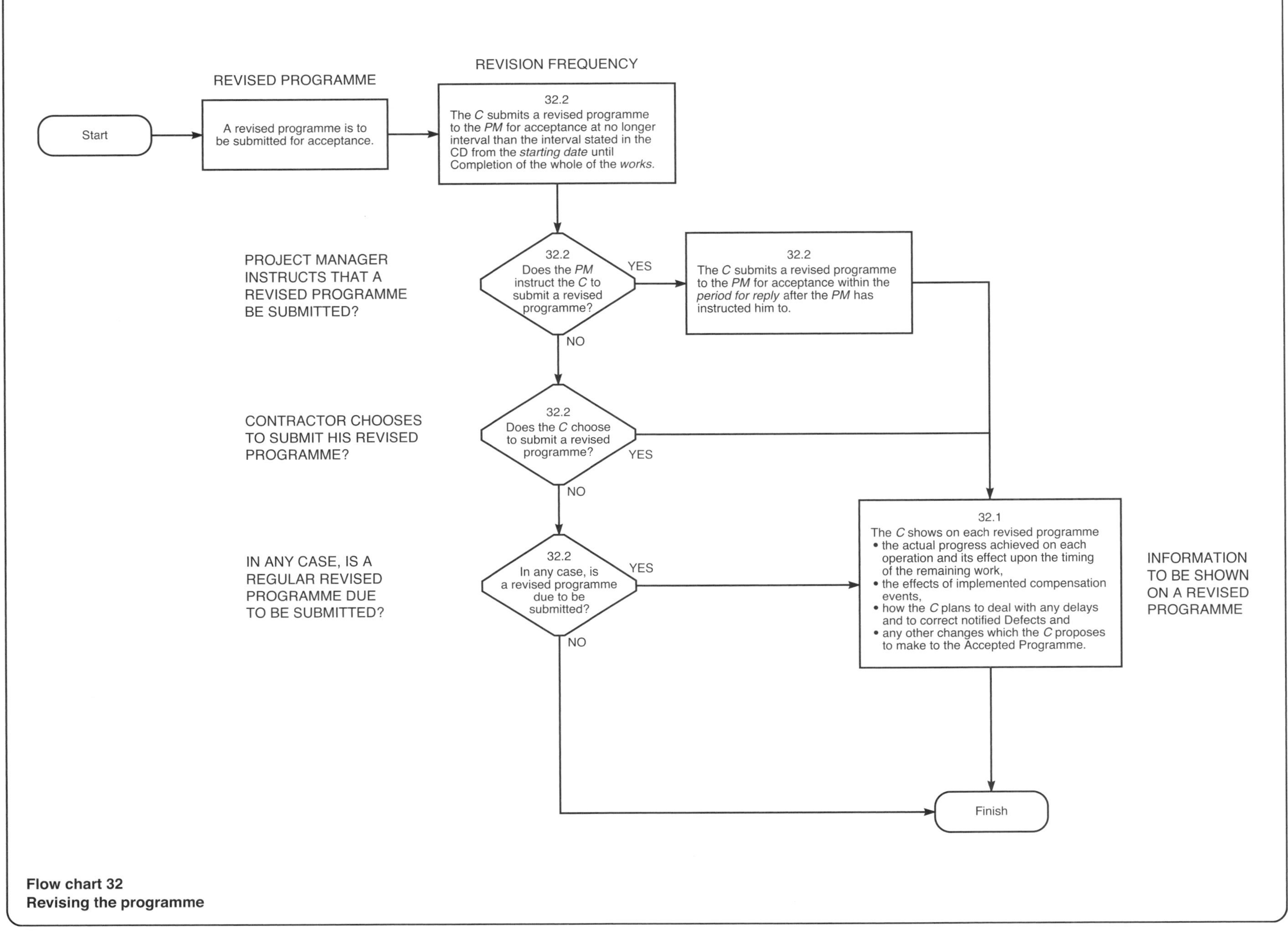
REVISED PROGRAMME
REVISION FREQUENCY
Start
A revised programme is to be submitted for acceptance.
32.2
The *C* submits a revised programme to the *PM* for acceptance at no longer interval than the interval stated in the CD from the *starting date* until Completion of the whole of the *works*.
PROJECT MANAGER INSTRUCTS THAT A REVISED PROGRAMME BE SUBMITTED?
32.2
Does the *PM* instruct the *C* to submit a revised programme?
YES
NO
32.2
The *C* submits a revised programme to the *PM* for acceptance within the *period for reply* after the *PM* has instructed him to.
CONTRACTOR CHOOSES TO SUBMIT HIS REVISED PROGRAMME?
32.2
Does the *C* choose to submit a revised programme?
YES
NO
IN ANY CASE, IS A REGULAR REVISED PROGRAMME DUE TO BE SUBMITTED?
32.2
In any case, is a revised programme due to be submitted?
YES
NO
32.1
The *C* shows on each revised programme
• the actual progress achieved on each operation and its effect upon the timing of the remaining work,
• the effects of implemented compensation events,
• how the *C* plans to deal with any delays and to correct notified Defects and
• any other changes which the *C* proposes to make to the Accepted Programme.
INFORMATION TO BE SHOWN ON A REVISED PROGRAMME
Finish

Flow chart 32
Revising the programme

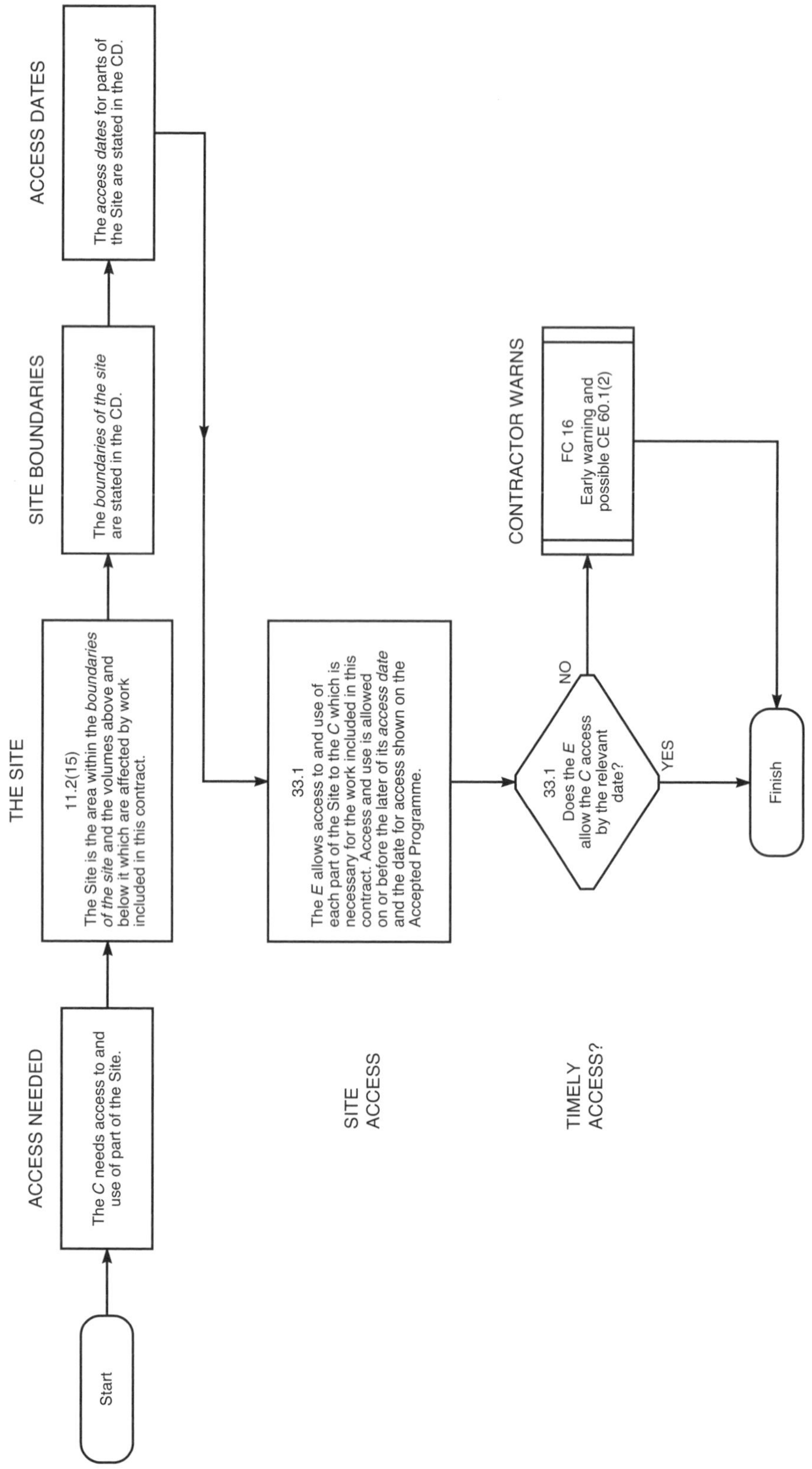

Flow chart 33
Access to and use of the Site

ACCESS NEEDED

Start

The *C* needs access to and use of part of the Site.

THE SITE

11.2(15)
The Site is the area within the *boundaries of the site* and the volumes above and below it which are affected by work included in this contract.

SITE BOUNDARIES

The *boundaries of the site* are stated in the CD.

ACCESS DATES

The *access dates* for parts of the Site are stated in the CD.

SITE ACCESS

33.1
The *E* allows access to and use of each part of the Site to the *C* which is necessary for the work included in this contract. Access and use is allowed on or before the later of its *access date* and the date for access shown on the Accepted Programme.

TIMELY ACCESS?

33.1
Does the *E* allow the *C* access by the relevant date?

NO

CONTRACTOR WARNS

FC 16
Early warning and possible CE 60.1(2)

YES

Finish

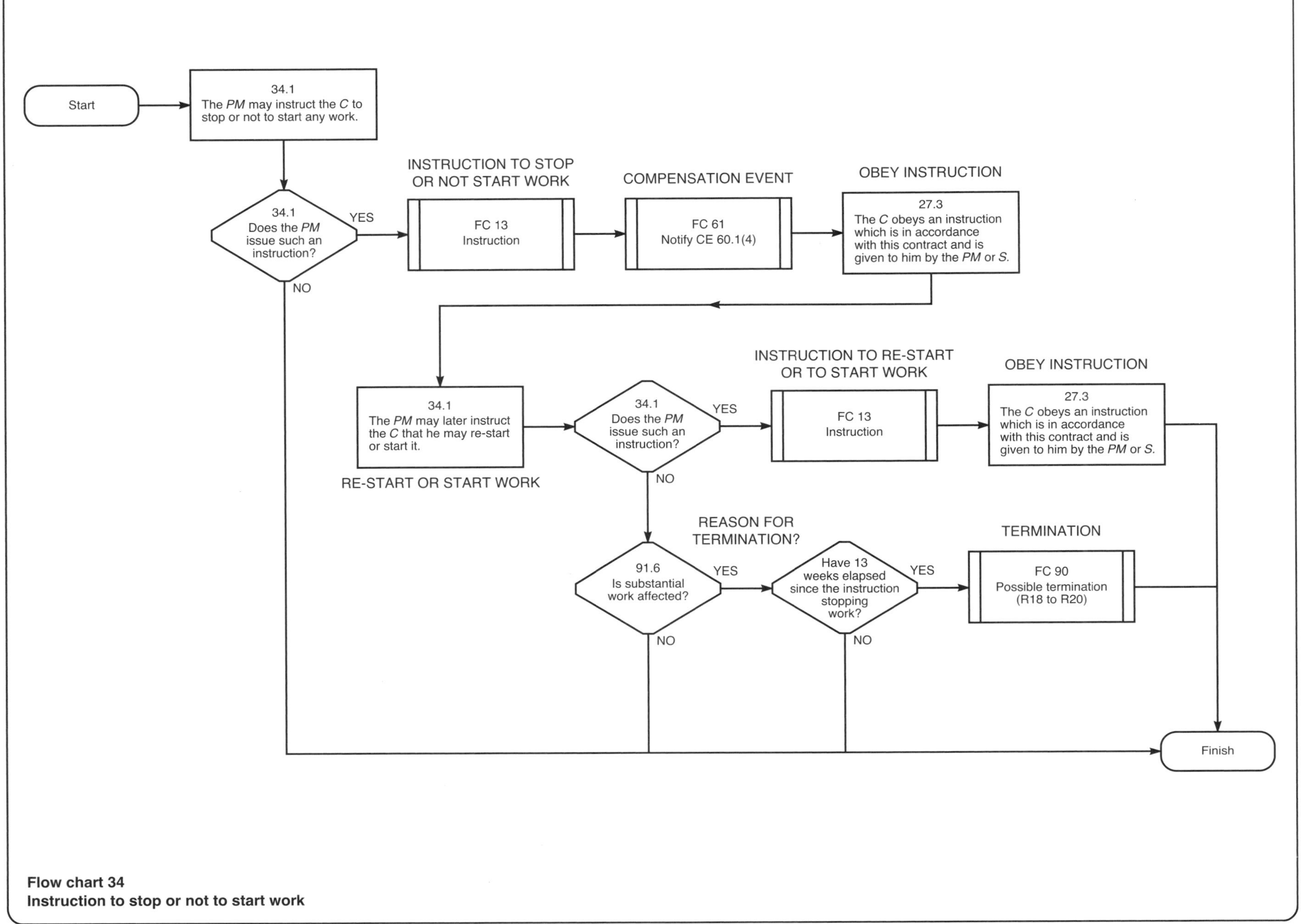
Start
34.1
The PM may instruct the C to stop or not to start any work.
34.1
Does the PM issue such an instruction?
YES
NO
INSTRUCTION TO STOP OR NOT START WORK
FC 13
Instruction
COMPENSATION EVENT
FC 61
Notify CE 60.1(4)
OBEY INSTRUCTION
27.3
The C obeys an instruction which is in accordance with this contract and is given to him by the PM or S.
34.1
The PM may later instruct the C that he may re-start or start it.
RE-START OR START WORK
34.1
Does the PM issue such an instruction?
YES
NO
INSTRUCTION TO RE-START OR TO START WORK
FC 13
Instruction
OBEY INSTRUCTION
27.3
The C obeys an instruction which is in accordance with this contract and is given to him by the PM or S.
REASON FOR TERMINATION?
91.6
Is substantial work affected?
YES
NO
Have 13 weeks elapsed since the instruction stopping work?
YES
NO
TERMINATION
FC 90
Possible termination (R18 to R20)
Finish

Flow chart 34
Instruction to stop or not to start work

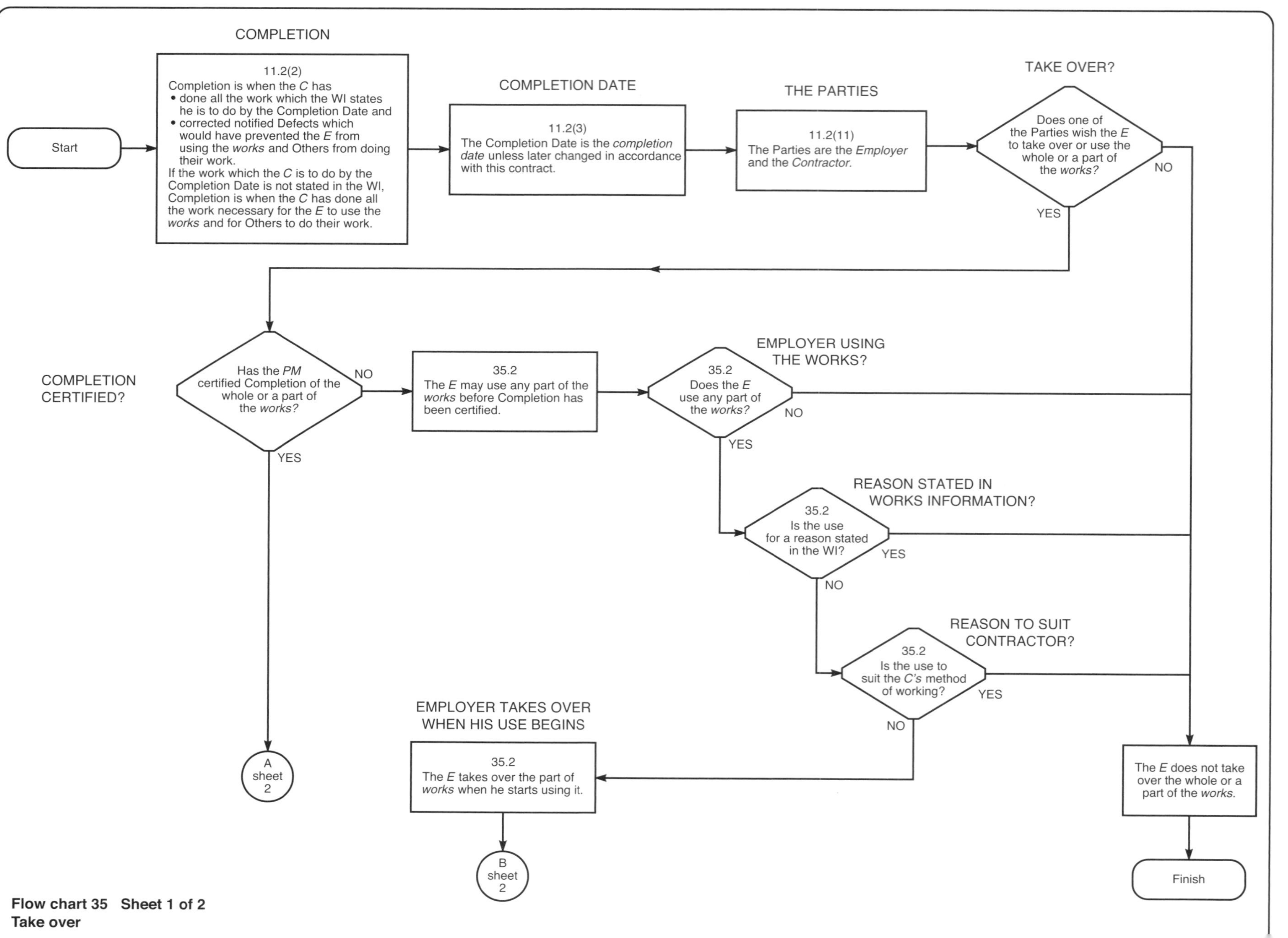
Start
COMPLETION
11.2(2)
Completion is when the C has
• done all the work which the WI states he is to do by the Completion Date and
• corrected notified Defects which would have prevented the E from using the works and Others from doing their work.
If the work which the C is to do by the Completion Date is not stated in the WI, Completion is when the C has done all the work necessary for the E to use the works and for Others to do their work.
COMPLETION DATE
11.2(3)
The Completion Date is the completion date unless later changed in accordance with this contract.
THE PARTIES
11.2(11)
The Parties are the Employer and the Contractor.
TAKE OVER?
Does one of the Parties wish the E to take over or use the whole or a part of the works?
NO
YES
COMPLETION CERTIFIED?
Has the PM certified Completion of the whole or a part of the works?
NO
YES
35.2
The E may use any part of the works before Completion has been certified.
EMPLOYER USING THE WORKS?
35.2
Does the E use any part of the works?
NO
YES
REASON STATED IN WORKS INFORMATION?
35.2
Is the use for a reason stated in the WI?
YES
NO
REASON TO SUIT CONTRACTOR?
35.2
Is the use to suit the C's method of working?
YES
NO
A sheet 2
EMPLOYER TAKES OVER WHEN HIS USE BEGINS
35.2
The E takes over the part of works when he starts using it.
B sheet 2
The E does not take over the whole or a part of the works.
Finish

Flow chart 35 Sheet 1 of 2
Take over

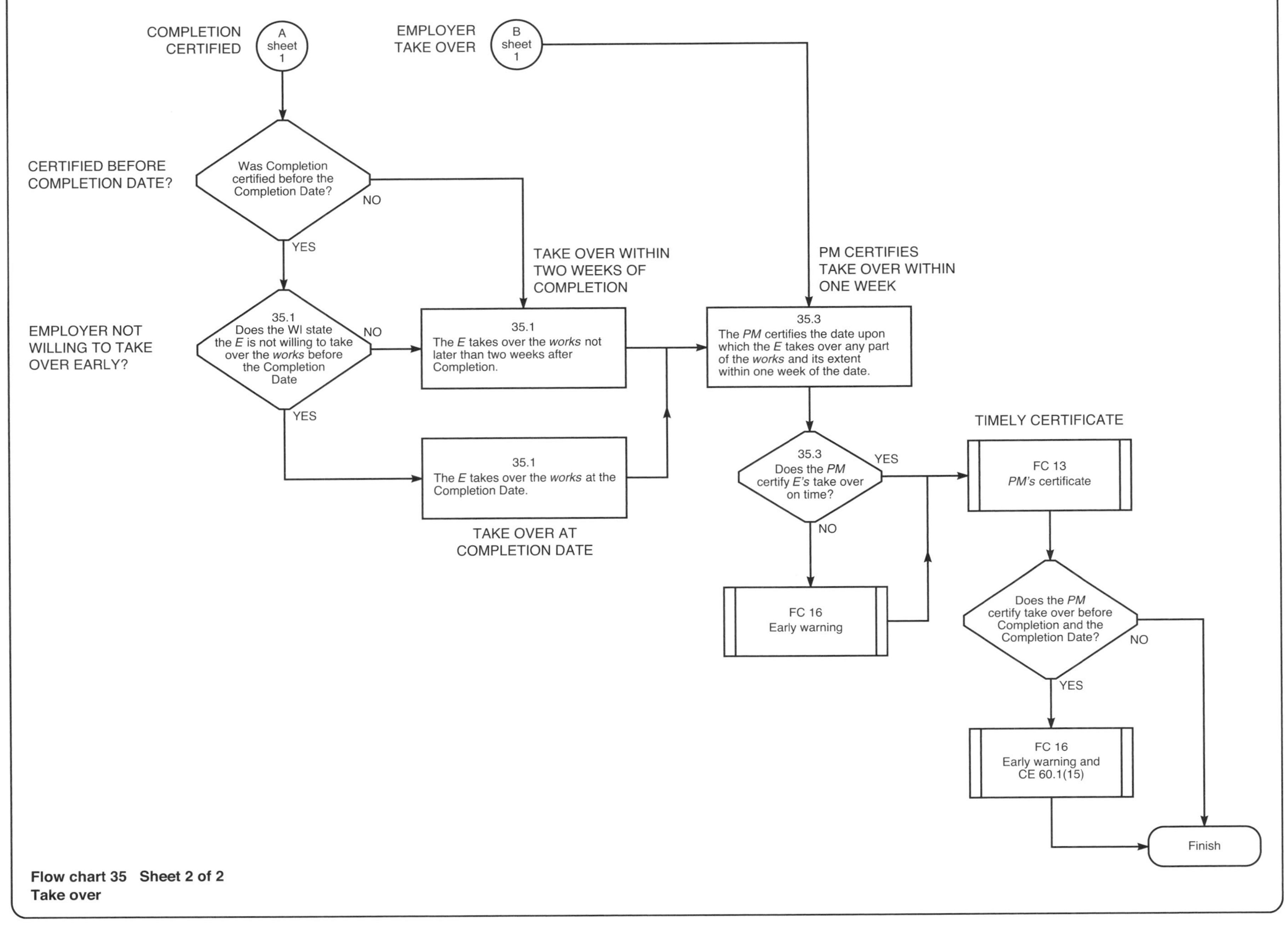
COMPLETION CERTIFIED
A sheet 1
EMPLOYER TAKE OVER
B sheet 1
CERTIFIED BEFORE COMPLETION DATE?
Was Completion certified before the Completion Date?
NO
YES
TAKE OVER WITHIN TWO WEEKS OF COMPLETION
PM CERTIFIES TAKE OVER WITHIN ONE WEEK
EMPLOYER NOT WILLING TO TAKE OVER EARLY?
35.1 Does the WI state the E is not willing to take over the works before the Completion Date
NO
YES
35.1 The E takes over the works not later than two weeks after Completion.
35.3 The PM certifies the date upon which the E takes over any part of the works and its extent within one week of the date.
35.1 The E takes over the works at the Completion Date.
TAKE OVER AT COMPLETION DATE
35.3 Does the PM certify E's take over on time?
YES
NO
TIMELY CERTIFICATE
FC 13 PM's certificate
FC 16 Early warning
Does the PM certify take over before Completion and the Completion Date?
NO
YES
FC 16 Early warning and CE 60.1(15)
Finish

Flow chart 35 Sheet 2 of 2
Take over

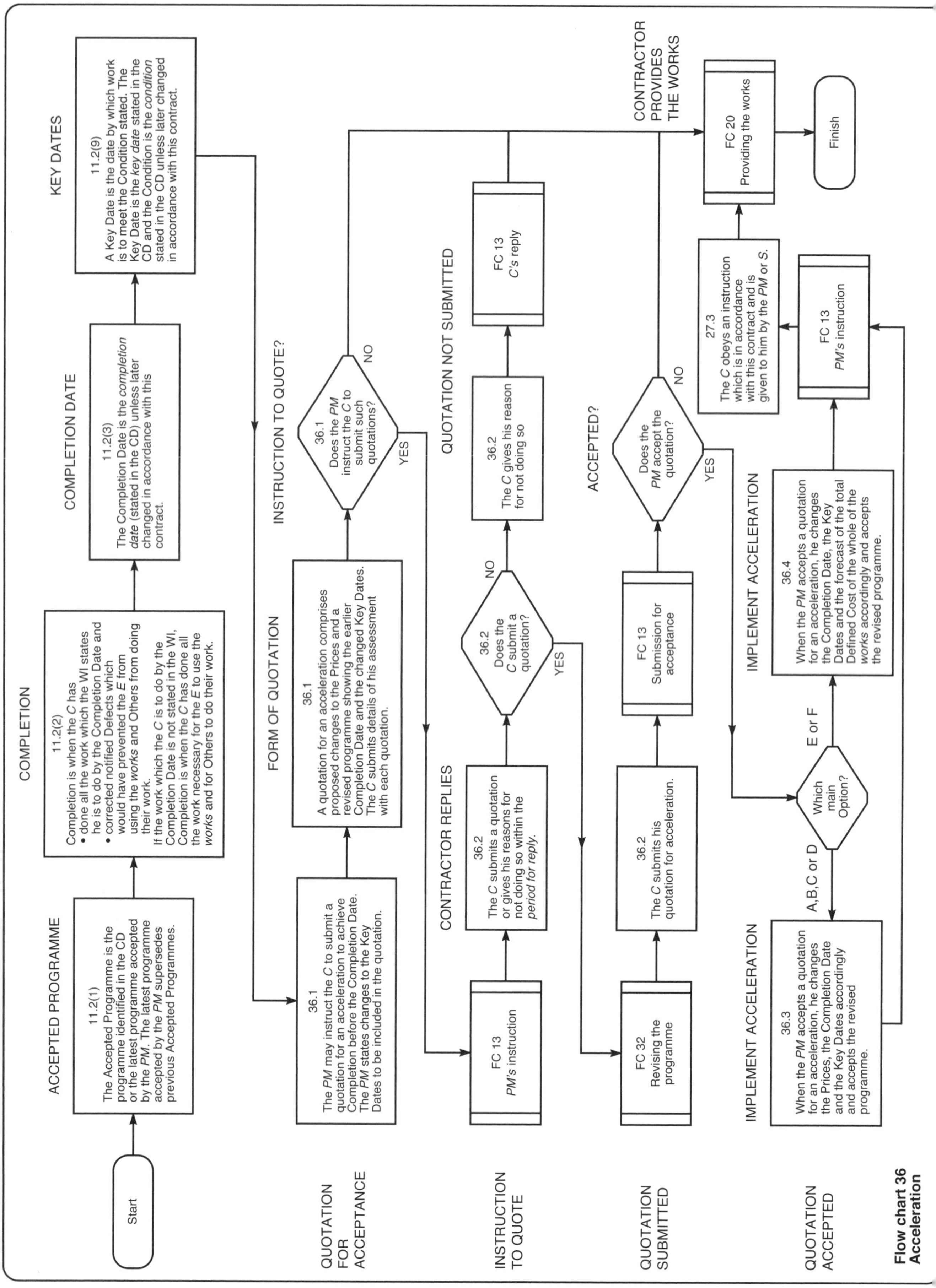

Flow chart 36
Acceleration

Start

ACCEPTED PROGRAMME

11.2(1)
The Accepted Programme is the programme identified in the CD or the latest programme accepted by the *PM*. The latest programme accepted by the *PM* supersedes previous Accepted Programmes.

COMPLETION

11.2(2)
Completion is when the *C* has
- done all the work which the WI states he is to do by the Completion Date and
- corrected notified Defects which would have prevented the *E* from using the *works* and Others from doing their work.

If the work which the *C* is to do by the Completion Date is not stated in the WI, Completion is when the *C* has done all the work necessary for the *E* to use the *works* and for Others to do their work.

COMPLETION DATE

11.2(3)
The Completion Date is the *completion date* (stated in the CD) unless later changed in accordance with this contract.

KEY DATES

11.2(9)
A Key Date is the date by which work is to meet the Condition stated. The Key Date is the *key date* stated in the CD and the Condition is the *condition* stated in the CD unless later changed in accordance with this contract.

QUOTATION FOR ACCEPTANCE

36.1
The *PM* may instruct the *C* to submit a quotation for an acceleration to achieve Completion before the Completion Date. The *PM* states changes to the Key Dates to be included in the quotation.

FORM OF QUOTATION

36.1
A quotation for an acceleration comprises proposed changes to the Prices and a revised programme showing the earlier Completion Date and the changed Key Dates. The *C* submits details of his assessment with each quotation.

INSTRUCTION TO QUOTE?

36.1
Does the *PM* instruct the *C* to submit such quotations?

YES / NO

INSTRUCTION TO QUOTE

FC 13
PM's instruction

CONTRACTOR REPLIES

36.2
The *C* submits a quotation or gives his reasons for not doing so within the *period for reply*.

36.2
Does the *C* submit a quotation?

YES / NO

QUOTATION NOT SUBMITTED

36.2
The *C* gives his reason for not doing so

FC 13
C's reply

QUOTATION SUBMITTED

FC 32
Revising the programme

36.2
The *C* submits his quotation for acceleration.

FC 13
Submission for acceptance

ACCEPTED?

Does the *PM* accept the quotation?

YES / NO

CONTRACTOR PROVIDES THE WORKS

FC 20
Providing the works

Finish

QUOTATION ACCEPTED

Which main Option?

A,B,C or D / E or F

IMPLEMENT ACCELERATION

36.3
When the *PM* accepts a quotation for an acceleration, he changes the Prices, the Completion Date and the Key Dates accordingly and accepts the revised programme.

IMPLEMENT ACCELERATION

36.4
When the *PM* accepts a quotation for an acceleration, he changes the Completion Date, the Key Dates and the forecast of the total Defined Cost of the whole of the *works* accordingly and accepts the revised programme.

FC 13
PM's instruction

27.3
The *C* obeys an instruction which is in accordance with this contract and is given to him by the *PM* or *S*.

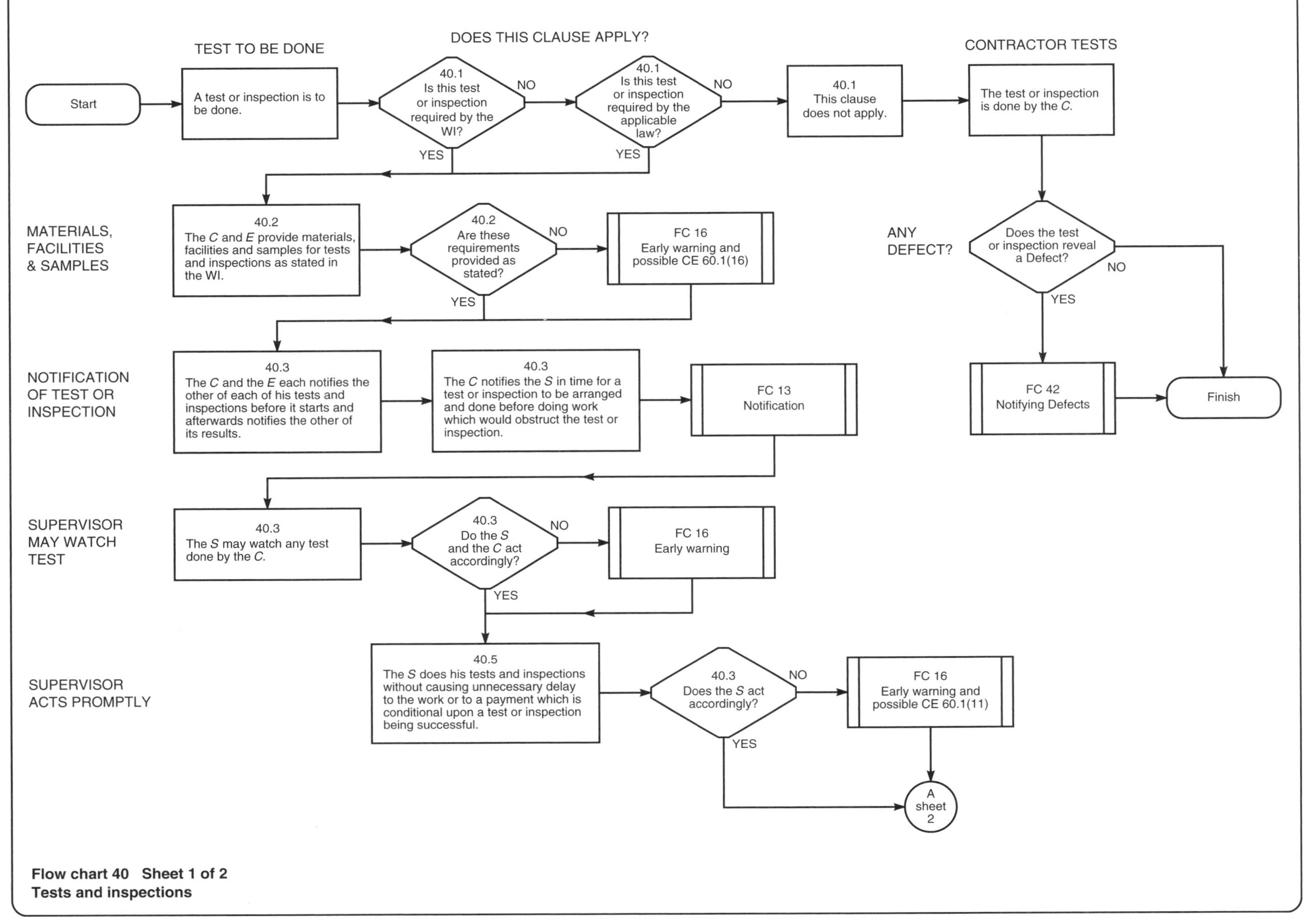
TEST TO BE DONE
DOES THIS CLAUSE APPLY?
CONTRACTOR TESTS
Start
A test or inspection is to be done.
40.1 Is this test or inspection required by the WI?
NO
YES
40.1 Is this test or inspection required by the applicable law?
NO
YES
40.1 This clause does not apply.
The test or inspection is done by the *C*.
ANY DEFECT?
Does the test or inspection reveal a Defect?
NO
YES
FC 42 Notifying Defects
Finish
MATERIALS, FACILITIES & SAMPLES
40.2 The *C* and *E* provide materials, facilities and samples for tests and inspections as stated in the WI.
40.2 Are these requirements provided as stated?
NO
YES
FC 16 Early warning and possible CE 60.1(16)
NOTIFICATION OF TEST OR INSPECTION
40.3 The *C* and the *E* each notifies the other of each of his tests and inspections before it starts and afterwards notifies the other of its results.
40.3 The *C* notifies the *S* in time for a test or inspection to be arranged and done before doing work which would obstruct the test or inspection.
FC 13 Notification
SUPERVISOR MAY WATCH TEST
40.3 The *S* may watch any test done by the *C*.
40.3 Do the *S* and the *C* act accordingly?
NO
YES
FC 16 Early warning
SUPERVISOR ACTS PROMPTLY
40.5 The *S* does his tests and inspections without causing unnecessary delay to the work or to a payment which is conditional upon a test or inspection being successful.
40.3 Does the *S* act accordingly?
NO
YES
FC 16 Early warning and possible CE 60.1(11)
A sheet 2

Flow chart 40 Sheet 1 of 2
Tests and inspections

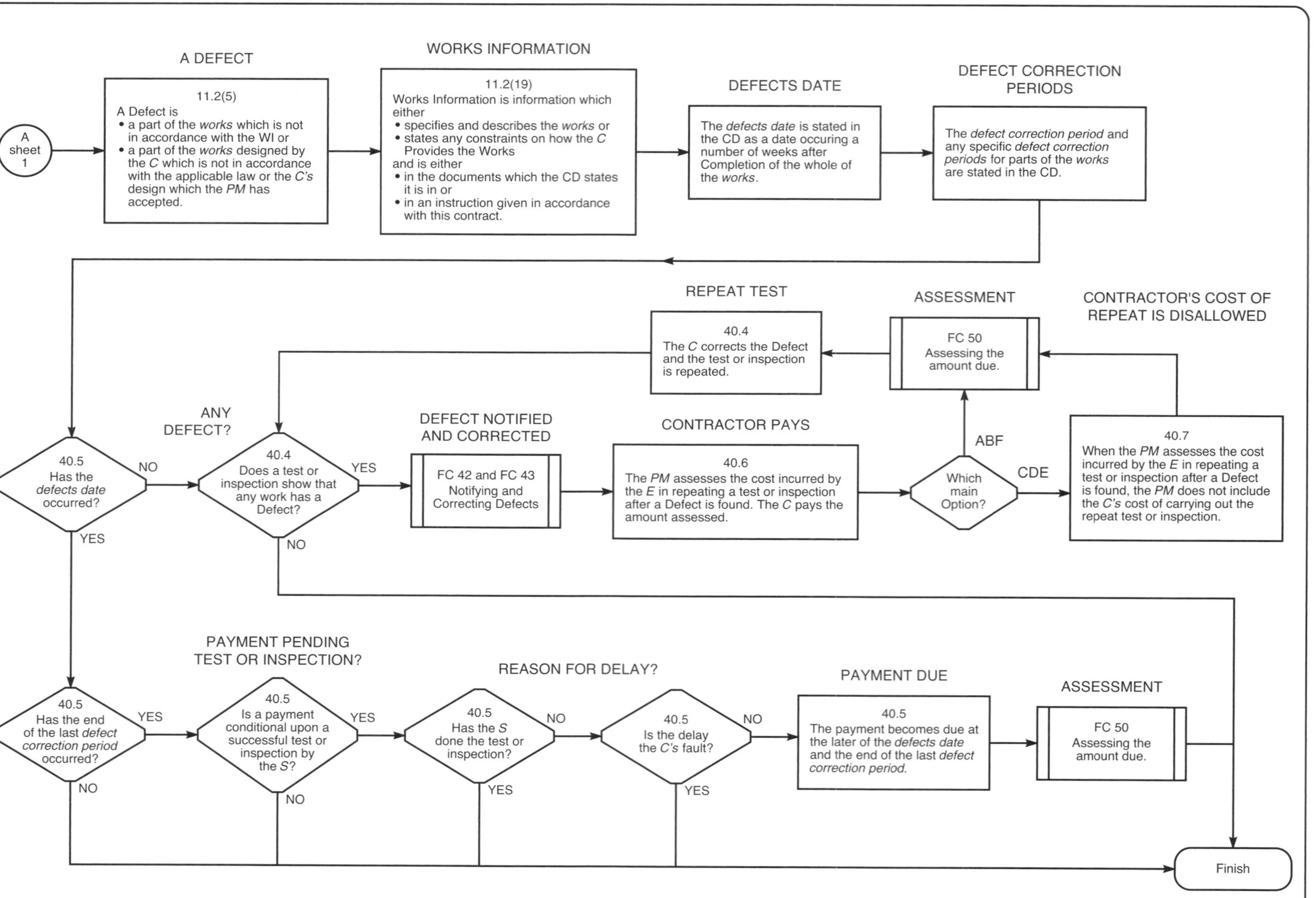
A sheet 1
A DEFECT
11.2(5)
A Defect is
• a part of the works which is not in accordance with the WI or
• a part of the works designed by the C which is not in accordance with the applicable law or the C's design which the PM has accepted.
WORKS INFORMATION
11.2(19)
Works Information is information which either
• specifies and describes the works or
• states any constraints on how the C Provides the Works
and is either
• in the documents which the CD states it is in or
• in an instruction given in accordance with this contract.
DEFECTS DATE
The defects date is stated in the CD as a date occuring a number of weeks after Completion of the whole of the works.
DEFECT CORRECTION PERIODS
The defect correction period and any specific defect correction periods for parts of the works are stated in the CD.
REPEAT TEST
40.4
The C corrects the Defect and the test or inspection is repeated.
ASSESSMENT
FC 50
Assessing the amount due.
CONTRACTOR'S COST OF REPEAT IS DISALLOWED
40.5
Has the defects date occurred?
NO
YES
ANY DEFECT?
40.4
Does a test or inspection show that any work has a Defect?
YES
NO
DEFECT NOTIFIED AND CORRECTED
FC 42 and FC 43
Notifying and Correcting Defects
CONTRACTOR PAYS
40.6
The PM assesses the cost incurred by the E in repeating a test or inspection after a Defect is found. The C pays the amount assessed.
Which main Option?
ABF
CDE
40.7
When the PM assesses the cost incurred by the E in repeating a test or inspection after a Defect is found, the PM does not include the C's cost of carrying out the repeat test or inspection.
PAYMENT PENDING TEST OR INSPECTION?
40.5
Has the end of the last defect correction period occurred?
YES
NO
40.5
Is a payment conditional upon a successful test or inspection by the S?
YES
NO
REASON FOR DELAY?
40.5
Has the S done the test or inspection?
NO
YES
40.5
Is the delay the C's fault?
NO
YES
PAYMENT DUE
40.5
The payment becomes due at the later of the defects date and the end of the last defect correction period.
ASSESSMENT
FC 50
Assessing the amount due.
Finish

Flow chart 40 Sheet 2 of 2
Tests and inspections

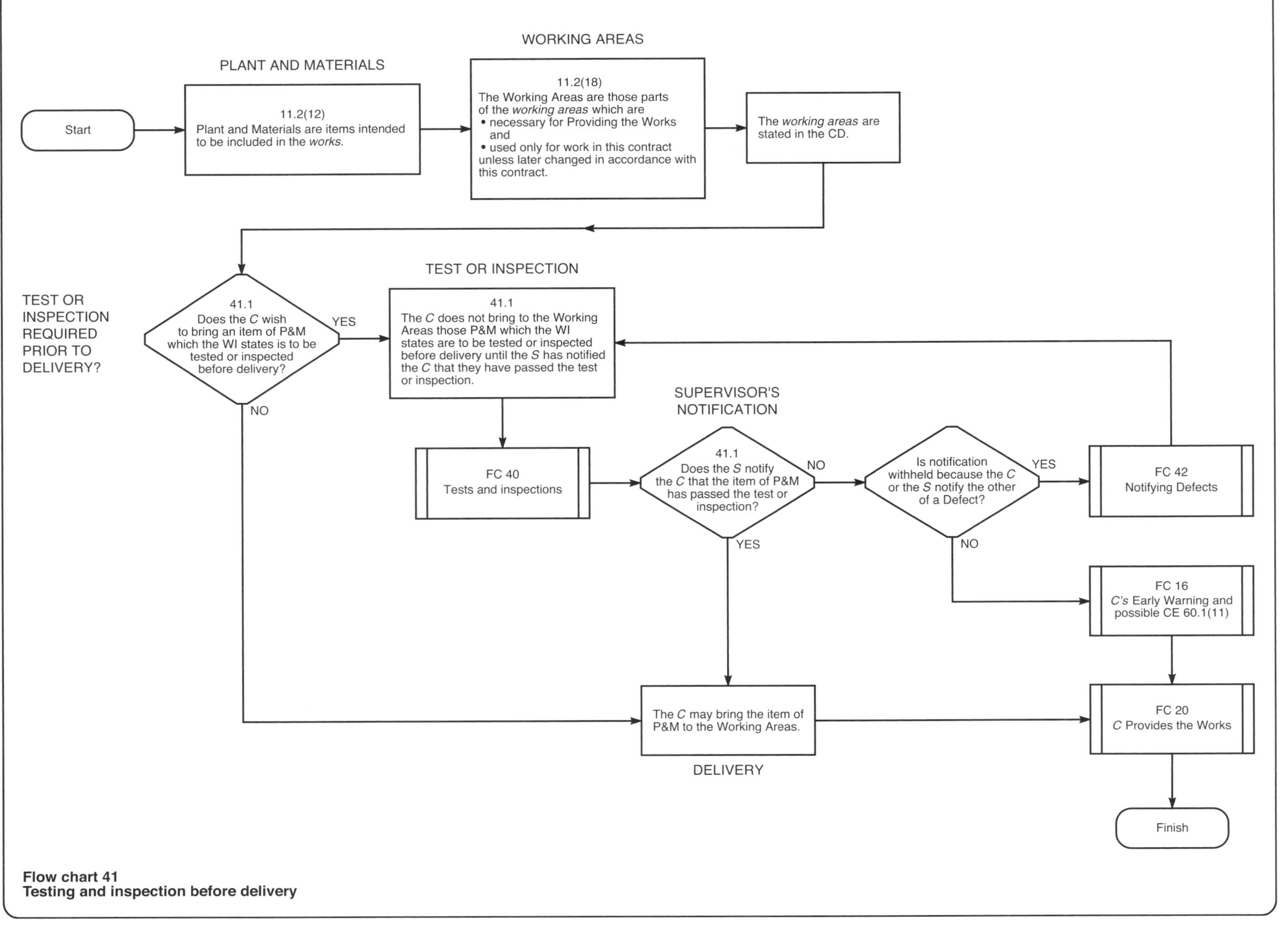
Start
PLANT AND MATERIALS
11.2(12)
Plant and Materials are items intended to be included in the *works*.
WORKING AREAS
11.2(18)
The Working Areas are those parts of the *working areas* which are
• necessary for Providing the Works and
• used only for work in this contract unless later changed in accordance with this contract.
The *working areas* are stated in the CD.
TEST OR INSPECTION REQUIRED PRIOR TO DELIVERY?
41.1
Does the *C* wish to bring an item of P&M which the WI states is to be tested or inspected before delivery?
YES
NO
TEST OR INSPECTION
41.1
The *C* does not bring to the Working Areas those P&M which the WI states are to be tested or inspected before delivery until the *S* has notified the *C* that they have passed the test or inspection.
FC 40
Tests and inspections
SUPERVISOR'S NOTIFICATION
41.1
Does the *S* notify the *C* that the item of P&M has passed the test or inspection?
NO
YES
Is notification withheld because the *C* or the *S* notify the other of a Defect?
YES
NO
FC 42
Notifying Defects
FC 16
C's Early Warning and possible CE 60.1(11)
The *C* may bring the item of P&M to the Working Areas.
DELIVERY
FC 20
C Provides the Works
Finish

Flow chart 41
Testing and inspection before delivery

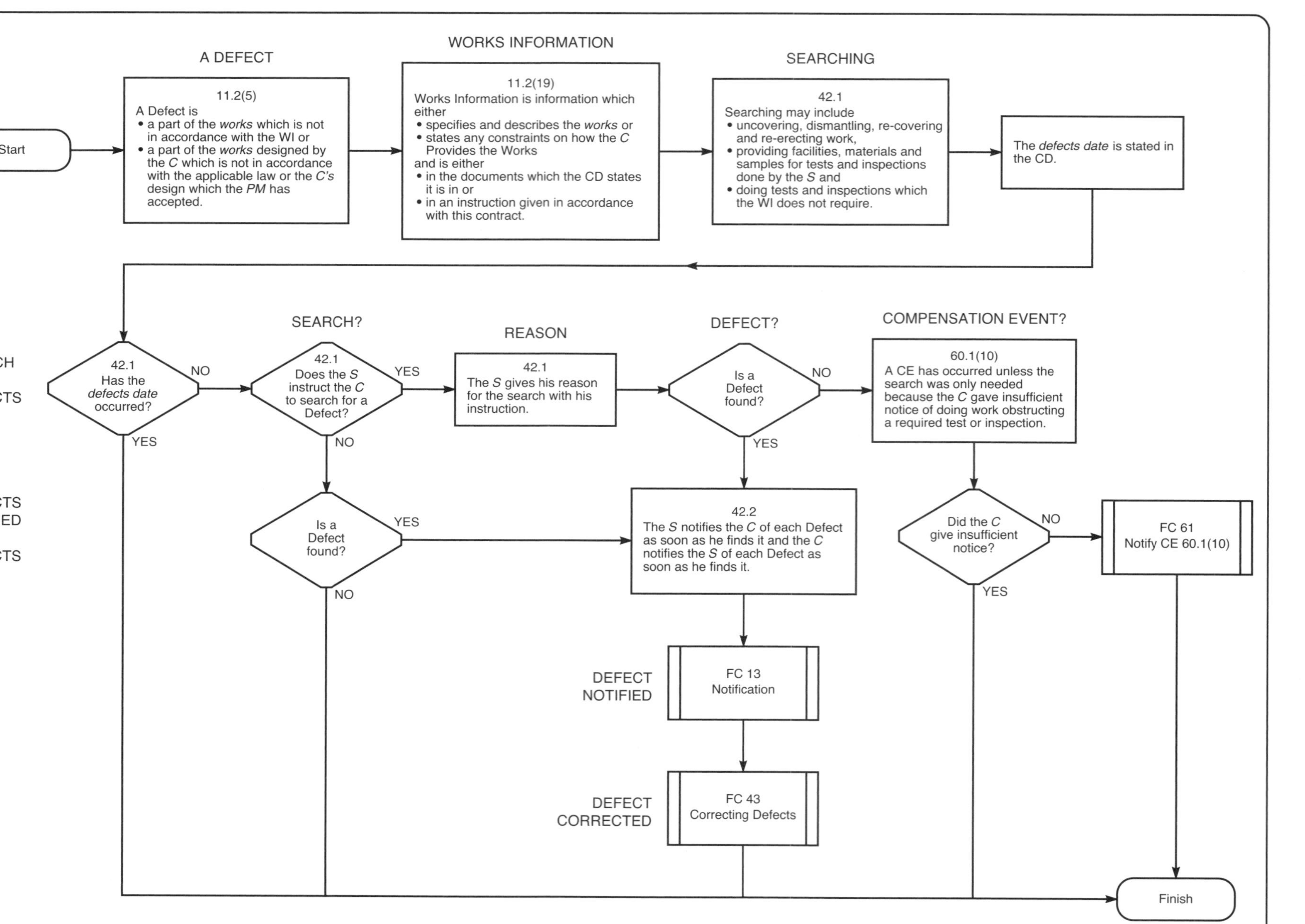
A DEFECT
WORKS INFORMATION
SEARCHING
Start
11.2(5)
A Defect is
• a part of the *works* which is not in accordance with the WI or
• a part of the *works* designed by the *C* which is not in accordance with the applicable law or the *C's* design which the *PM* has accepted.
11.2(19)
Works Information is information which either
• specifies and describes the *works* or
• states any constraints on how the *C* Provides the Works
and is either
• in the documents which the CD states it is in or
• in an instruction given in accordance with this contract.
42.1
Searching may include
• uncovering, dismantling, re-covering and re-erecting work,
• providing facilities, materials and samples for tests and inspections done by the *S* and
• doing tests and inspections which the WI does not require.
The *defects date* is stated in the CD.
SEARCH?
REASON
DEFECT?
COMPENSATION EVENT?
SEARCH UNTIL DEFECTS DATE
42.1
Has the *defects date* occurred?
NO
YES
42.1
Does the *S* instruct the *C* to search for a Defect?
YES
NO
42.1
The *S* gives his reason for the search with his instruction.
Is a Defect found?
NO
YES
60.1(10)
A CE has occurred unless the search was only needed because the *C* gave insufficient notice of doing work obstructing a required test or inspection.
DEFECTS NOTIFIED UNTIL DEFECTS DATE
Is a Defect found?
YES
NO
42.2
The *S* notifies the *C* of each Defect as soon as he finds it and the *C* notifies the *S* of each Defect as soon as he finds it.
Did the *C* give insufficient notice?
NO
YES
FC 61
Notify CE 60.1(10)
DEFECT NOTIFIED
FC 13
Notification
DEFECT CORRECTED
FC 43
Correcting Defects
Finish

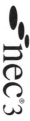

Flow chart 42
Searching for and notifying Defects

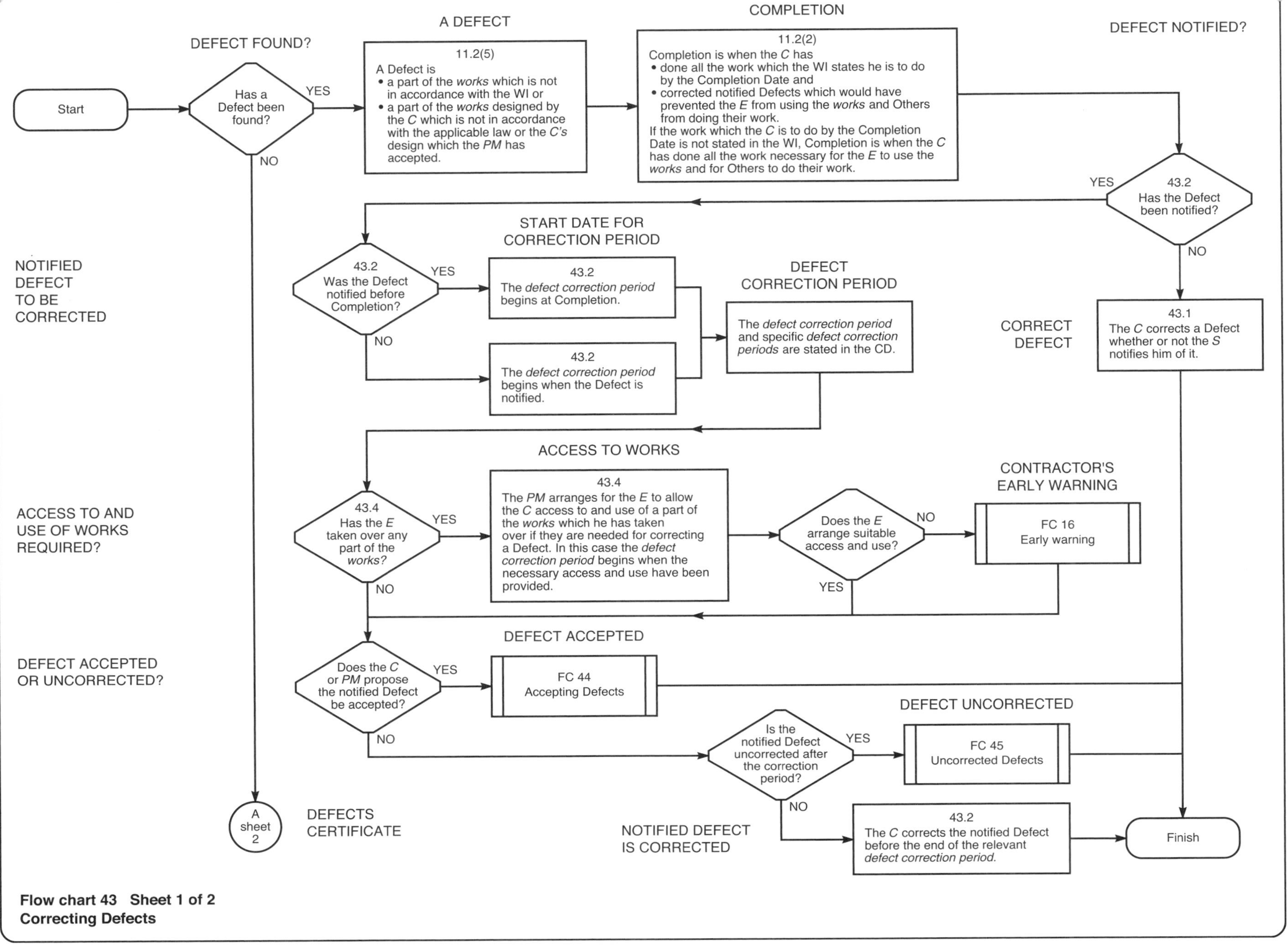
Start
DEFECT FOUND?
Has a Defect been found?
YES
NO
A DEFECT
11.2(5)
A Defect is
• a part of the *works* which is not in accordance with the WI or
• a part of the *works* designed by the *C* which is not in accordance with the applicable law or the *C's* design which the *PM* has accepted.
COMPLETION
11.2(2)
Completion is when the *C* has
• done all the work which the WI states he is to do by the Completion Date and
• corrected notified Defects which would have prevented the *E* from using the *works* and Others from doing their work.
If the work which the *C* is to do by the Completion Date is not stated in the WI, Completion is when the *C* has done all the work necessary for the *E* to use the *works* and for Others to do their work.
DEFECT NOTIFIED?
43.2
Has the Defect been notified?
YES
NO
CORRECT DEFECT
43.1
The *C* corrects a Defect whether or not the *S* notifies him of it.
NOTIFIED DEFECT TO BE CORRECTED
START DATE FOR CORRECTION PERIOD
43.2
Was the Defect notified before Completion?
YES
NO
43.2
The *defect correction period* begins at Completion.
43.2
The *defect correction period* begins when the Defect is notified.
DEFECT CORRECTION PERIOD
The *defect correction period* and specific *defect correction periods* are stated in the CD.
ACCESS TO AND USE OF WORKS REQUIRED?
ACCESS TO WORKS
43.4
Has the *E* taken over any part of the *works?*
YES
NO
43.4
The *PM* arranges for the *E* to allow the *C* access to and use of a part of the *works* which he has taken over if they are needed for correcting a Defect. In this case the *defect correction period* begins when the necessary access and use have been provided.
Does the *E* arrange suitable access and use?
NO
YES
CONTRACTOR'S EARLY WARNING
FC 16
Early warning
DEFECT ACCEPTED OR UNCORRECTED?
Does the *C* or *PM* propose the notified Defect be accepted?
YES
NO
DEFECT ACCEPTED
FC 44
Accepting Defects
DEFECT UNCORRECTED
Is the notified Defect uncorrected after the correction period?
YES
NO
FC 45
Uncorrected Defects
NOTIFIED DEFECT IS CORRECTED
43.2
The *C* corrects the notified Defect before the end of the relevant *defect correction period.*
Finish
A sheet 2
DEFECTS CERTIFICATE

Flow chart 43 Sheet 1 of 2
Correcting Defects

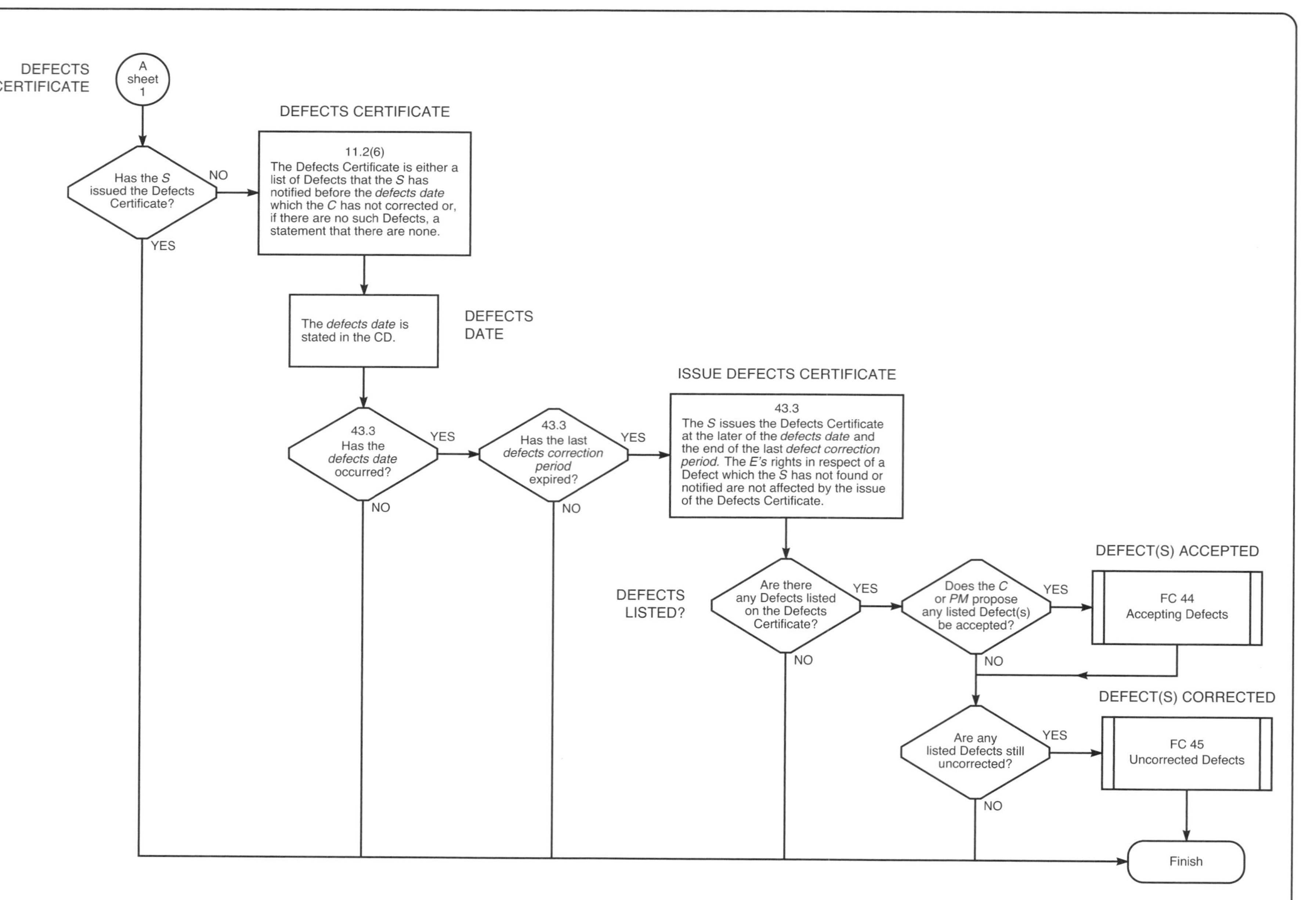
DEFECTS CERTIFICATE
A sheet 1
Has the S issued the Defects Certificate?
NO
YES
DEFECTS CERTIFICATE
11.2(6) The Defects Certificate is either a list of Defects that the S has notified before the defects date which the C has not corrected or, if there are no such Defects, a statement that there are none.
The defects date is stated in the CD.
DEFECTS DATE
43.3 Has the defects date occurred?
YES
NO
43.3 Has the last defects correction period expired?
YES
NO
ISSUE DEFECTS CERTIFICATE
43.3 The S issues the Defects Certificate at the later of the defects date and the end of the last defect correction period. The E's rights in respect of a Defect which the S has not found or notified are not affected by the issue of the Defects Certificate.
DEFECTS LISTED?
Are there any Defects listed on the Defects Certificate?
YES
NO
Does the C or PM propose any listed Defect(s) be accepted?
YES
NO
DEFECT(S) ACCEPTED
FC 44 Accepting Defects
DEFECT(S) CORRECTED
Are any listed Defects still uncorrected?
YES
NO
FC 45 Uncorrected Defects
Finish

Flow chart 43 Sheet 2 of 2
Correcting Defects

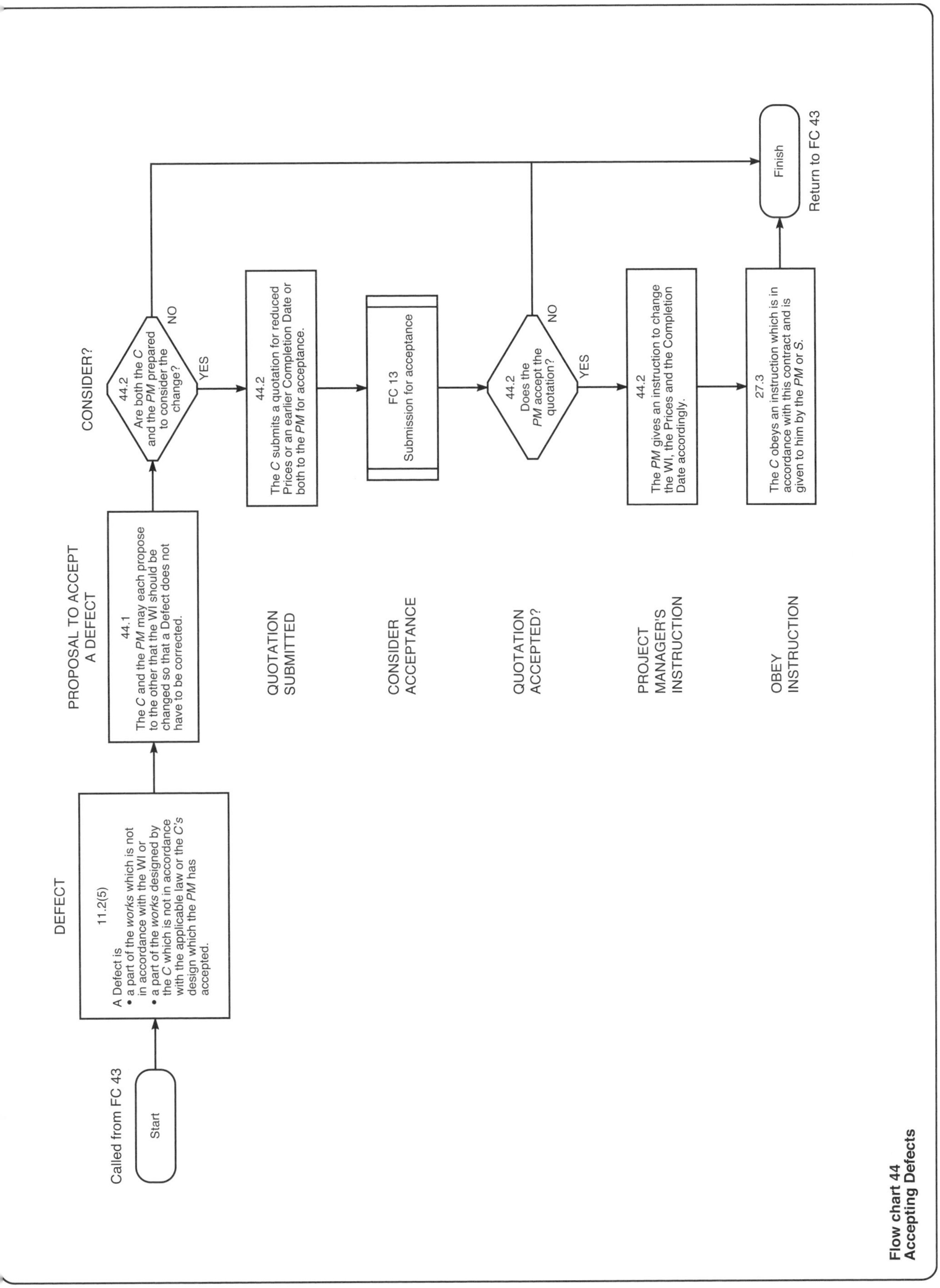

Flow chart 44
Accepting Defects

Called from FC 43

Start

DEFECT

11.2(5)
A Defect is
- a part of the *works* which is not in accordance with the WI or
- a part of the *works* designed by the *C* which is not in accordance with the applicable law or the *C's* design which the *PM* has accepted.

PROPOSAL TO ACCEPT A DEFECT

44.1
The *C* and the *PM* may each propose to the other that the WI should be changed so that a Defect does not have to be corrected.

CONSIDER?

44.2
Are both the *C* and the *PM* prepared to consider the change?

NO → Finish

YES

QUOTATION SUBMITTED

44.2
The *C* submits a quotation for reduced Prices or an earlier Completion Date or both to the *PM* for acceptance.

CONSIDER ACCEPTANCE

FC 13
Submission for acceptance

QUOTATION ACCEPTED?

44.2
Does the *PM* accept the quotation?

NO → Finish

YES

PROJECT MANAGER'S INSTRUCTION

44.2
The *PM* gives an instruction to change the WI, the Prices and the Completion Date accordingly.

OBEY INSTRUCTION

27.3
The *C* obeys an instruction which is in accordance with this contract and is given to him by the *PM* or *S*.

Finish

Return to FC 43

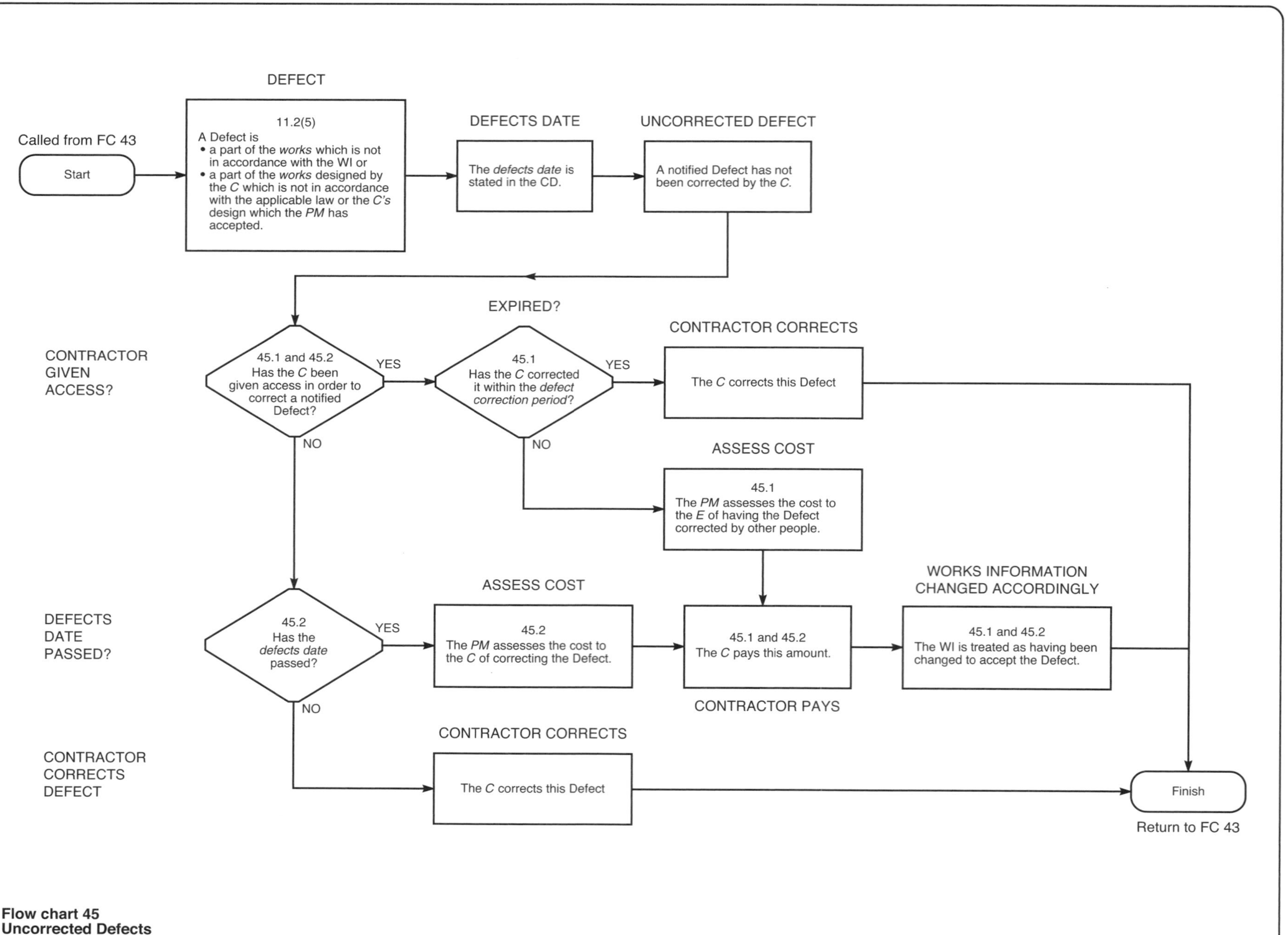
DEFECT
Called from FC 43
Start
11.2(5)
A Defect is
• a part of the works which is not in accordance with the WI or
• a part of the works designed by the C which is not in accordance with the applicable law or the C's design which the PM has accepted.
DEFECTS DATE
The defects date is stated in the CD.
UNCORRECTED DEFECT
A notified Defect has not been corrected by the C.
EXPIRED?
CONTRACTOR CORRECTS
CONTRACTOR GIVEN ACCESS?
45.1 and 45.2
Has the C been given access in order to correct a notified Defect?
YES
45.1
Has the C corrected it within the defect correction period?
YES
The C corrects this Defect
NO
NO
ASSESS COST
45.1
The PM assesses the cost to the E of having the Defect corrected by other people.
WORKS INFORMATION CHANGED ACCORDINGLY
ASSESS COST
DEFECTS DATE PASSED?
45.2
Has the defects date passed?
YES
45.2
The PM assesses the cost to the C of correcting the Defect.
45.1 and 45.2
The C pays this amount.
45.1 and 45.2
The WI is treated as having been changed to accept the Defect.
NO
CONTRACTOR PAYS
CONTRACTOR CORRECTS
CONTRACTOR CORRECTS DEFECT
The C corrects this Defect
Finish
Return to FC 43
Flow chart 45
Uncorrected Defects

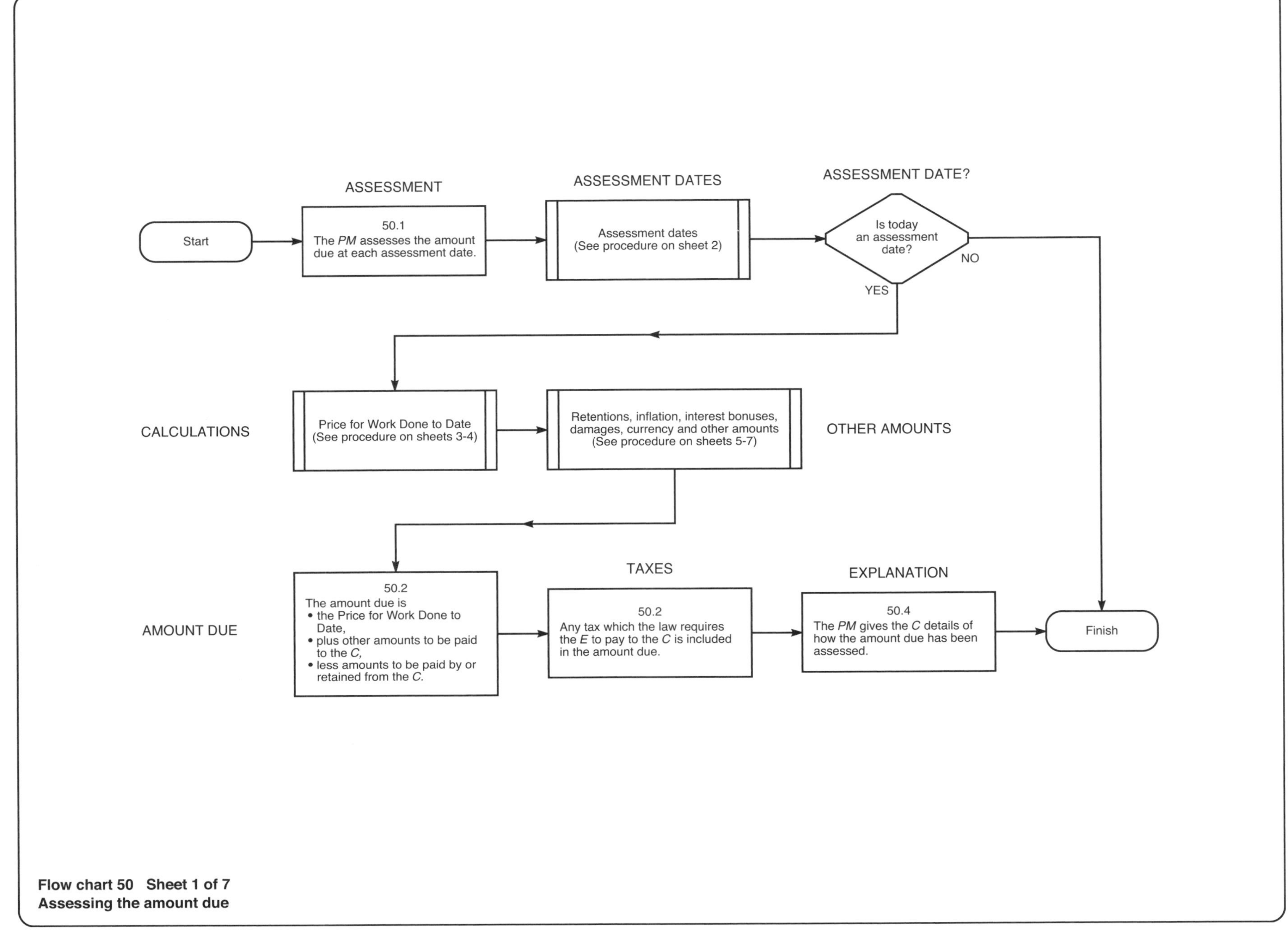
ASSESSMENT
ASSESSMENT DATES
ASSESSMENT DATE?
Start
50.1
The PM assesses the amount due at each assessment date.
Assessment dates
(See procedure on sheet 2)
Is today an assessment date?
NO
YES
CALCULATIONS
Price for Work Done to Date
(See procedure on sheets 3-4)
Retentions, inflation, interest bonuses, damages, currency and other amounts
(See procedure on sheets 5-7)
OTHER AMOUNTS
TAXES
EXPLANATION
AMOUNT DUE
50.2
The amount due is
• the Price for Work Done to Date,
• plus other amounts to be paid to the C,
• less amounts to be paid by or retained from the C.
50.2
Any tax which the law requires the E to pay to the C is included in the amount due.
50.4
The PM gives the C details of how the amount due has been assessed.
Finish

Flow chart 50 Sheet 1 of 7
Assessing the amount due

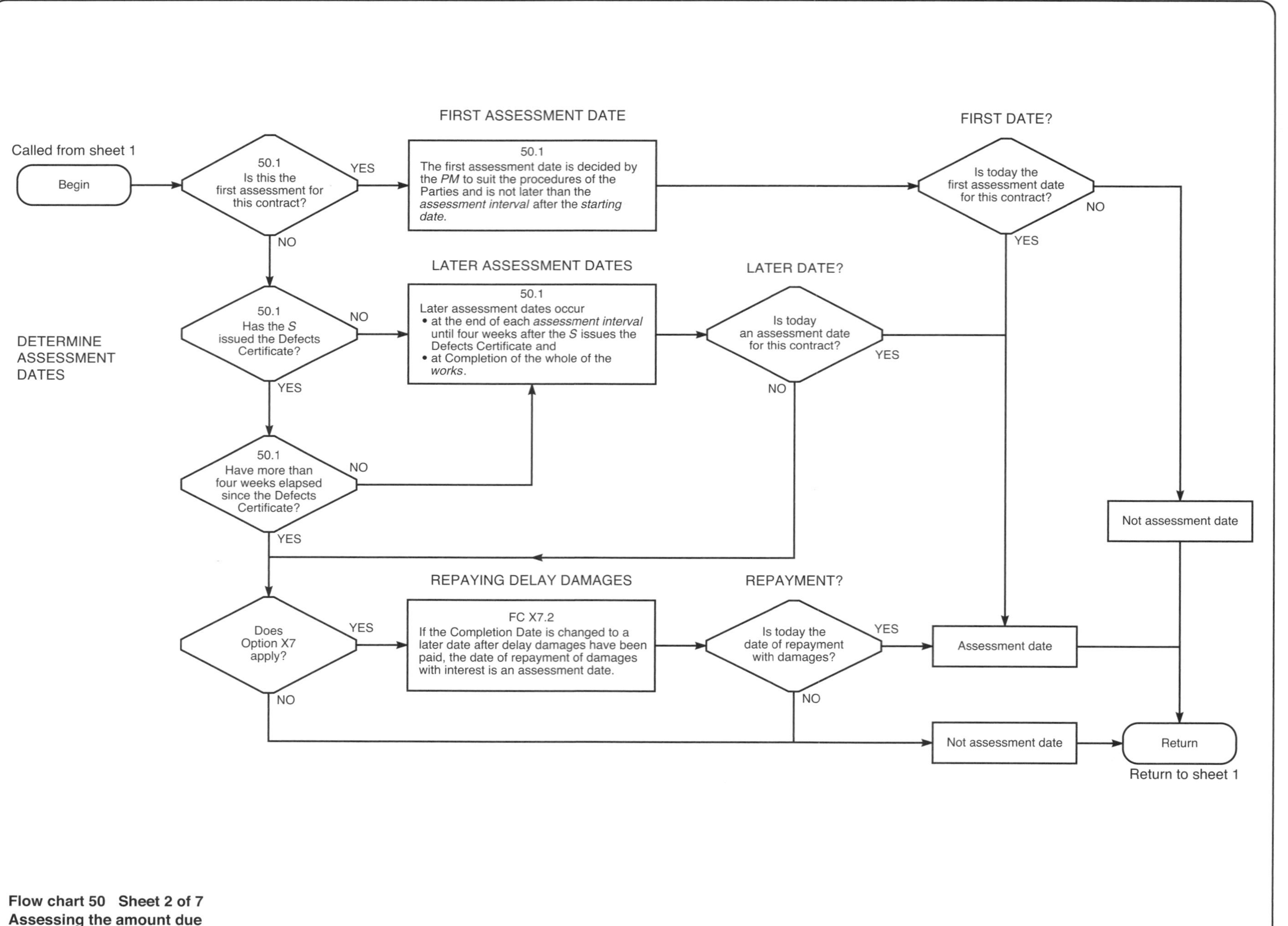
Called from sheet 1
Begin
DETERMINE ASSESSMENT DATES
FIRST ASSESSMENT DATE
50.1 Is this the first assessment for this contract?
YES
NO
50.1 The first assessment date is decided by the PM to suit the procedures of the Parties and is not later than the assessment interval after the starting date.
FIRST DATE?
Is today the first assessment date for this contract?
NO
YES
Not assessment date
LATER ASSESSMENT DATES
50.1 Has the S issued the Defects Certificate?
NO
YES
50.1 Later assessment dates occur
• at the end of each assessment interval until four weeks after the S issues the Defects Certificate and
• at Completion of the whole of the works.
LATER DATE?
Is today an assessment date for this contract?
YES
NO
50.1 Have more than four weeks elapsed since the Defects Certificate?
NO
YES
REPAYING DELAY DAMAGES
Does Option X7 apply?
YES
NO
FC X7.2 If the Completion Date is changed to a later date after delay damages have been paid, the date of repayment of damages with interest is an assessment date.
REPAYMENT?
Is today the date of repayment with damages?
YES
NO
Assessment date
Not assessment date
Return
Return to sheet 1
Flow chart 50 Sheet 2 of 7
Assessing the amount due

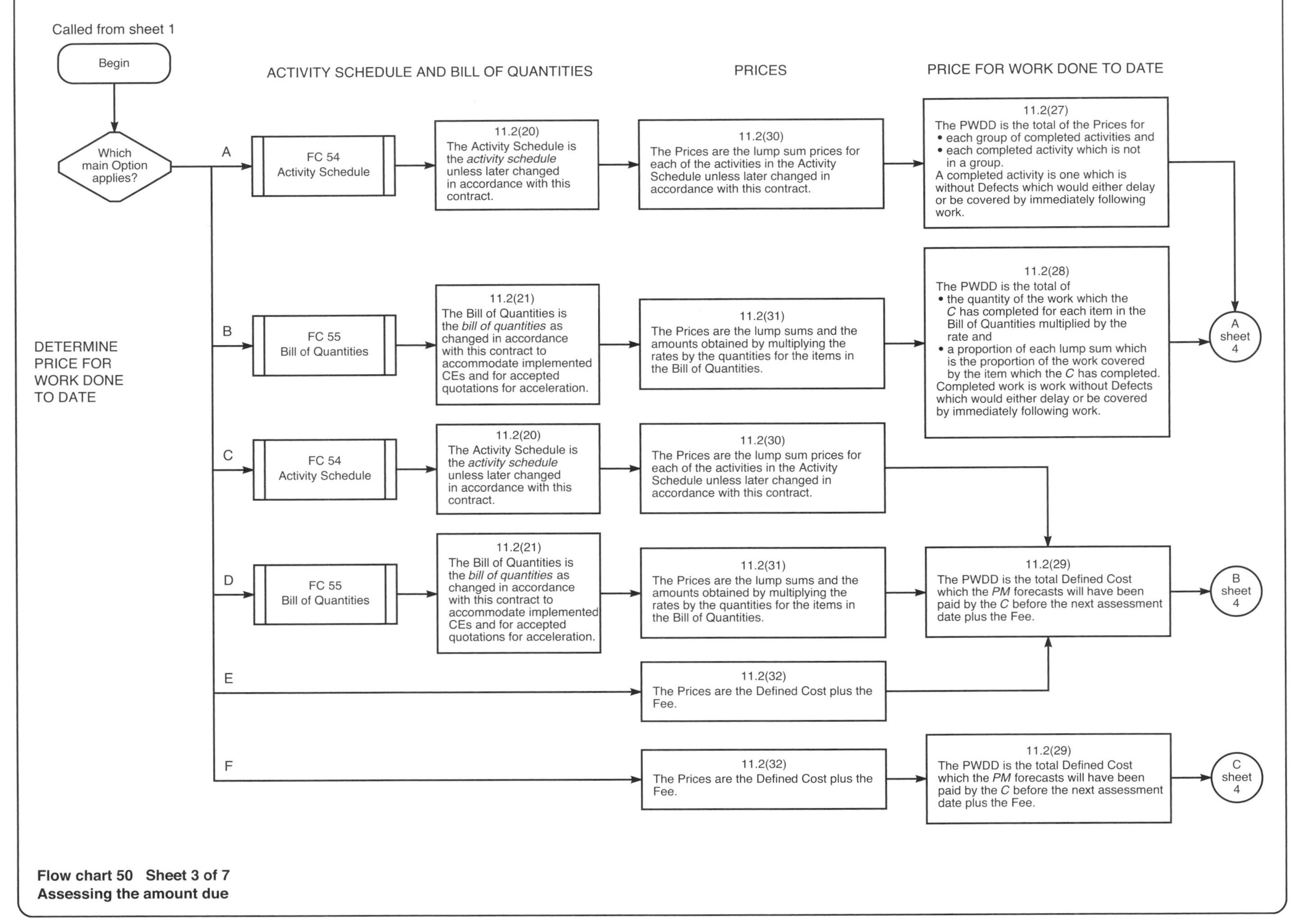

Called from sheet 1
Begin
Which main Option applies?
ACTIVITY SCHEDULE AND BILL OF QUANTITIES
PRICES
PRICE FOR WORK DONE TO DATE
DETERMINE PRICE FOR WORK DONE TO DATE
A
FC 54 Activity Schedule
11.2(20) The Activity Schedule is the *activity schedule* unless later changed in accordance with this contract.
11.2(30) The Prices are the lump sum prices for each of the activities in the Activity Schedule unless later changed in accordance with this contract.
11.2(27) The PWDD is the total of the Prices for
• each group of completed activities and
• each completed activity which is not in a group.
A completed activity is one which is without Defects which would either delay or be covered by immediately following work.
B
FC 55 Bill of Quantities
11.2(21) The Bill of Quantities is the *bill of quantities* as changed in accordance with this contract to accommodate implemented CEs and for accepted quotations for acceleration.
11.2(31) The Prices are the lump sums and the amounts obtained by multiplying the rates by the quantities for the items in the Bill of Quantities.
11.2(28) The PWDD is the total of
• the quantity of the work which the *C* has completed for each item in the Bill of Quantities multiplied by the rate and
• a proportion of each lump sum which is the proportion of the work covered by the item which the *C* has completed.
Completed work is work without Defects which would either delay or be covered by immediately following work.
A sheet 4
C
FC 54 Activity Schedule
11.2(20) The Activity Schedule is the *activity schedule* unless later changed in accordance with this contract.
11.2(30) The Prices are the lump sum prices for each of the activities in the Activity Schedule unless later changed in accordance with this contract.
D
FC 55 Bill of Quantities
11.2(21) The Bill of Quantities is the *bill of quantities* as changed in accordance with this contract to accommodate implemented CEs and for accepted quotations for acceleration.
11.2(31) The Prices are the lump sums and the amounts obtained by multiplying the rates by the quantities for the items in the Bill of Quantities.
11.2(29) The PWDD is the total Defined Cost which the *PM* forecasts will have been paid by the *C* before the next assessment date plus the Fee.
B sheet 4
E
11.2(32) The Prices are the Defined Cost plus the Fee.
F
11.2(32) The Prices are the Defined Cost plus the Fee.
11.2(29) The PWDD is the total Defined Cost which the *PM* forecasts will have been paid by the *C* before the next assessment date plus the Fee.
C sheet 4

Flow chart 50 Sheet 3 of 7
Assessing the amount due

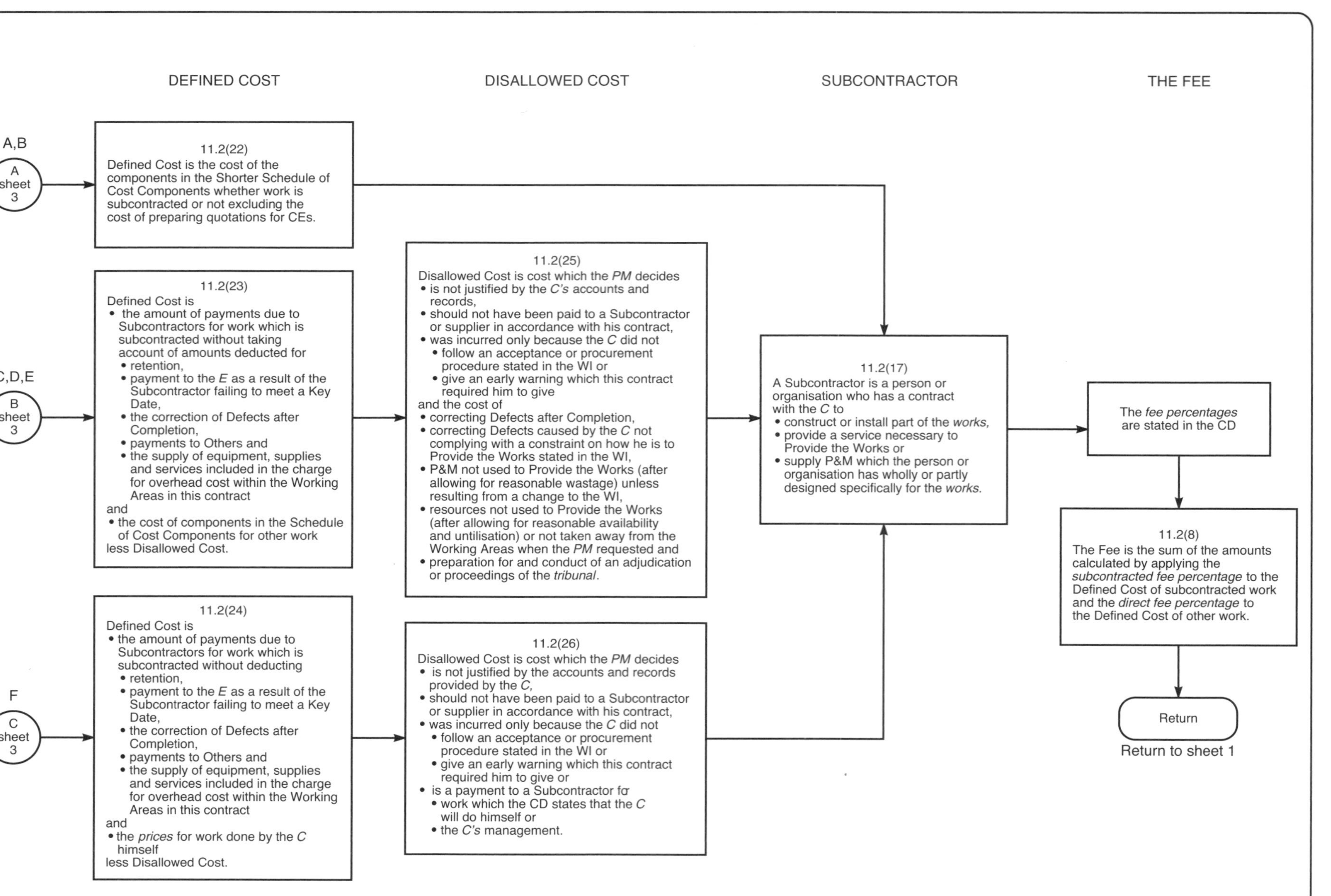
DEFINED COST
DISALLOWED COST
SUBCONTRACTOR
THE FEE
A,B
A sheet 3
11.2(22) Defined Cost is the cost of the components in the Shorter Schedule of Cost Components whether work is subcontracted or not excluding the cost of preparing quotations for CEs.
C,D,E
B sheet 3
11.2(23) Defined Cost is • the amount of payments due to Subcontractors for work which is subcontracted without taking account of amounts deducted for • retention, • payment to the E as a result of the Subcontractor failing to meet a Key Date, • the correction of Defects after Completion, • payments to Others and • the supply of equipment, supplies and services included in the charge for overhead cost within the Working Areas in this contract and • the cost of components in the Schedule of Cost Components for other work less Disallowed Cost.
F
C sheet 3
11.2(24) Defined Cost is • the amount of payments due to Subcontractors for work which is subcontracted without deducting • retention, • payment to the E as a result of the Subcontractor failing to meet a Key Date, • the correction of Defects after Completion, • payments to Others and • the supply of equipment, supplies and services included in the charge for overhead cost within the Working Areas in this contract and • the prices for work done by the C himself less Disallowed Cost.
11.2(25) Disallowed Cost is cost which the PM decides • is not justified by the C's accounts and records, • should not have been paid to a Subcontractor or supplier in accordance with his contract, • was incurred only because the C did not • follow an acceptance or procurement procedure stated in the WI or • give an early warning which this contract required him to give and the cost of • correcting Defects after Completion, • correcting Defects caused by the C not complying with a constraint on how he is to Provide the Works stated in the WI, • P&M not used to Provide the Works (after allowing for reasonable wastage) unless resulting from a change to the WI, • resources not used to Provide the Works (after allowing for reasonable availability and untilisation) or not taken away from the Working Areas when the PM requested and • preparation for and conduct of an adjudication or proceedings of the tribunal.
11.2(26) Disallowed Cost is cost which the PM decides • is not justified by the accounts and records provided by the C, • should not have been paid to a Subcontractor or supplier in accordance with his contract, • was incurred only because the C did not • follow an acceptance or procurement procedure stated in the WI or • give an early warning which this contract required him to give or • is a payment to a Subcontractor for • work which the CD states that the C will do himself or • the C's management.
11.2(17) A Subcontractor is a person or organisation who has a contract with the C to • construct or install part of the works, • provide a service necessary to Provide the Works or • supply P&M which the person or organisation has wholly or partly designed specifically for the works.
The fee percentages are stated in the CD
11.2(8) The Fee is the sum of the amounts calculated by applying the subcontracted fee percentage to the Defined Cost of subcontracted work and the direct fee percentage to the Defined Cost of other work.
Return
Return to sheet 1

Flow chart 50 Sheet 4 of 7
Assessing the amount due

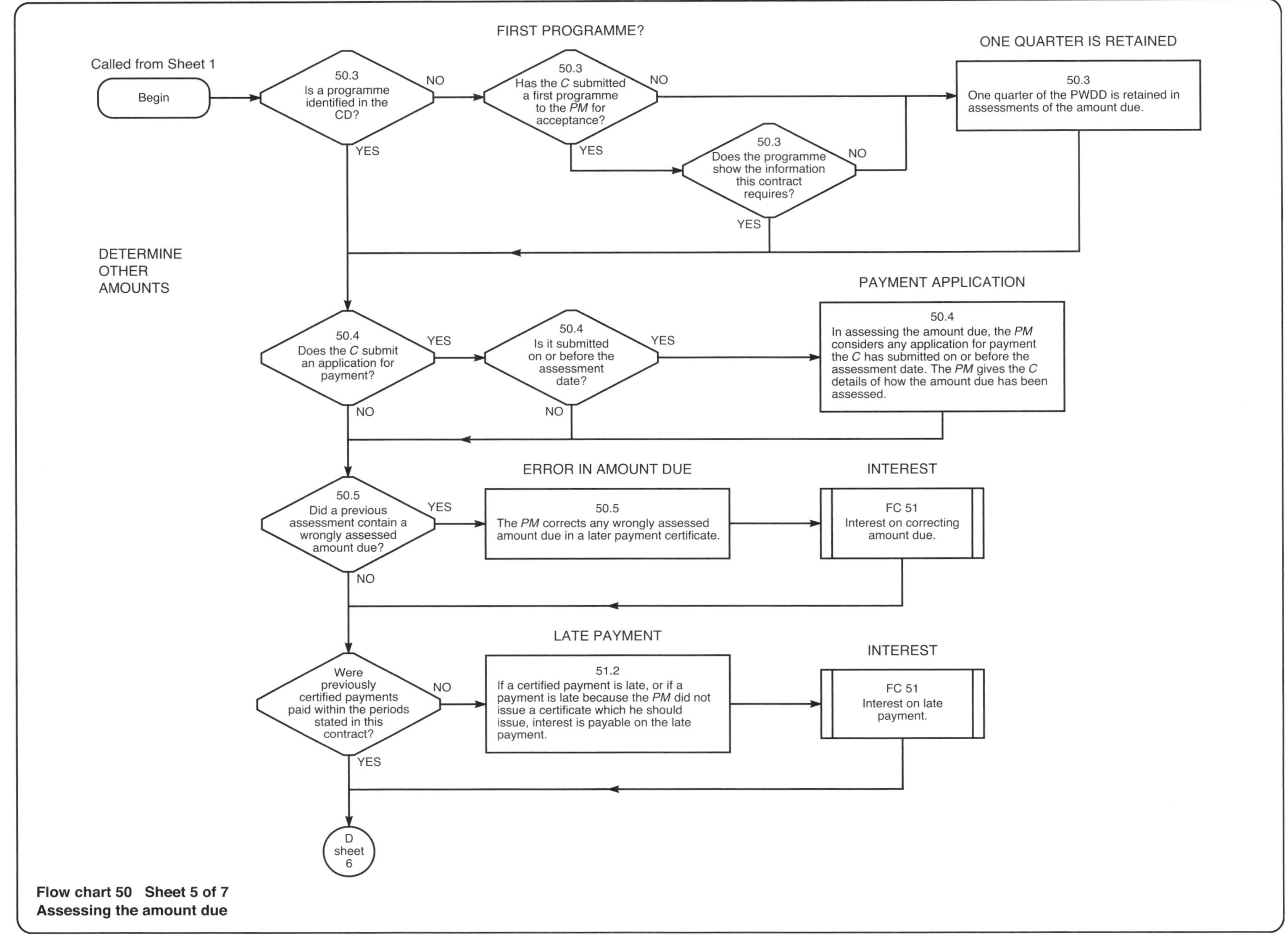
Called from Sheet 1
Begin
FIRST PROGRAMME?
50.3 Is a programme identified in the CD?
NO
YES
50.3 Has the C submitted a first programme to the PM for acceptance?
NO
YES
50.3 Does the programme show the information this contract requires?
NO
YES
ONE QUARTER IS RETAINED
50.3 One quarter of the PWDD is retained in assessments of the amount due.
DETERMINE OTHER AMOUNTS
50.4 Does the C submit an application for payment?
YES
NO
50.4 Is it submitted on or before the assessment date?
YES
NO
PAYMENT APPLICATION
50.4 In assessing the amount due, the PM considers any application for payment the C has submitted on or before the assessment date. The PM gives the C details of how the amount due has been assessed.
50.5 Did a previous assessment contain a wrongly assessed amount due?
YES
NO
ERROR IN AMOUNT DUE
50.5 The PM corrects any wrongly assessed amount due in a later payment certificate.
INTEREST
FC 51 Interest on correcting amount due.
Were previously certified payments paid within the periods stated in this contract?
NO
YES
LATE PAYMENT
51.2 If a certified payment is late, or if a payment is late because the PM did not issue a certificate which he should issue, interest is payable on the late payment.
INTEREST
FC 51 Interest on late payment.
D sheet 6
Flow chart 50 Sheet 5 of 7
Assessing the amount due

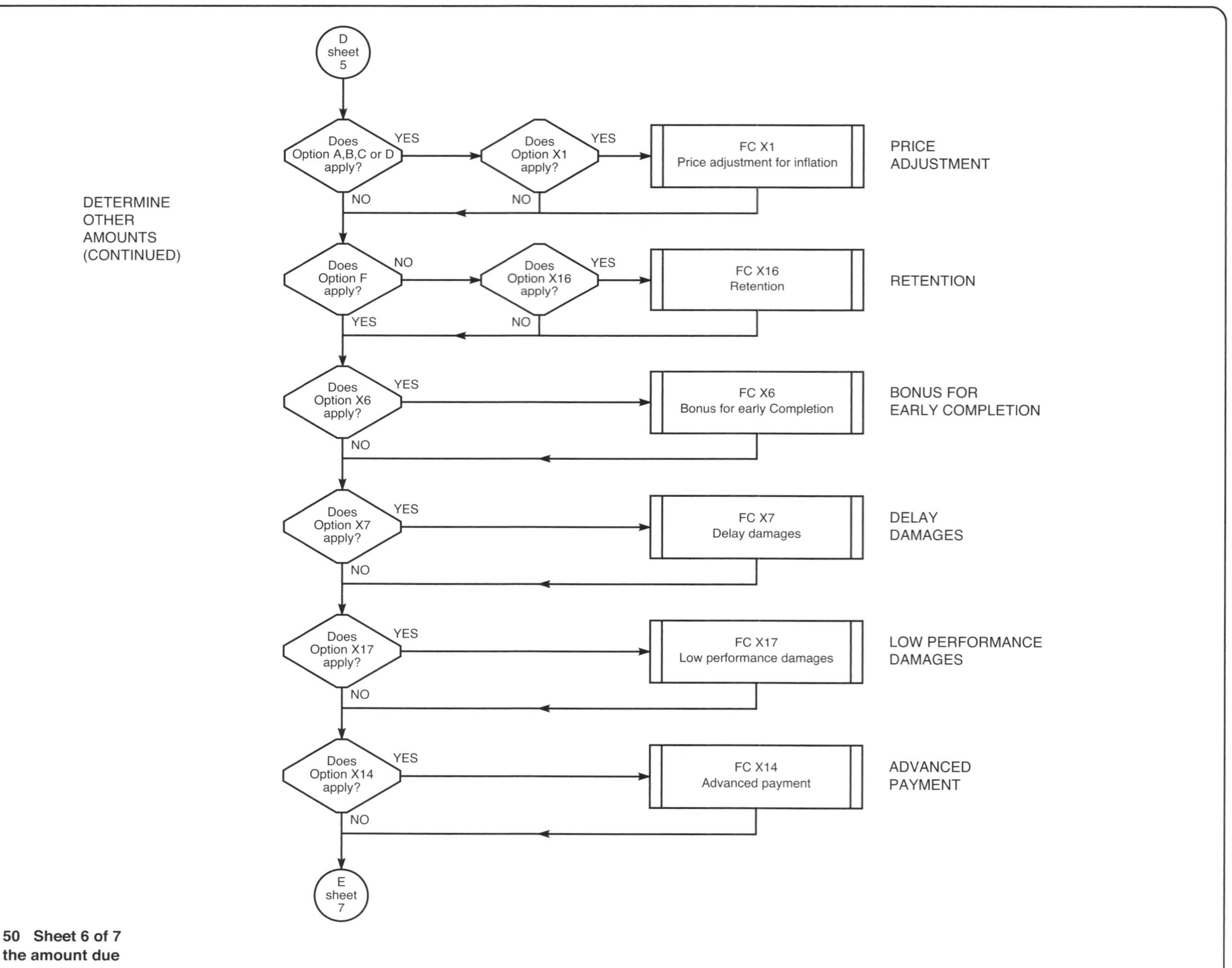
D sheet 5
DETERMINE OTHER AMOUNTS (CONTINUED)
Does Option A,B,C or D apply?
YES
NO
Does Option X1 apply?
YES
NO
FC X1 Price adjustment for inflation
PRICE ADJUSTMENT
Does Option F apply?
NO
YES
Does Option X16 apply?
YES
NO
FC X16 Retention
RETENTION
Does Option X6 apply?
YES
NO
FC X6 Bonus for early Completion
BONUS FOR EARLY COMPLETION
Does Option X7 apply?
YES
NO
FC X7 Delay damages
DELAY DAMAGES
Does Option X17 apply?
YES
NO
FC X17 Low performance damages
LOW PERFORMANCE DAMAGES
Does Option X14 apply?
YES
NO
FC X14 Advanced payment
ADVANCED PAYMENT
E sheet 7

Flow chart 50 Sheet 6 of 7
Assessing the amount due

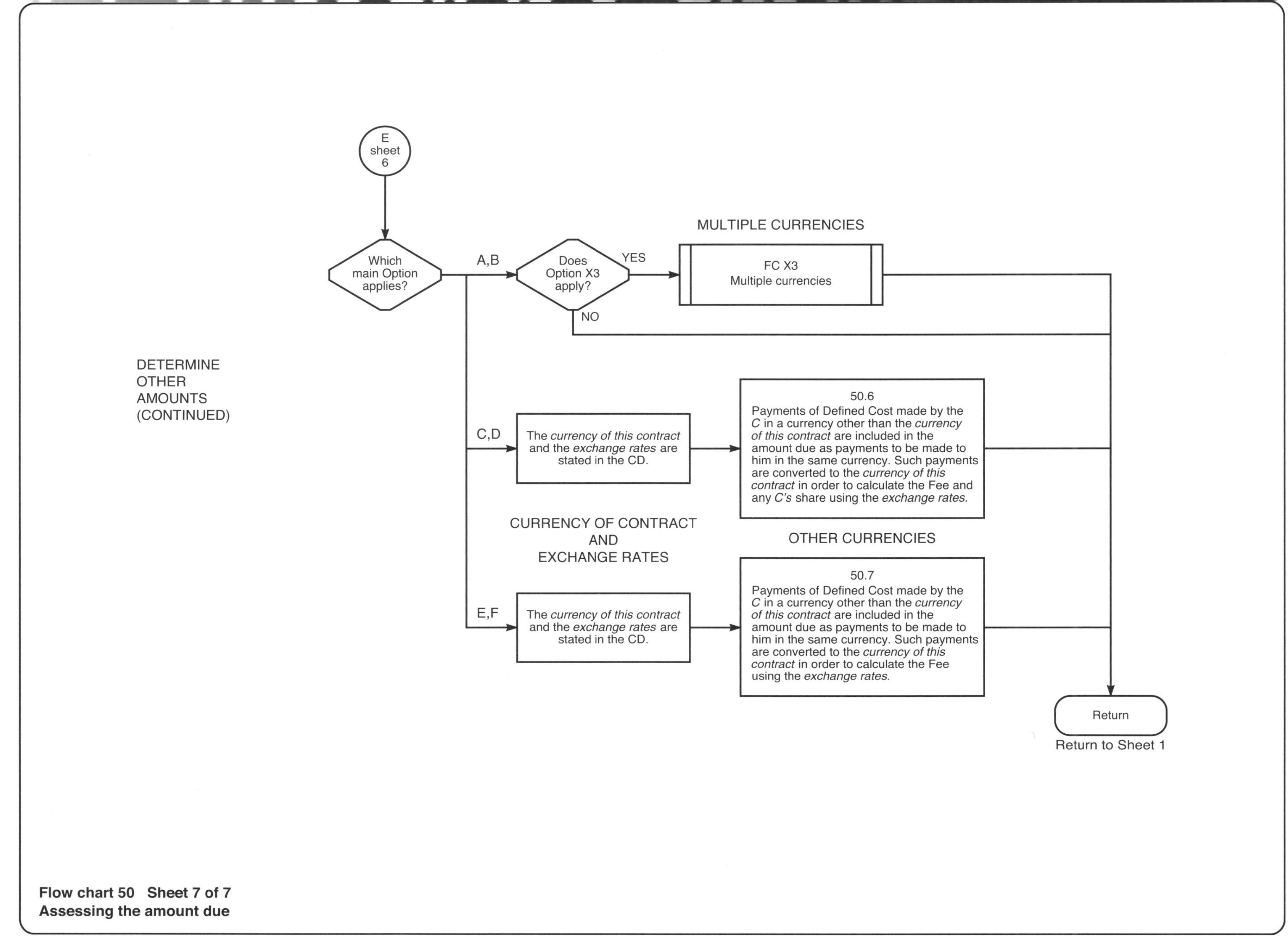
E sheet 6
Which main Option applies?
A,B
Does Option X3 apply?
YES
NO
MULTIPLE CURRENCIES
FC X3 Multiple currencies
DETERMINE OTHER AMOUNTS (CONTINUED)
C,D
The currency of this contract and the exchange rates are stated in the CD.
50.6
Payments of Defined Cost made by the C in a currency other than the currency of this contract are included in the amount due as payments to be made to him in the same currency. Such payments are converted to the currency of this contract in order to calculate the Fee and any C's share using the exchange rates.
CURRENCY OF CONTRACT AND EXCHANGE RATES
OTHER CURRENCIES
E,F
The currency of this contract and the exchange rates are stated in the CD.
50.7
Payments of Defined Cost made by the C in a currency other than the currency of this contract are included in the amount due as payments to be made to him in the same currency. Such payments are converted to the currency of this contract in order to calculate the Fee using the exchange rates.
Return
Return to Sheet 1

Flow chart 50 Sheet 7 of 7
Assessing the amount due

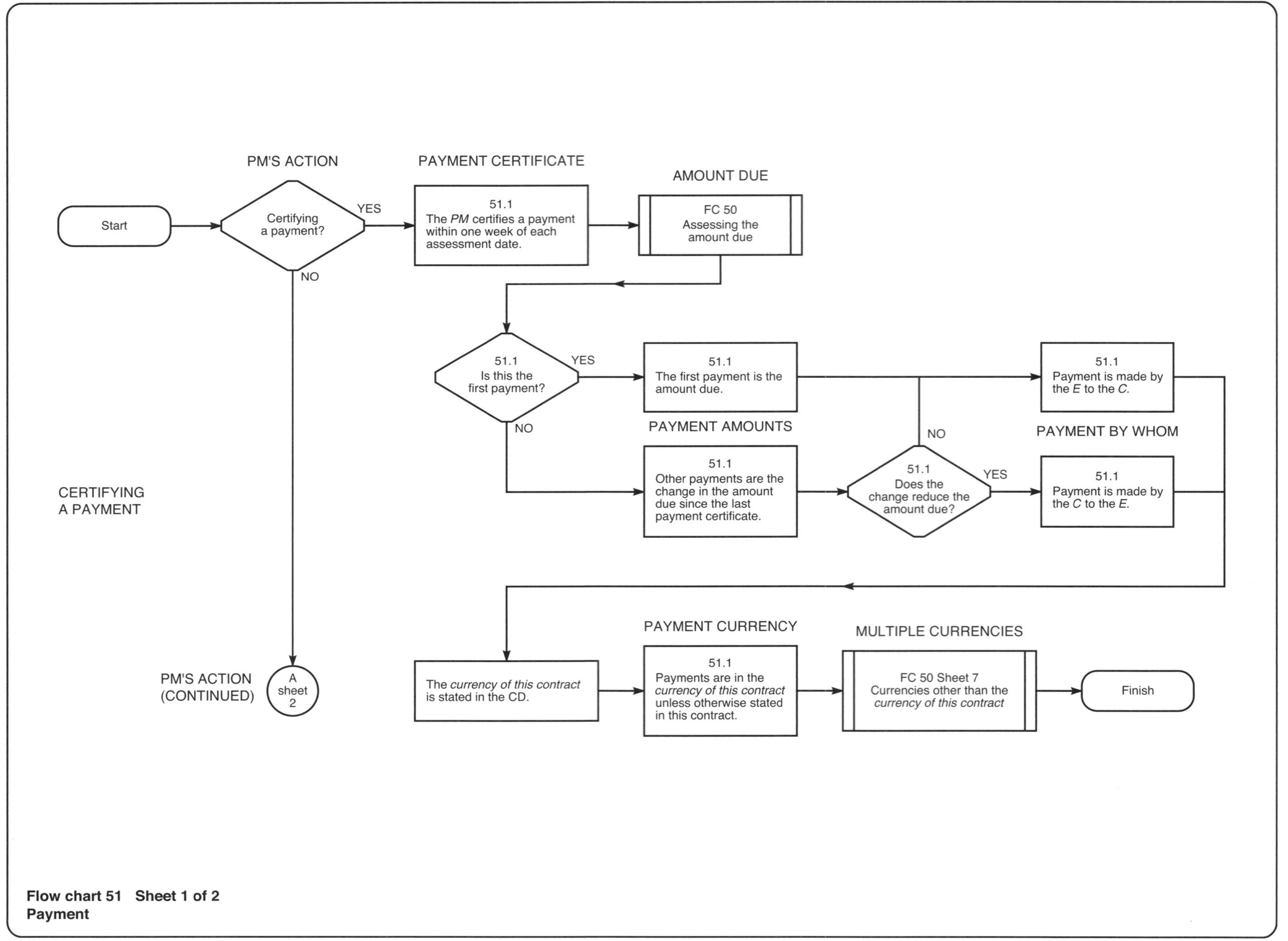

CERTIFYING A PAYMENT
Start
PM'S ACTION
Certifying a payment?
YES
NO
PAYMENT CERTIFICATE
51.1 The PM certifies a payment within one week of each assessment date.
AMOUNT DUE
FC 50 Assessing the amount due
51.1 Is this the first payment?
YES
NO
PAYMENT AMOUNTS
51.1 The first payment is the amount due.
51.1 Other payments are the change in the amount due since the last payment certificate.
51.1 Does the change reduce the amount due?
NO
YES
PAYMENT BY WHOM
51.1 Payment is made by the E to the C.
51.1 Payment is made by the C to the E.
The currency of this contract is stated in the CD.
PAYMENT CURRENCY
51.1 Payments are in the currency of this contract unless otherwise stated in this contract.
MULTIPLE CURRENCIES
FC 50 Sheet 7 Currencies other than the currency of this contract
Finish
PM'S ACTION (CONTINUED)
A sheet 2

Flow chart 51 Sheet 1 of 2
Payment

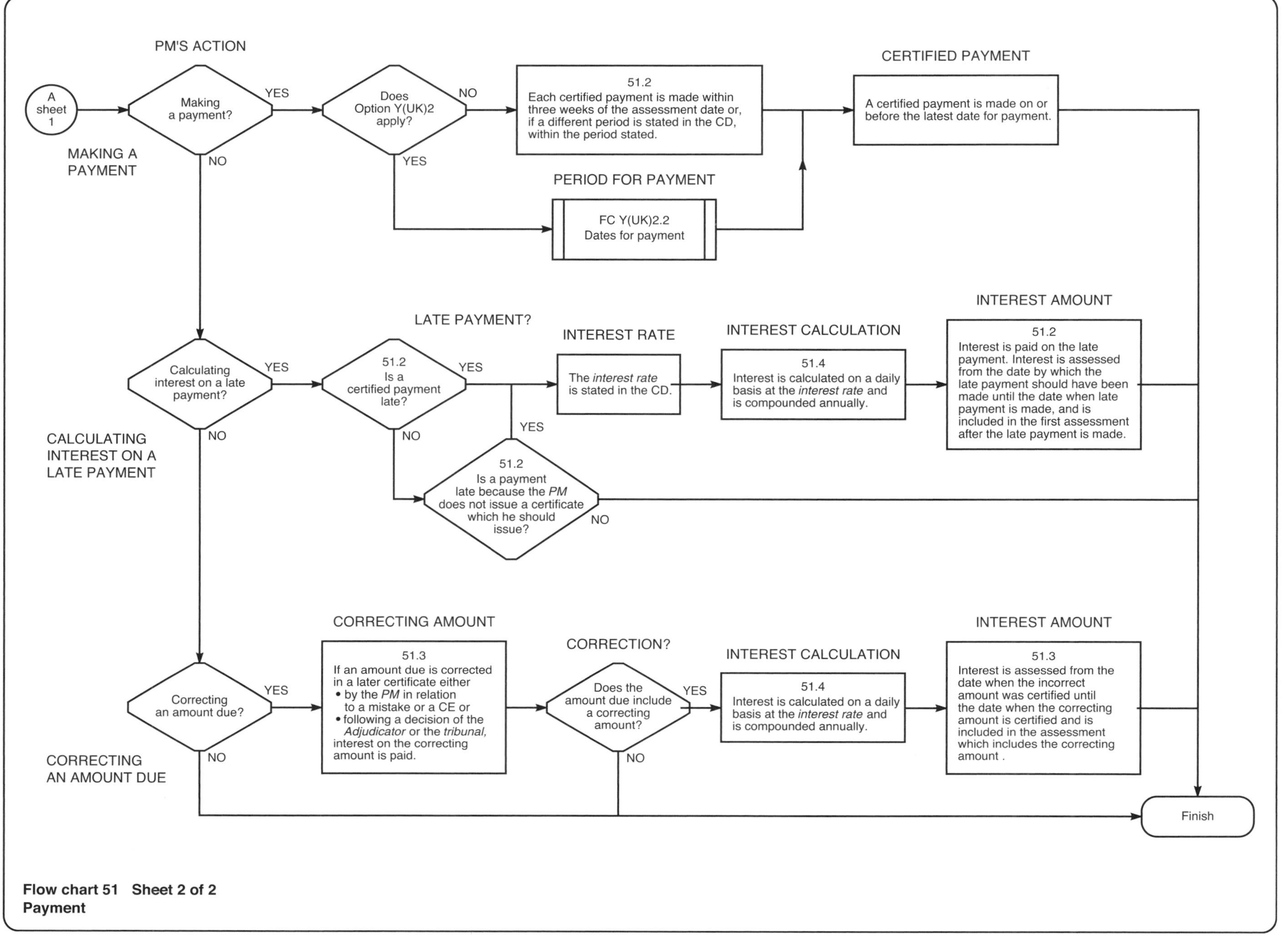
PM'S ACTION
A sheet 1
MAKING A PAYMENT
Making a payment?
YES
NO
Does Option Y(UK)2 apply?
NO
YES
51.2
Each certified payment is made within three weeks of the assessment date or, if a different period is stated in the CD, within the period stated.
PERIOD FOR PAYMENT
FC Y(UK)2.2
Dates for payment
CERTIFIED PAYMENT
A certified payment is made on or before the latest date for payment.
CALCULATING INTEREST ON A LATE PAYMENT
Calculating interest on a late payment?
YES
NO
LATE PAYMENT?
51.2
Is a certified payment late?
YES
NO
51.2
Is a payment late because the PM does not issue a certificate which he should issue?
YES
NO
INTEREST RATE
The interest rate is stated in the CD.
INTEREST CALCULATION
51.4
Interest is calculated on a daily basis at the interest rate and is compounded annually.
INTEREST AMOUNT
51.2
Interest is paid on the late payment. Interest is assessed from the date by which the late payment should have been made until the date when late payment is made, and is included in the first assessment after the late payment is made.
CORRECTING AN AMOUNT DUE
Correcting an amount due?
YES
NO
CORRECTING AMOUNT
51.3
If an amount due is corrected in a later certificate either
• by the PM in relation to a mistake or a CE or
• following a decision of the Adjudicator or the tribunal,
interest on the correcting amount is paid.
CORRECTION?
Does the amount due include a correcting amount?
YES
NO
INTEREST CALCULATION
51.4
Interest is calculated on a daily basis at the interest rate and is compounded annually.
INTEREST AMOUNT
51.3
Interest is assessed from the date when the incorrect amount was certified until the date when the correcting amount is certified and is included in the assessment which includes the correcting amount .
Finish

Flow chart 51 Sheet 2 of 2
Payment

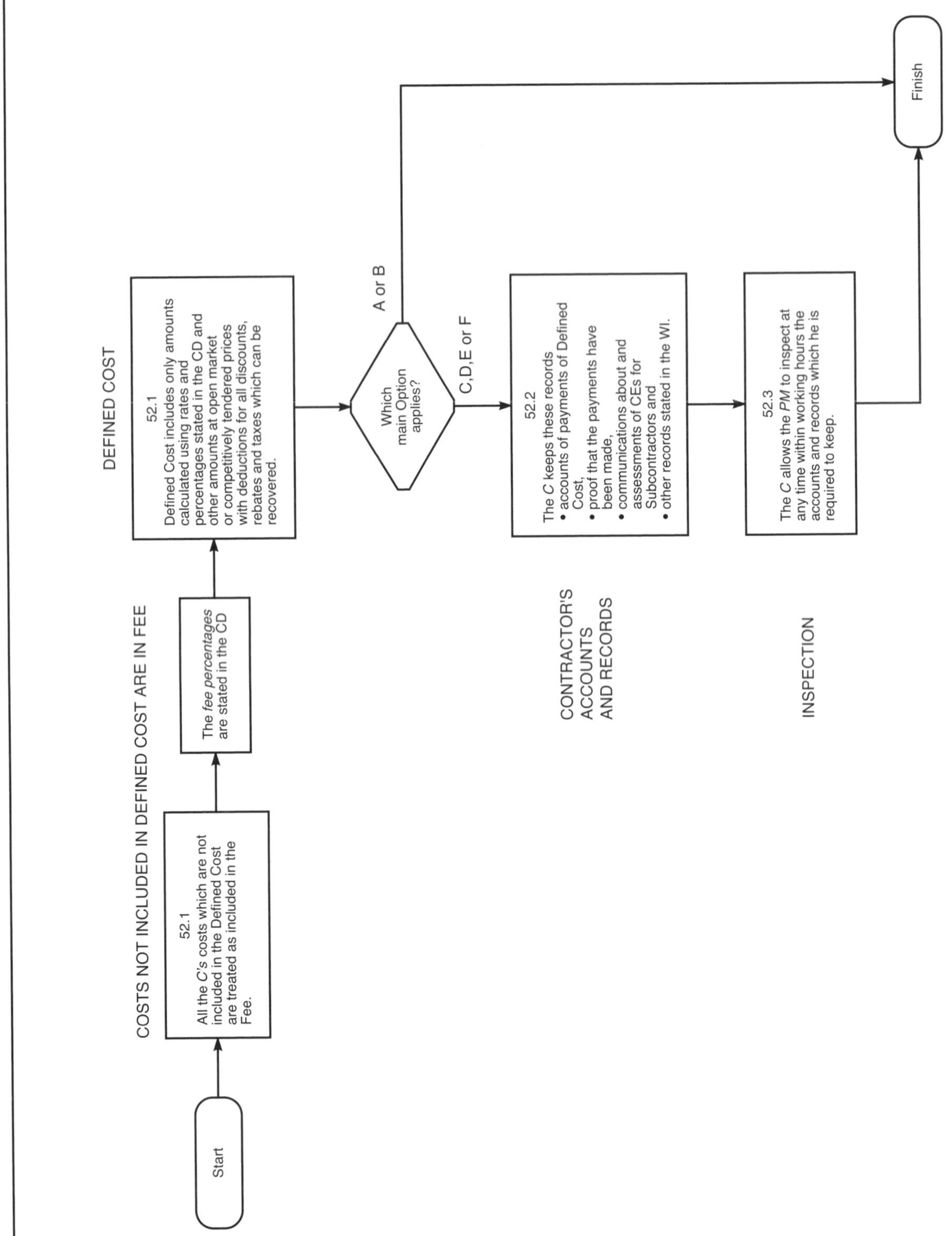

Flow chart 52
Defined Cost

COSTS NOT INCLUDED IN DEFINED COST ARE IN FEE

Start

52.1
All the *C's* costs which are not included in the Defined Cost are treated as included in the Fee.

The *fee percentages* are stated in the CD

DEFINED COST

52.1
Defined Cost includes only amounts calculated using rates and percentages stated in the CD and other amounts at open market or competitively tendered prices with deductions for all discounts, rebates and taxes which can be recovered.

Which main Option applies?

A or B → Finish

C,D,E or F

CONTRACTOR'S ACCOUNTS AND RECORDS

52.2
The *C* keeps these records
- accounts of payments of Defined Cost,
- proof that the payments have been made,
- communications about and assessments of CEs for Subcontractors and
- other records stated in the WI.

INSPECTION

52.3
The *C* allows the *PM* to inspect at any time within working hours the accounts and records which he is required to keep.

Finish

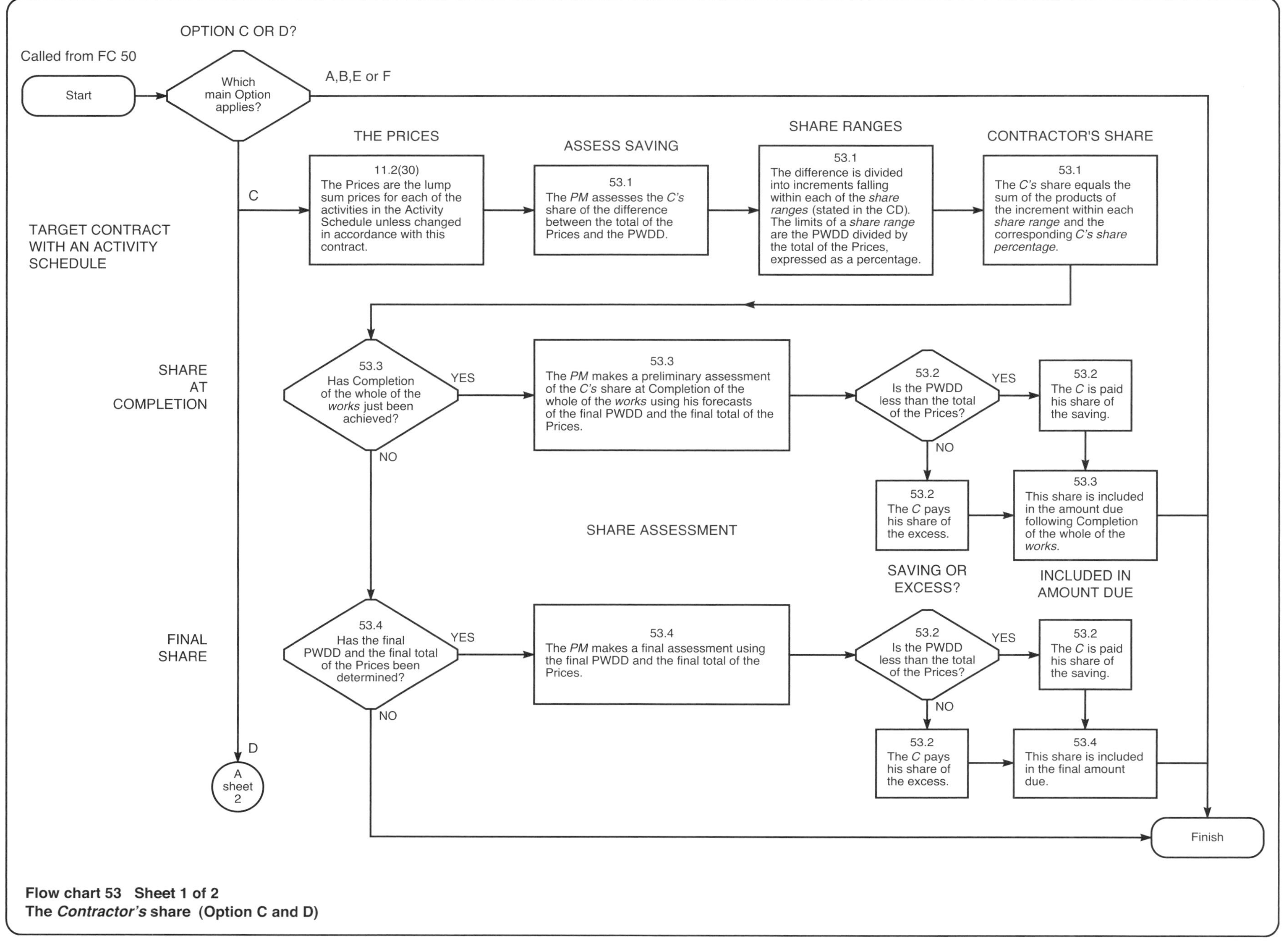
Called from FC 50
Start
OPTION C OR D?
Which main Option applies?
A,B,E or F
C
D
A sheet 2
TARGET CONTRACT WITH AN ACTIVITY SCHEDULE
THE PRICES
11.2(30) The Prices are the lump sum prices for each of the activities in the Activity Schedule unless changed in accordance with this contract.
ASSESS SAVING
53.1 The PM assesses the C's share of the difference between the total of the Prices and the PWDD.
SHARE RANGES
53.1 The difference is divided into increments falling within each of the share ranges (stated in the CD). The limits of a share range are the PWDD divided by the total of the Prices, expressed as a percentage.
CONTRACTOR'S SHARE
53.1 The C's share equals the sum of the products of the increment within each share range and the corresponding C's share percentage.
SHARE AT COMPLETION
53.3 Has Completion of the whole of the works just been achieved?
YES
NO
SHARE ASSESSMENT
53.3 The PM makes a preliminary assessment of the C's share at Completion of the whole of the works using his forecasts of the final PWDD and the final total of the Prices.
SAVING OR EXCESS?
53.2 Is the PWDD less than the total of the Prices?
YES
NO
53.2 The C is paid his share of the saving.
53.2 The C pays his share of the excess.
INCLUDED IN AMOUNT DUE
53.3 This share is included in the amount due following Completion of the whole of the works.
FINAL SHARE
53.4 Has the final PWDD and the final total of the Prices been determined?
YES
NO
53.4 The PM makes a final assessment using the final PWDD and the final total of the Prices.
53.2 Is the PWDD less than the total of the Prices?
YES
NO
53.2 The C is paid his share of the saving.
53.2 The C pays his share of the excess.
53.4 This share is included in the final amount due.
Finish

Flow chart 53 Sheet 1 of 2
The *Contractor's* share (Option C and D)

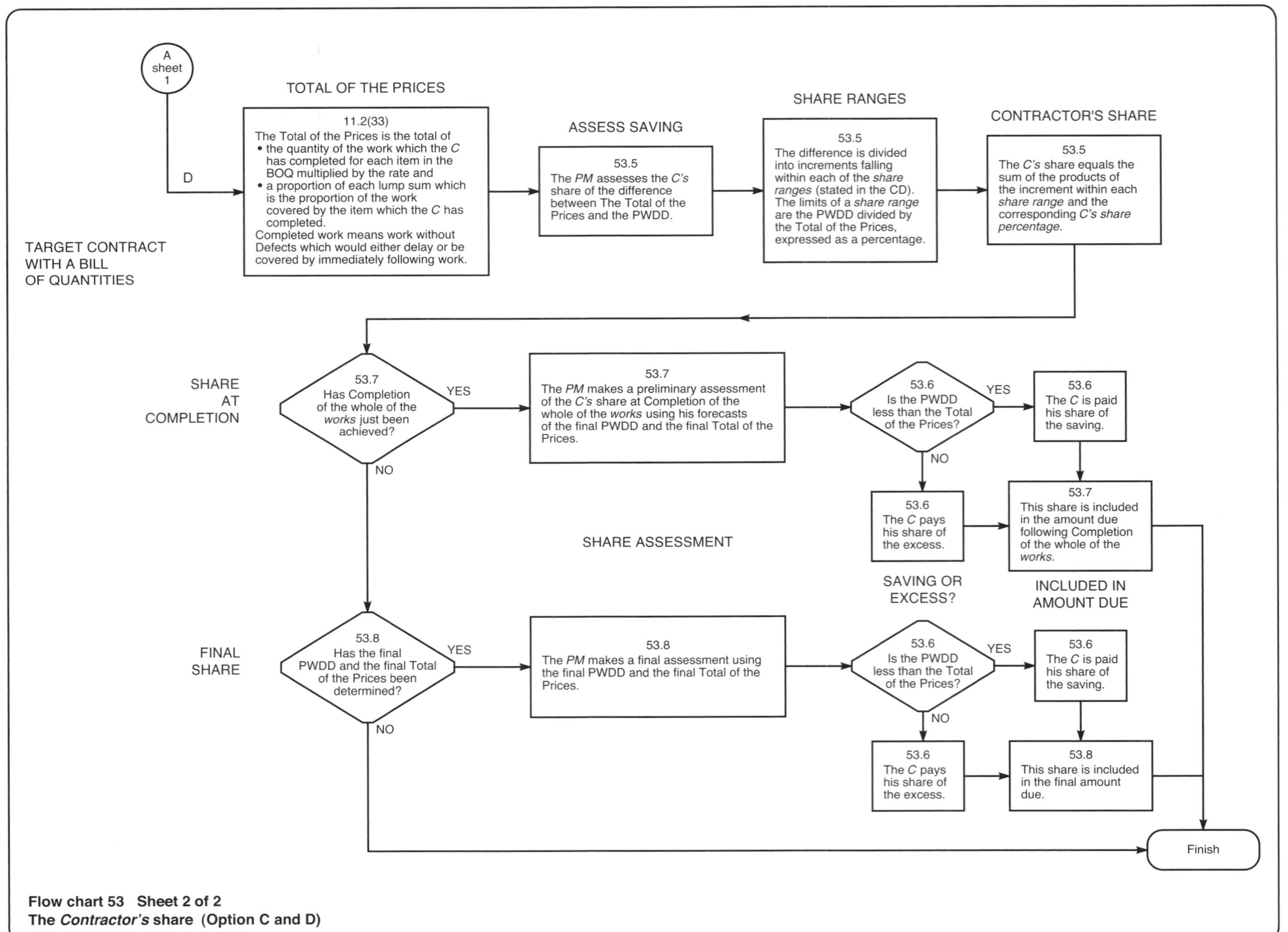

A sheet 1
D
TOTAL OF THE PRICES
11.2(33) The Total of the Prices is the total of • the quantity of the work which the C has completed for each item in the BOQ multiplied by the rate and • a proportion of each lump sum which is the proportion of the work covered by the item which the C has completed. Completed work means work without Defects which would either delay or be covered by immediately following work.
TARGET CONTRACT WITH A BILL OF QUANTITIES
ASSESS SAVING
53.5 The PM assesses the C's share of the difference between The Total of the Prices and the PWDD.
SHARE RANGES
53.5 The difference is divided into increments falling within each of the share ranges (stated in the CD). The limits of a share range are the PWDD divided by the Total of the Prices, expressed as a percentage.
CONTRACTOR'S SHARE
53.5 The C's share equals the sum of the products of the increment within each share range and the corresponding C's share percentage.
SHARE AT COMPLETION
53.7 Has Completion of the whole of the works just been achieved?
YES
NO
53.7 The PM makes a preliminary assessment of the C's share at Completion of the whole of the works using his forecasts of the final PWDD and the final Total of the Prices.
53.6 Is the PWDD less than the Total of the Prices?
YES
NO
53.6 The C is paid his share of the saving.
53.6 The C pays his share of the excess.
53.7 This share is included in the amount due following Completion of the whole of the works.
SHARE ASSESSMENT
SAVING OR EXCESS?
INCLUDED IN AMOUNT DUE
FINAL SHARE
53.8 Has the final PWDD and the final Total of the Prices been determined?
YES
NO
53.8 The PM makes a final assessment using the final PWDD and the final Total of the Prices.
53.6 Is the PWDD less than the Total of the Prices?
YES
NO
53.6 The C is paid his share of the saving.
53.6 The C pays his share of the excess.
53.8 This share is included in the final amount due.
Finish
Flow chart 53 Sheet 2 of 2
The Contractor's share (Option C and D)

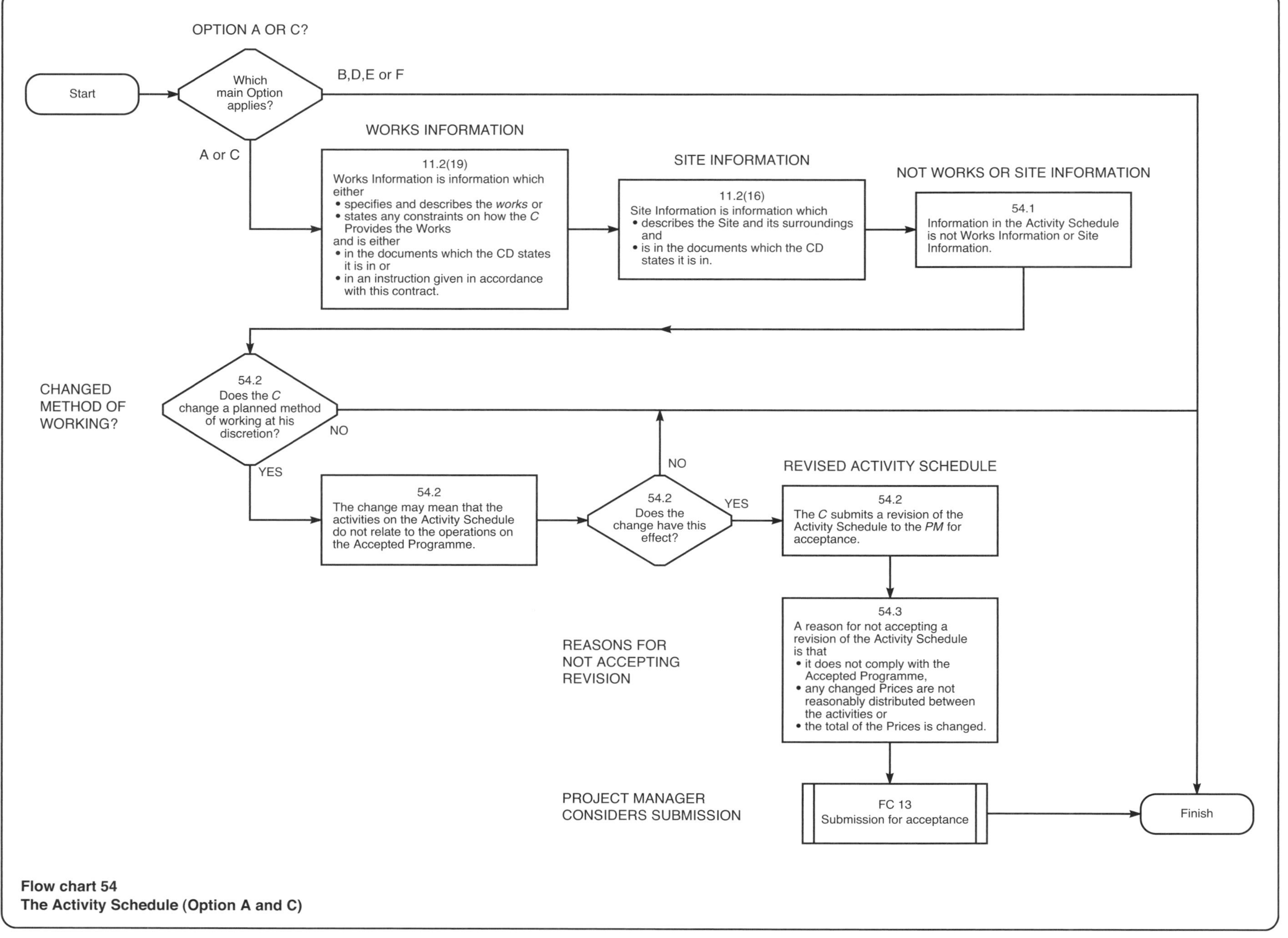
OPTION A OR C?
Start
Which main Option applies?
B,D,E or F
A or C
WORKS INFORMATION
11.2(19)
Works Information is information which either
• specifies and describes the *works* or
• states any constraints on how the *C* Provides the Works
and is either
• in the documents which the CD states it is in or
• in an instruction given in accordance with this contract.
SITE INFORMATION
11.2(16)
Site Information is information which
• describes the Site and its surroundings and
• is in the documents which the CD states it is in.
NOT WORKS OR SITE INFORMATION
54.1
Information in the Activity Schedule is not Works Information or Site Information.
CHANGED METHOD OF WORKING?
54.2
Does the *C* change a planned method of working at his discretion?
NO
YES
54.2
The change may mean that the activities on the Activity Schedule do not relate to the operations on the Accepted Programme.
NO
54.2
Does the change have this effect?
YES
REVISED ACTIVITY SCHEDULE
54.2
The *C* submits a revision of the Activity Schedule to the *PM* for acceptance.
REASONS FOR NOT ACCEPTING REVISION
54.3
A reason for not accepting a revision of the Activity Schedule is that
• it does not comply with the Accepted Programme,
• any changed Prices are not reasonably distributed between the activities or
• the total of the Prices is changed.
PROJECT MANAGER CONSIDERS SUBMISSION
FC 13
Submission for acceptance
Finish

Flow chart 54
The Activity Schedule (Option A and C)

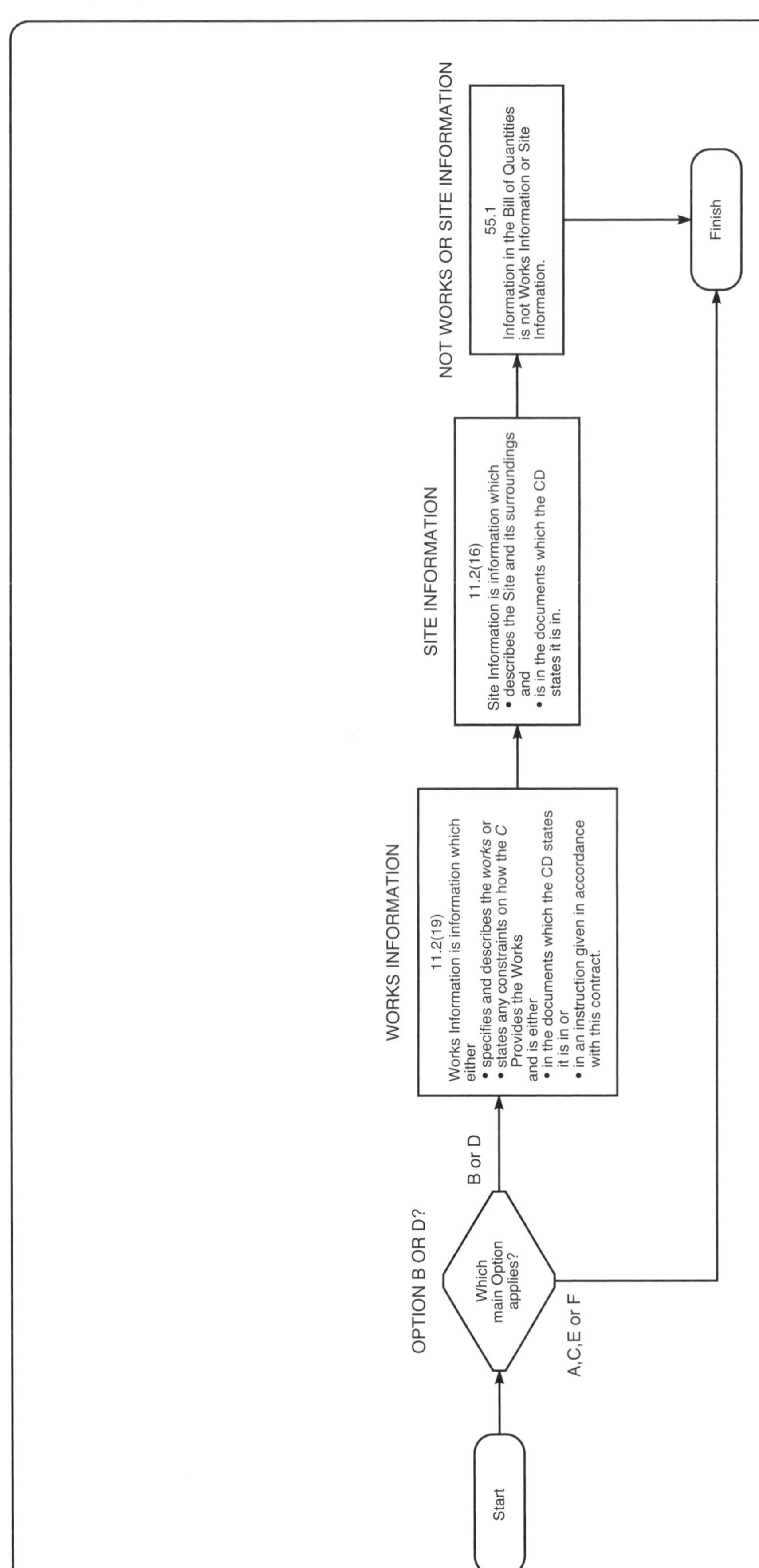
Start
OPTION B OR D?
Which main Option applies?
B or D
A,C,E or F
WORKS INFORMATION
11.2(19)
Works Information is information which either
• specifies and describes the *works* or
• states any constraints on how the *C* Provides the Works
and is either
• in the documents which the CD states it is in or
• in an instruction given in accordance with this contract.
SITE INFORMATION
11.2(16)
Site Information is information which
• describes the Site and its surroundings
and
• is in the documents which the CD states it is in.
NOT WORKS OR SITE INFORMATION
55.1
Information in the Bill of Quantities is not Works Information or Site Information.
Finish

Flow chart 55
The Bill of Quantities (Option B and D)

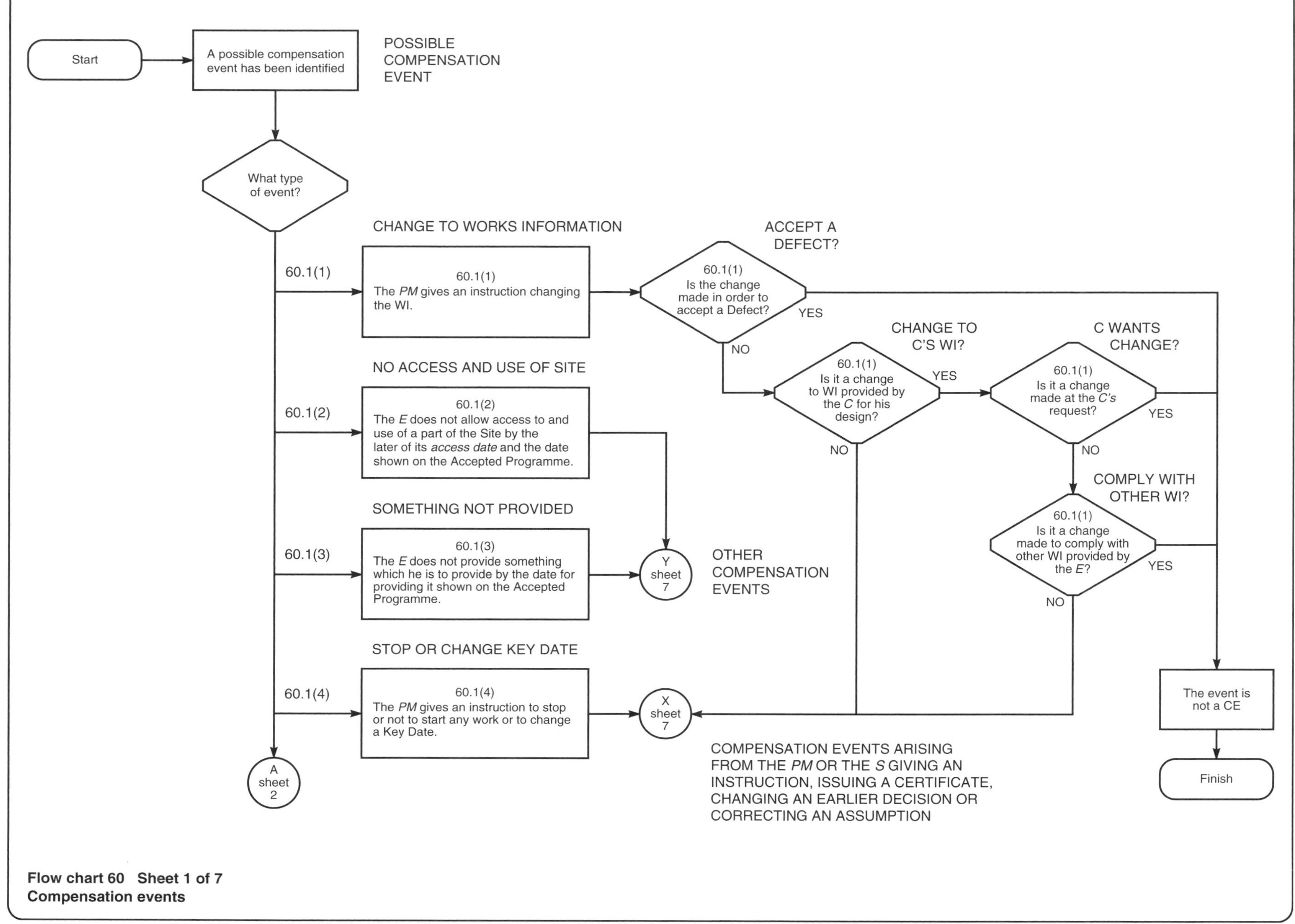
Start
A possible compensation event has been identified
POSSIBLE COMPENSATION EVENT
What type of event?
CHANGE TO WORKS INFORMATION
60.1(1)
60.1(1) The PM gives an instruction changing the WI.
NO ACCESS AND USE OF SITE
60.1(2)
60.1(2) The E does not allow access to and use of a part of the Site by the later of its access date and the date shown on the Accepted Programme.
SOMETHING NOT PROVIDED
60.1(3)
60.1(3) The E does not provide something which he is to provide by the date for providing it shown on the Accepted Programme.
STOP OR CHANGE KEY DATE
60.1(4)
60.1(4) The PM gives an instruction to stop or not to start any work or to change a Key Date.
A sheet 2
ACCEPT A DEFECT?
60.1(1) Is the change made in order to accept a Defect?
YES
NO
CHANGE TO C'S WI?
60.1(1) Is it a change to WI provided by the C for his design?
YES
NO
C WANTS CHANGE?
60.1(1) Is it a change made at the C's request?
YES
NO
COMPLY WITH OTHER WI?
60.1(1) Is it a change made to comply with other WI provided by the E?
YES
NO
Y sheet 7
OTHER COMPENSATION EVENTS
X sheet 7
COMPENSATION EVENTS ARISING FROM THE PM OR THE S GIVING AN INSTRUCTION, ISSUING A CERTIFICATE, CHANGING AN EARLIER DECISION OR CORRECTING AN ASSUMPTION
The event is not a CE
Finish

Flow chart 60 Sheet 1 of 7
Compensation events

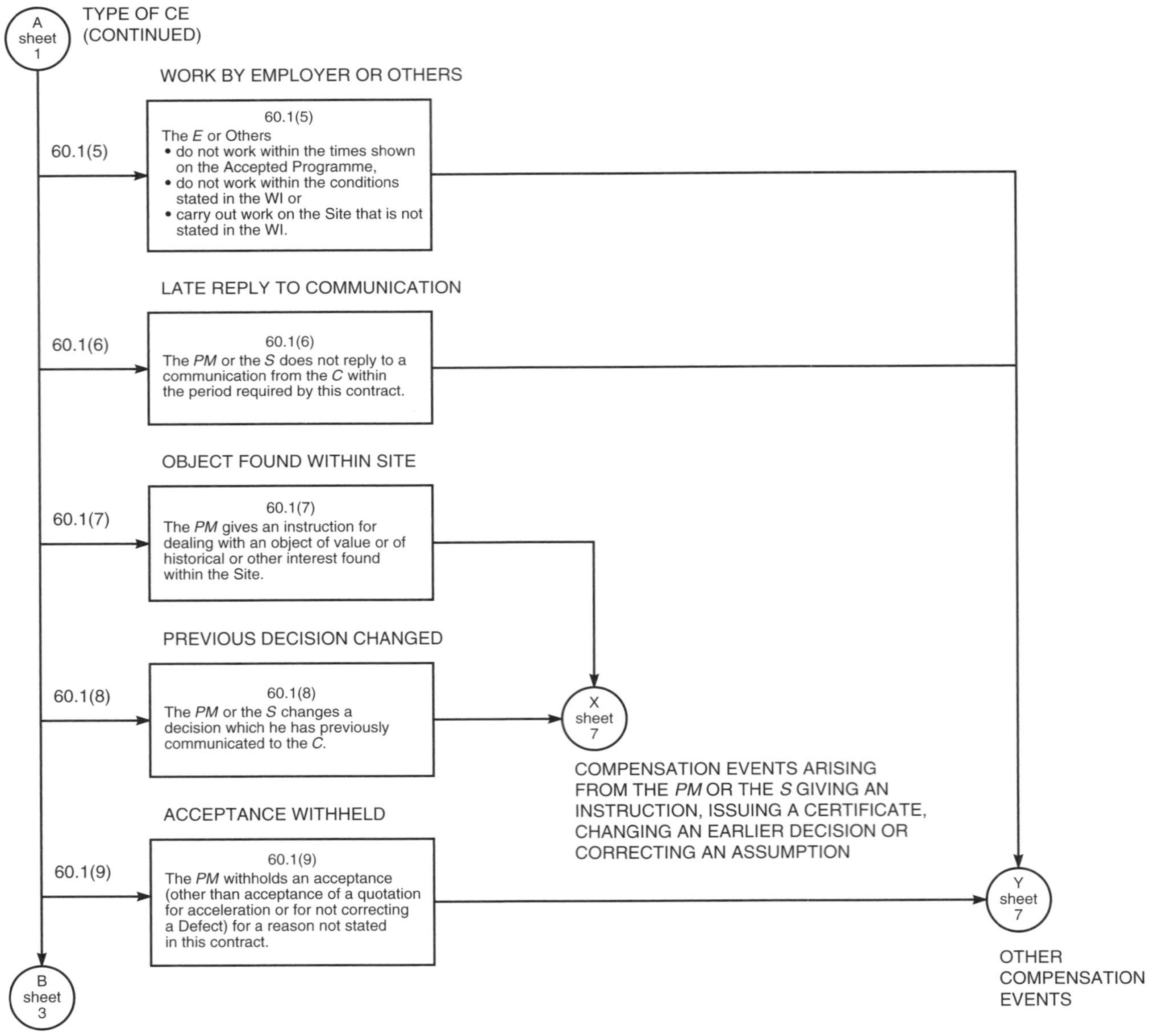

A sheet 1

TYPE OF CE (CONTINUED)

WORK BY EMPLOYER OR OTHERS

60.1(5)

60.1(5)
The *E* or Others
- do not work within the times shown on the Accepted Programme,
- do not work within the conditions stated in the WI or
- carry out work on the Site that is not stated in the WI.

LATE REPLY TO COMMUNICATION

60.1(6)

60.1(6)
The *PM* or the *S* does not reply to a communication from the *C* within the period required by this contract.

OBJECT FOUND WITHIN SITE

60.1(7)

60.1(7)
The *PM* gives an instruction for dealing with an object of value or of historical or other interest found within the Site.

PREVIOUS DECISION CHANGED

60.1(8)

60.1(8)
The *PM* or the *S* changes a decision which he has previously communicated to the *C*.

ACCEPTANCE WITHHELD

60.1(9)

60.1(9)
The *PM* withholds an acceptance (other than acceptance of a quotation for acceleration or for not correcting a Defect) for a reason not stated in this contract.

X sheet 7

COMPENSATION EVENTS ARISING FROM THE *PM* OR THE *S* GIVING AN INSTRUCTION, ISSUING A CERTIFICATE, CHANGING AN EARLIER DECISION OR CORRECTING AN ASSUMPTION

Y sheet 7

OTHER COMPENSATION EVENTS

B sheet 3

Flow chart 60 Sheet 2 of 7
Compensation events

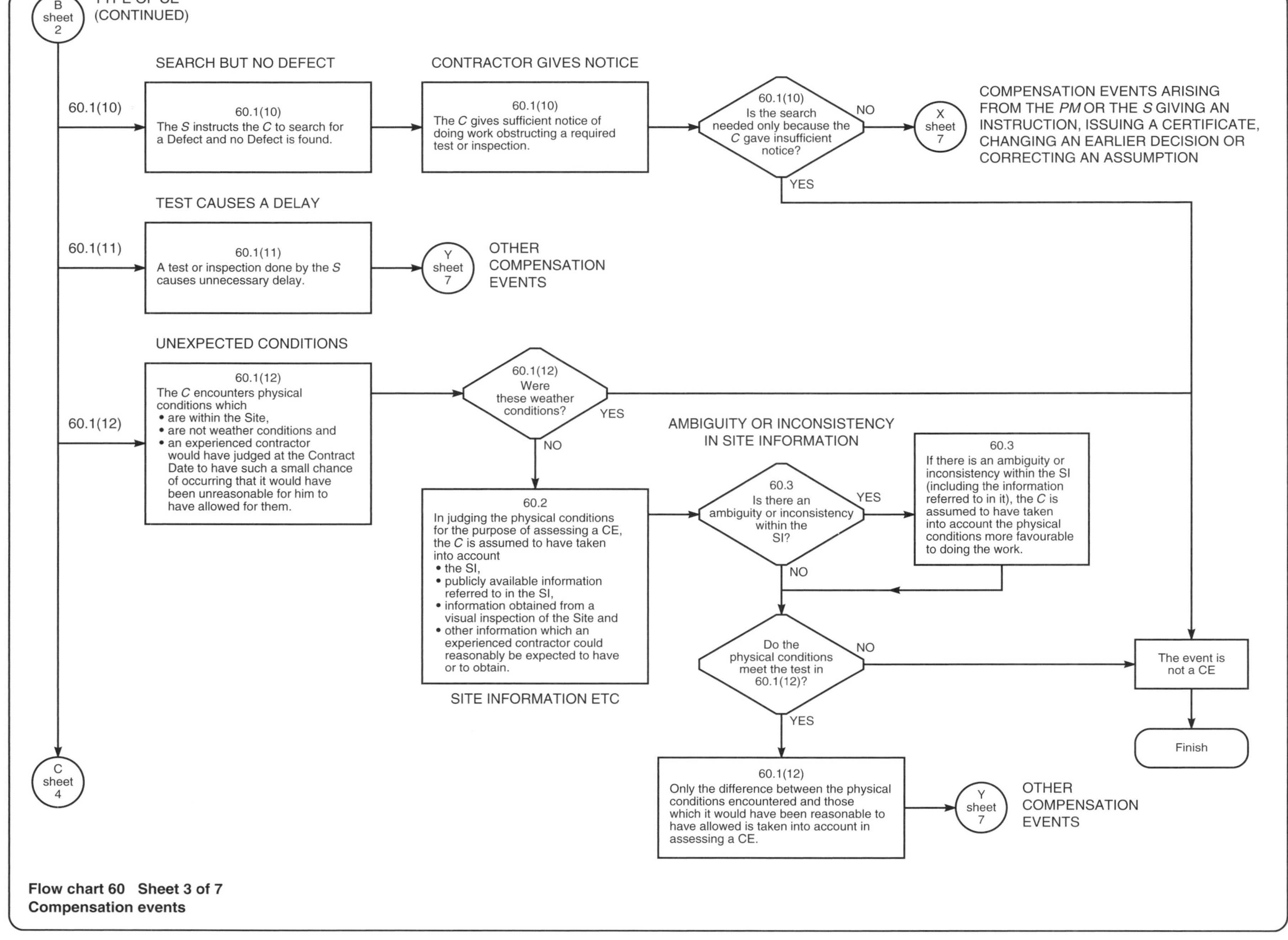
TYPE OF CE (CONTINUED)
B sheet 2
60.1(10)
SEARCH BUT NO DEFECT
60.1(10) The S instructs the C to search for a Defect and no Defect is found.
CONTRACTOR GIVES NOTICE
60.1(10) The C gives sufficient notice of doing work obstructing a required test or inspection.
60.1(10) Is the search needed only because the C gave insufficient notice?
NO
X sheet 7
COMPENSATION EVENTS ARISING FROM THE PM OR THE S GIVING AN INSTRUCTION, ISSUING A CERTIFICATE, CHANGING AN EARLIER DECISION OR CORRECTING AN ASSUMPTION
YES
60.1(11)
TEST CAUSES A DELAY
60.1(11) A test or inspection done by the S causes unnecessary delay.
Y sheet 7
OTHER COMPENSATION EVENTS
60.1(12)
UNEXPECTED CONDITIONS
60.1(12) The C encounters physical conditions which
• are within the Site,
• are not weather conditions and
• an experienced contractor would have judged at the Contract Date to have such a small chance of occurring that it would have been unreasonable for him to have allowed for them.
60.1(12) Were these weather conditions?
YES
NO
60.2 In judging the physical conditions for the purpose of assessing a CE, the C is assumed to have taken into account
• the SI,
• publicly available information referred to in the SI,
• information obtained from a visual inspection of the Site and
• other information which an experienced contractor could reasonably be expected to have or to obtain.
SITE INFORMATION ETC
AMBIGUITY OR INCONSISTENCY IN SITE INFORMATION
60.3 Is there an ambiguity or inconsistency within the SI?
YES
NO
60.3 If there is an ambiguity or inconsistency within the SI (including the information referred to in it), the C is assumed to have taken into account the physical conditions more favourable to doing the work.
Do the physical conditions meet the test in 60.1(12)?
NO
YES
The event is not a CE
Finish
60.1(12) Only the difference between the physical conditions encountered and those which it would have been reasonable to have allowed is taken into account in assessing a CE.
Y sheet 7
OTHER COMPENSATION EVENTS
C sheet 4
Flow chart 60 Sheet 3 of 7
Compensation events

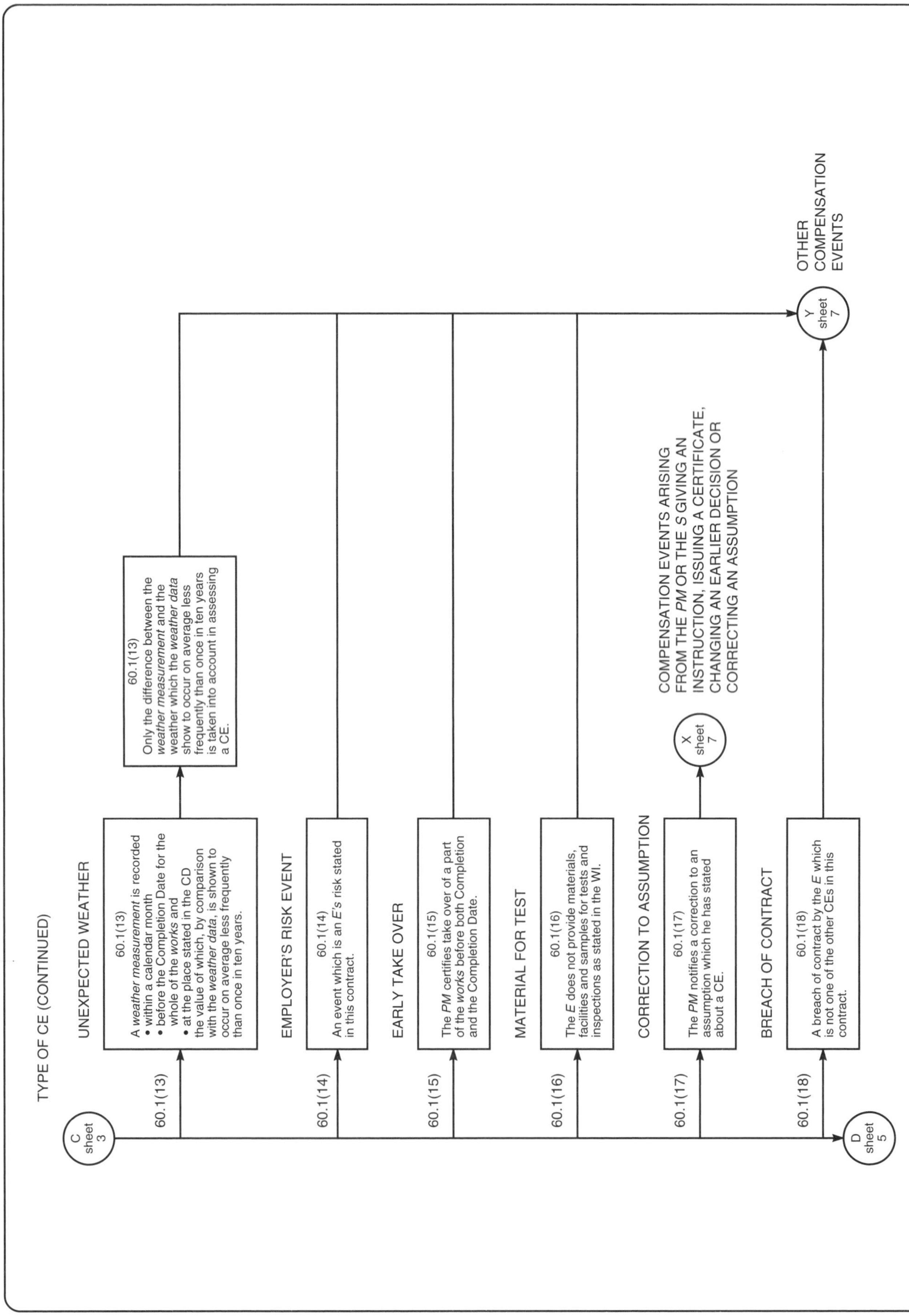

TYPE OF CE (CONTINUED)

C sheet 3

UNEXPECTED WEATHER

60.1(13)

60.1(13)
A *weather measurement* is recorded
- within a calendar month
- before the Completion Date for the whole of the *works* and
- at the place stated in the CD

the value of which, by comparison with the *weather data*, is shown to occur on average less frequently than once in ten years.

60.1(13)
Only the difference between the *weather measurement* and the weather which the *weather data* show to occur on average less frequently than once in ten years is taken into account in assessing a CE.

EMPLOYER'S RISK EVENT

60.1(14)

60.1(14)
An event which is an *E's* risk stated in this contract.

EARLY TAKE OVER

60.1(15)

60.1(15)
The *PM* certifies take over of a part of the *works* before both Completion and the Completion Date.

MATERIAL FOR TEST

60.1(16)

60.1(16)
The *E* does not provide materials, facilities and samples for tests and inspections as stated in the WI.

CORRECTION TO ASSUMPTION

60.1(17)

60.1(17)
The *PM* notifies a correction to an assumption which he has stated about a CE.

X sheet 7

COMPENSATION EVENTS ARISING FROM THE *PM* OR THE *S* GIVING AN INSTRUCTION, ISSUING A CERTIFICATE, CHANGING AN EARLIER DECISION OR CORRECTING AN ASSUMPTION

BREACH OF CONTRACT

60.1(18)

60.1(18)
A breach of contract by the *E* which is not one of the other CEs in this contract.

Y sheet 7

OTHER COMPENSATION EVENTS

D sheet 5

Flow chart 60 Sheet 4 of 7
Compensation events

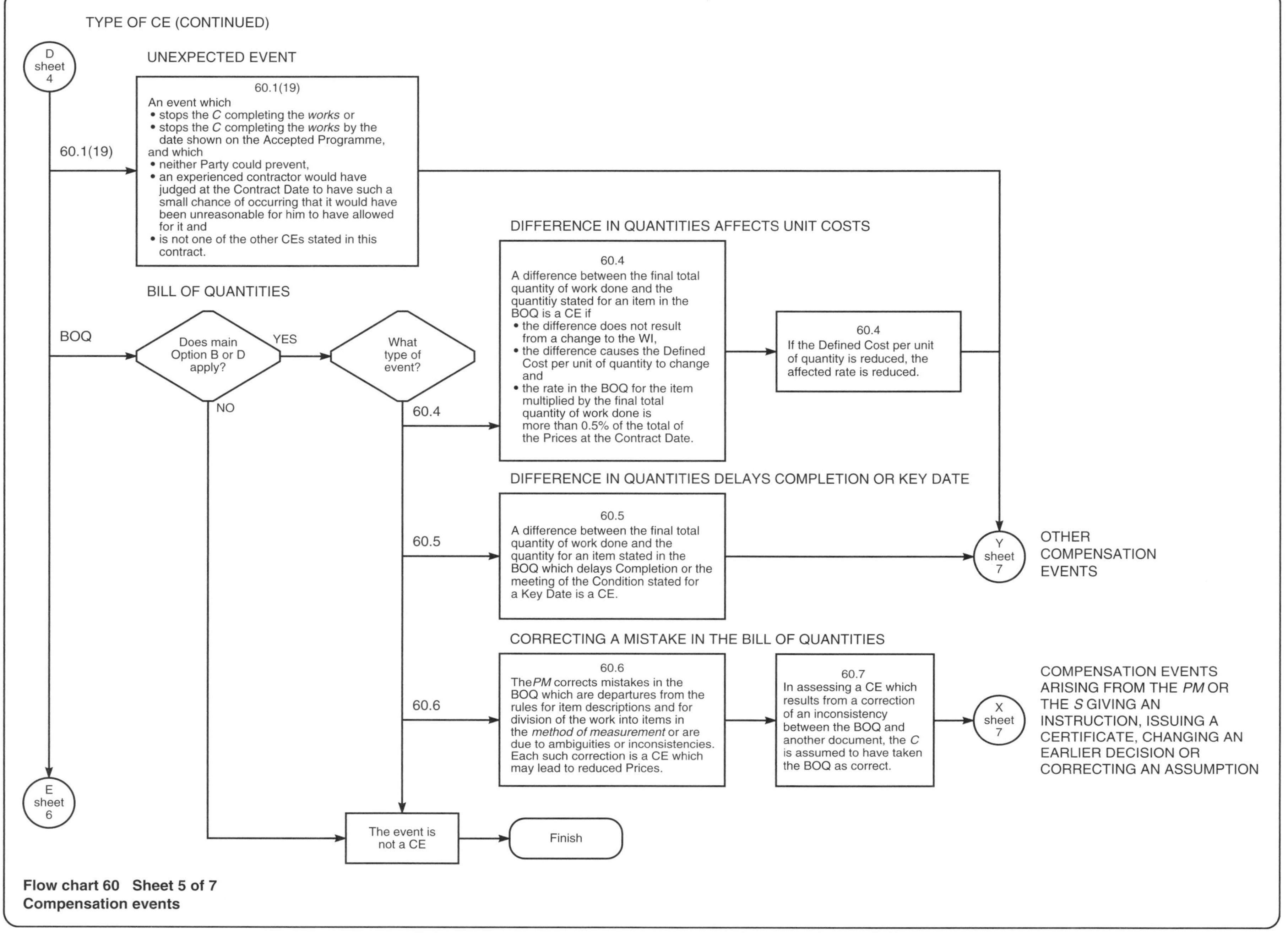
TYPE OF CE (CONTINUED)
D sheet 4
UNEXPECTED EVENT
60.1(19)
60.1(19)
An event which
• stops the *C* completing the *works* or
• stops the *C* completing the *works* by the date shown on the Accepted Programme, and which
• neither Party could prevent,
• an experienced contractor would have judged at the Contract Date to have such a small chance of occurring that it would have been unreasonable for him to have allowed for it and
• is not one of the other CEs stated in this contract.
BILL OF QUANTITIES
BOQ
Does main Option B or D apply?
YES
NO
What type of event?
60.4
60.5
60.6
DIFFERENCE IN QUANTITIES AFFECTS UNIT COSTS
60.4
A difference between the final total quantity of work done and the quantitiy stated for an item in the BOQ is a CE if
• the difference does not result from a change to the WI,
• the difference causes the Defined Cost per unit of quantity to change and
• the rate in the BOQ for the item multiplied by the final total quantity of work done is more than 0.5% of the total of the Prices at the Contract Date.
60.4
If the Defined Cost per unit of quantity is reduced, the affected rate is reduced.
DIFFERENCE IN QUANTITIES DELAYS COMPLETION OR KEY DATE
60.5
A difference between the final total quantity of work done and the quantity for an item stated in the BOQ which delays Completion or the meeting of the Condition stated for a Key Date is a CE.
Y sheet 7
OTHER COMPENSATION EVENTS
CORRECTING A MISTAKE IN THE BILL OF QUANTITIES
60.6
The *PM* corrects mistakes in the BOQ which are departures from the rules for item descriptions and for division of the work into items in the *method of measurement* or are due to ambiguities or inconsistencies. Each such correction is a CE which may lead to reduced Prices.
60.7
In assessing a CE which results from a correction of an inconsistency between the BOQ and another document, the *C* is assumed to have taken the BOQ as correct.
X sheet 7
COMPENSATION EVENTS ARISING FROM THE *PM* OR THE *S* GIVING AN INSTRUCTION, ISSUING A CERTIFICATE, CHANGING AN EARLIER DECISION OR CORRECTING AN ASSUMPTION
E sheet 6
The event is not a CE
Finish

Flow chart 60 Sheet 5 of 7
Compensation events

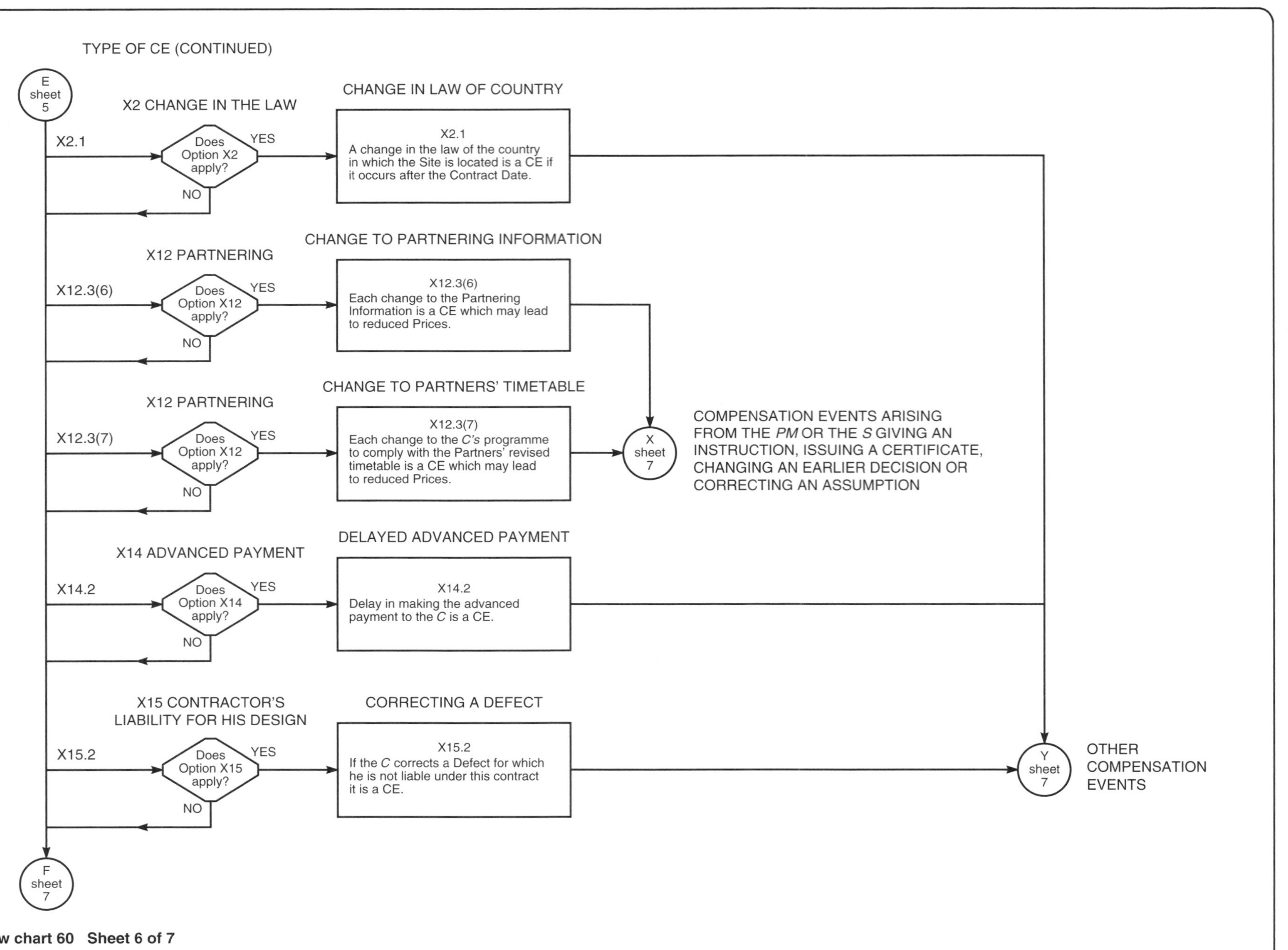
TYPE OF CE (CONTINUED)
E sheet 5
X2 CHANGE IN THE LAW
X2.1
Does Option X2 apply?
YES
NO
CHANGE IN LAW OF COUNTRY
X2.1
A change in the law of the country in which the Site is located is a CE if it occurs after the Contract Date.
X12 PARTNERING
X12.3(6)
Does Option X12 apply?
YES
NO
CHANGE TO PARTNERING INFORMATION
X12.3(6)
Each change to the Partnering Information is a CE which may lead to reduced Prices.
X12 PARTNERING
X12.3(7)
Does Option X12 apply?
YES
NO
CHANGE TO PARTNERS' TIMETABLE
X12.3(7)
Each change to the C's programme to comply with the Partners' revised timetable is a CE which may lead to reduced Prices.
X sheet 7
COMPENSATION EVENTS ARISING FROM THE PM OR THE S GIVING AN INSTRUCTION, ISSUING A CERTIFICATE, CHANGING AN EARLIER DECISION OR CORRECTING AN ASSUMPTION
X14 ADVANCED PAYMENT
X14.2
Does Option X14 apply?
YES
NO
DELAYED ADVANCED PAYMENT
X14.2
Delay in making the advanced payment to the C is a CE.
X15 CONTRACTOR'S LIABILITY FOR HIS DESIGN
X15.2
Does Option X15 apply?
YES
NO
CORRECTING A DEFECT
X15.2
If the C corrects a Defect for which he is not liable under this contract it is a CE.
Y sheet 7
OTHER COMPENSATION EVENTS
F sheet 7

Flow chart 60 Sheet 6 of 7
Compensation events

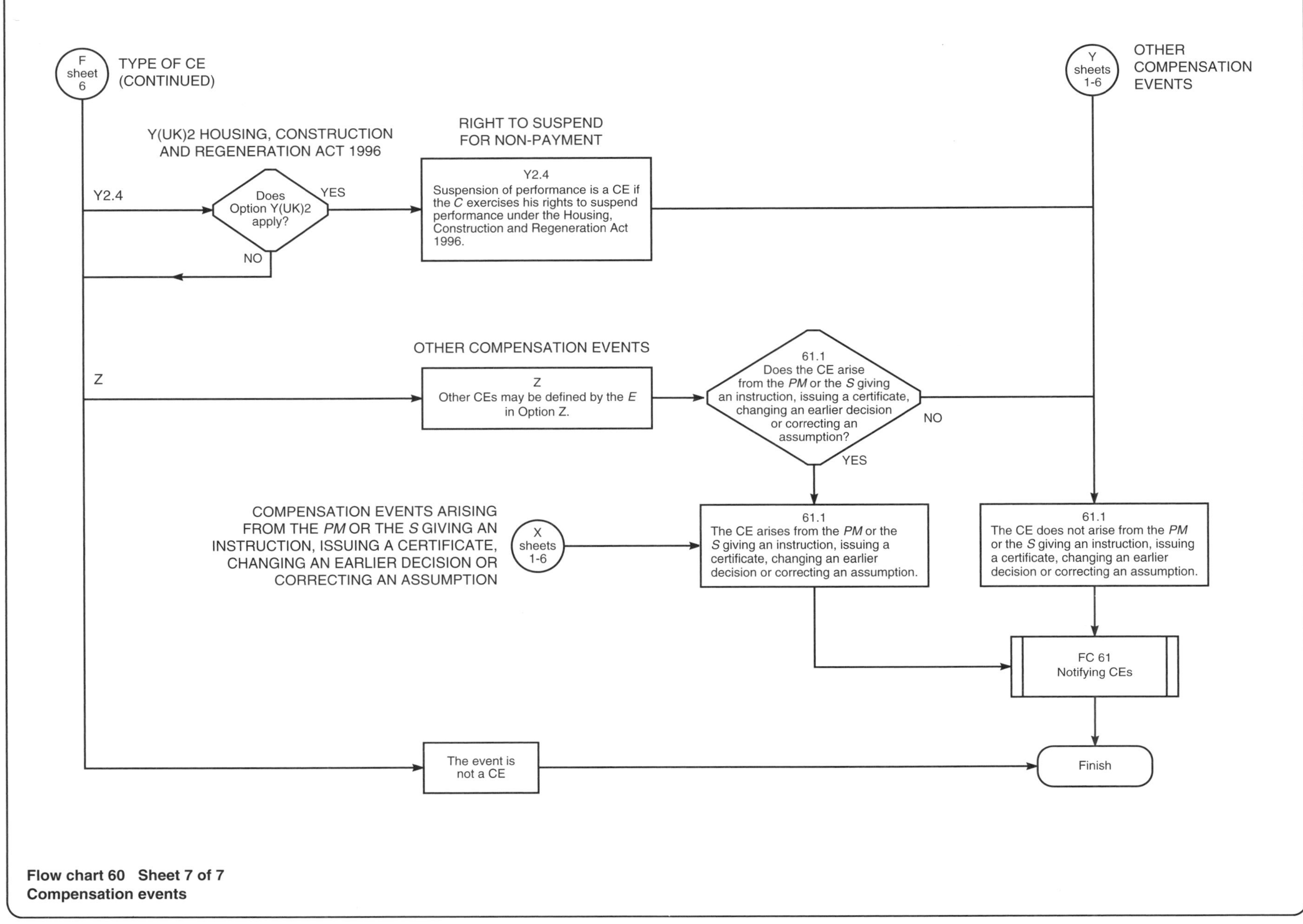

F sheet 6
TYPE OF CE (CONTINUED)
Y(UK)2 HOUSING, CONSTRUCTION AND REGENERATION ACT 1996
Y2.4
Does Option Y(UK)2 apply?
YES
NO
RIGHT TO SUSPEND FOR NON-PAYMENT
Y2.4 Suspension of performance is a CE if the C exercises his rights to suspend performance under the Housing, Construction and Regeneration Act 1996.
Y sheets 1-6
OTHER COMPENSATION EVENTS
Z
OTHER COMPENSATION EVENTS
Z Other CEs may be defined by the E in Option Z.
61.1 Does the CE arise from the PM or the S giving an instruction, issuing a certificate, changing an earlier decision or correcting an assumption?
NO
YES
COMPENSATION EVENTS ARISING FROM THE PM OR THE S GIVING AN INSTRUCTION, ISSUING A CERTIFICATE, CHANGING AN EARLIER DECISION OR CORRECTING AN ASSUMPTION
X sheets 1-6
61.1 The CE arises from the PM or the S giving an instruction, issuing a certificate, changing an earlier decision or correcting an assumption.
61.1 The CE does not arise from the PM or the S giving an instruction, issuing a certificate, changing an earlier decision or correcting an assumption.
FC 61 Notifying CEs
The event is not a CE
Finish

Flow chart 60 Sheet 7 of 7
Compensation events

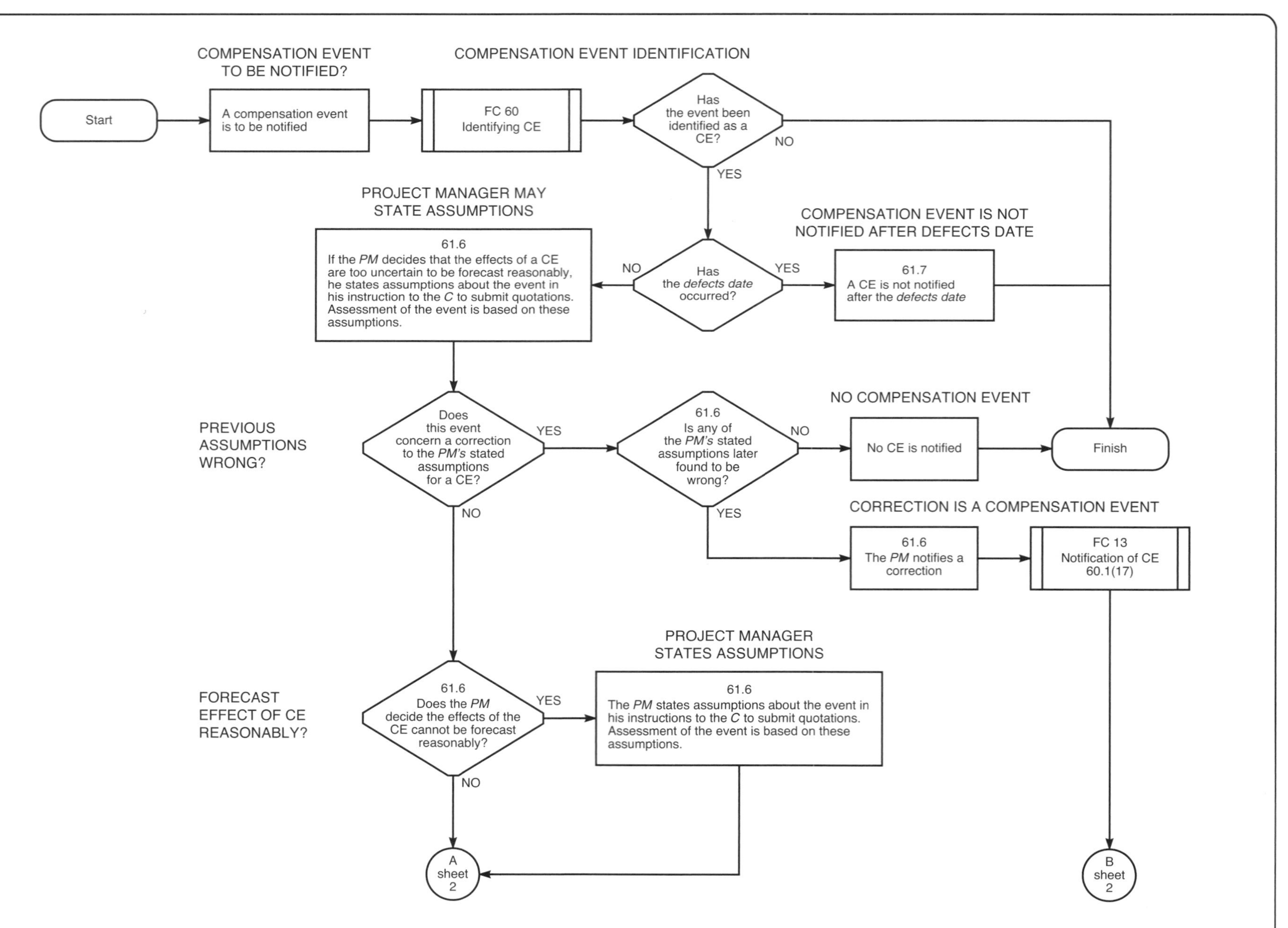
COMPENSATION EVENT TO BE NOTIFIED?
Start
A compensation event is to be notified
COMPENSATION EVENT IDENTIFICATION
FC 60 Identifying CE
Has the event been identified as a CE?
NO
YES
PROJECT MANAGER MAY STATE ASSUMPTIONS
61.6 If the *PM* decides that the effects of a CE are too uncertain to be forecast reasonably, he states assumptions about the event in his instruction to the *C* to submit quotations. Assessment of the event is based on these assumptions.
NO
Has the *defects date* occurred?
YES
COMPENSATION EVENT IS NOT NOTIFIED AFTER DEFECTS DATE
61.7 A CE is not notified after the *defects date*
PREVIOUS ASSUMPTIONS WRONG?
Does this event concern a correction to the *PM's* stated assumptions for a CE?
YES
NO
61.6 Is any of the *PM's* stated assumptions later found to be wrong?
NO
YES
NO COMPENSATION EVENT
No CE is notified
Finish
CORRECTION IS A COMPENSATION EVENT
61.6 The *PM* notifies a correction
FC 13 Notification of CE 60.1(17)
FORECAST EFFECT OF CE REASONABLY?
61.6 Does the *PM* decide the effects of the CE cannot be forecast reasonably?
YES
NO
PROJECT MANAGER STATES ASSUMPTIONS
61.6 The *PM* states assumptions about the event in his instructions to the *C* to submit quotations. Assessment of the event is based on these assumptions.
A sheet 2
B sheet 2

Flow chart 61 Sheet 1 of 4
Notifying compensation events

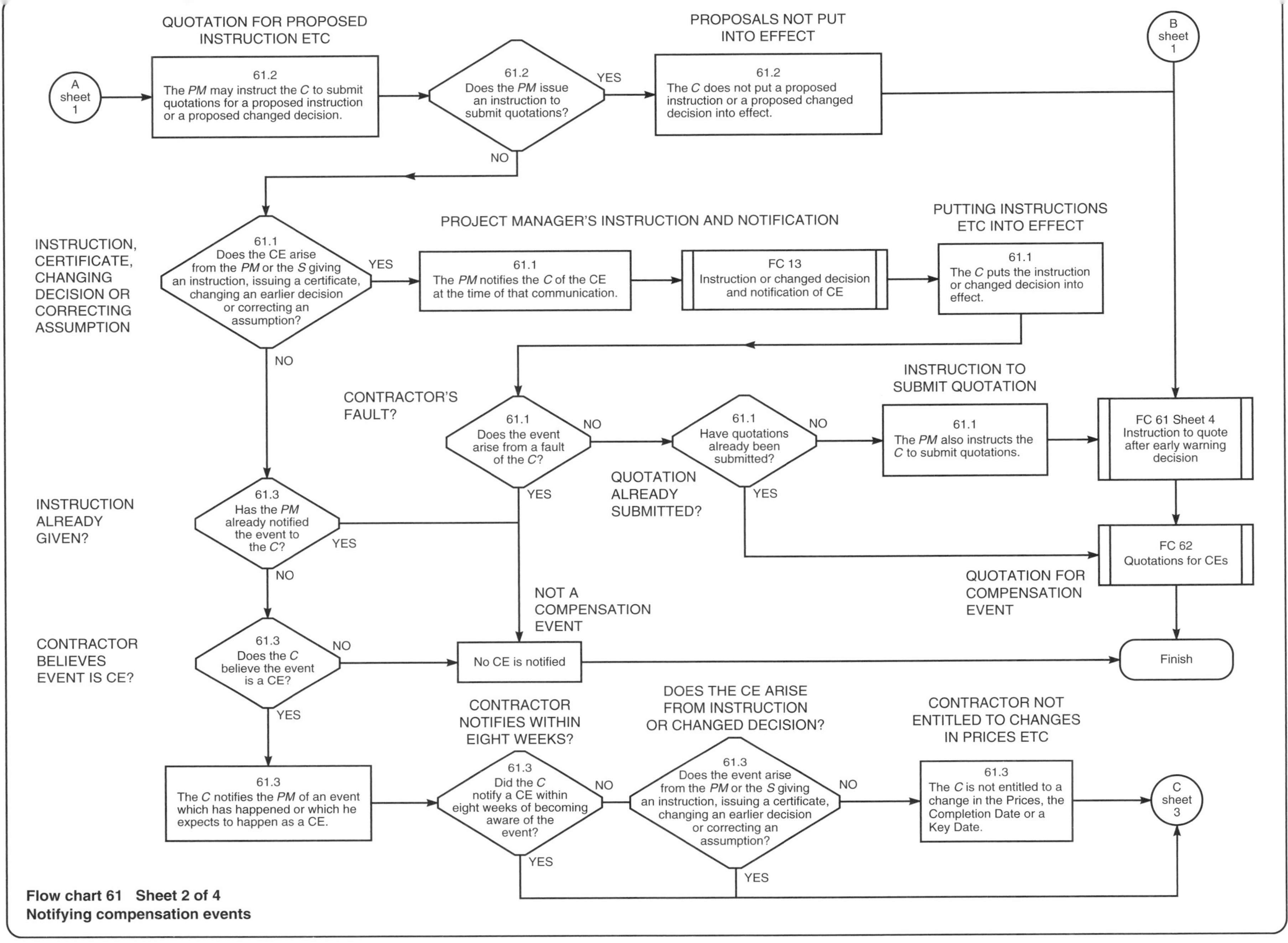

QUOTATION FOR PROPOSED INSTRUCTION ETC
A sheet 1
61.2 The PM may instruct the C to submit quotations for a proposed instruction or a proposed changed decision.
61.2 Does the PM issue an instruction to submit quotations?
YES
NO
PROPOSALS NOT PUT INTO EFFECT
61.2 The C does not put a proposed instruction or a proposed changed decision into effect.
B sheet 1
INSTRUCTION, CERTIFICATE, CHANGING DECISION OR CORRECTING ASSUMPTION
61.1 Does the CE arise from the PM or the S giving an instruction, issuing a certificate, changing an earlier decision or correcting an assumption?
YES
NO
PROJECT MANAGER'S INSTRUCTION AND NOTIFICATION
61.1 The PM notifies the C of the CE at the time of that communication.
FC 13 Instruction or changed decision and notification of CE
PUTTING INSTRUCTIONS ETC INTO EFFECT
61.1 The C puts the instruction or changed decision into effect.
CONTRACTOR'S FAULT?
61.1 Does the event arise from a fault of the C?
NO
YES
61.1 Have quotations already been submitted?
NO
YES
QUOTATION ALREADY SUBMITTED?
INSTRUCTION TO SUBMIT QUOTATION
61.1 The PM also instructs the C to submit quotations.
FC 61 Sheet 4 Instruction to quote after early warning decision
INSTRUCTION ALREADY GIVEN?
61.3 Has the PM already notified the event to the C?
YES
NO
FC 62 Quotations for CEs
QUOTATION FOR COMPENSATION EVENT
NOT A COMPENSATION EVENT
CONTRACTOR BELIEVES EVENT IS CE?
61.3 Does the C believe the event is a CE?
NO
YES
No CE is notified
Finish
CONTRACTOR NOTIFIES WITHIN EIGHT WEEKS?
DOES THE CE ARISE FROM INSTRUCTION OR CHANGED DECISION?
CONTRACTOR NOT ENTITLED TO CHANGES IN PRICES ETC
61.3 The C notifies the PM of an event which has happened or which he expects to happen as a CE.
61.3 Did the C notify a CE within eight weeks of becoming aware of the event?
NO
YES
61.3 Does the event arise from the PM or the S giving an instruction, issuing a certificate, changing an earlier decision or correcting an assumption?
NO
YES
61.3 The C is not entitled to a change in the Prices, the Completion Date or a Key Date.
C sheet 3

Flow chart 61 Sheet 2 of 4
Notifying compensation events

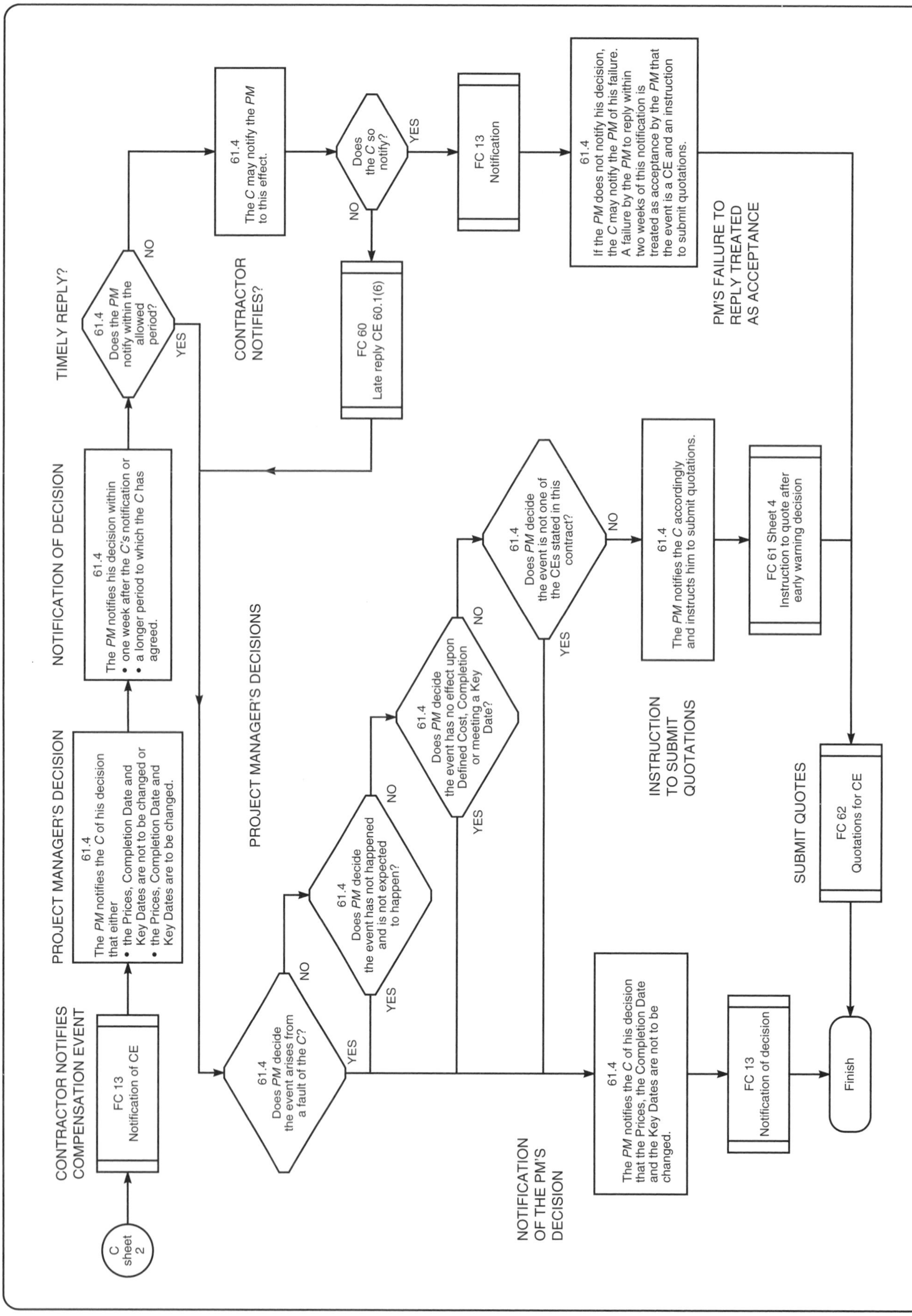

C sheet 2

CONTRACTOR NOTIFIES COMPENSATION EVENT

FC 13
Notification of CE

PROJECT MANAGER'S DECISION

61.4
The *PM* notifies the *C* of his decision that either
- the Prices, Completion Date and Key Dates are not to be changed or
- the Prices, Completion Date and Key Dates are to be changed.

NOTIFICATION OF DECISION

61.4
The *PM* notifies his decision within
- one week after the *C's* notification or
- a longer period to which the *C* has agreed.

TIMELY REPLY?

61.4
Does the *PM* notify within the allowed period?
YES / NO

CONTRACTOR NOTIFIES?

61.4
The *C* may notify the *PM* to this effect.

Does the *C* so notify?
NO / YES

FC 60
Late reply CE 60.1(6)

FC 13
Notification

61.4
If the *PM* does not notify his decision, the *C* may notify the *PM* of his failure. A failure by the *PM* to reply within two weeks of this notification is treated as acceptance by the *PM* that the event is a CE and an instruction to submit quotations.

PM'S FAILURE TO REPLY TREATED AS ACCEPTANCE

PROJECT MANAGER'S DECISIONS

61.4
Does *PM* decide the event arises from a fault of the *C*?
YES / NO

61.4
Does *PM* decide the event has not happened and is not expected to happen?
YES / NO

61.4
Does *PM* decide the event has no effect upon Defined Cost, Completion or meeting a Key Date?
YES / NO

61.4
Does *PM* decide the event is not one of the CEs stated in this contract?
YES / NO

NOTIFICATION OF THE PM'S DECISION

61.4
The *PM* notifies the *C* of his decision that the Prices, the Completion Date and the Key Dates are not to be changed.

FC 13
Notification of decision

Finish

INSTRUCTION TO SUBMIT QUOTATIONS

61.4
The *PM* notifies the *C* accordingly and instructs him to submit quotations.

FC 61 Sheet 4
Instruction to quote after early warning decision

SUBMIT QUOTES

FC 62
Quotations for CE

Flow chart 61 Sheet 3 of 4
Notifying compensation events

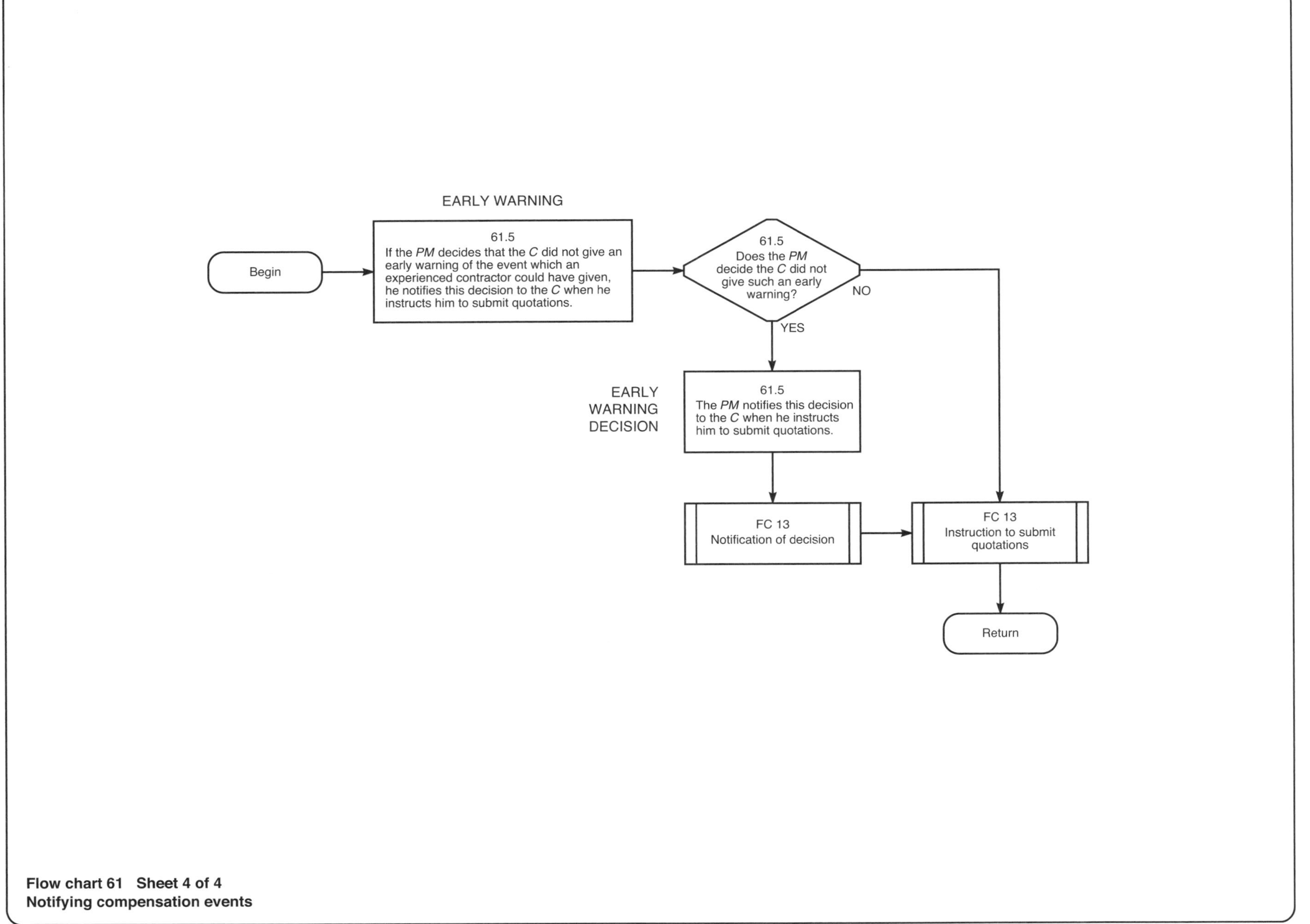
EARLY WARNING
Begin
61.5
If the *PM* decides that the *C* did not give an early warning of the event which an experienced contractor could have given, he notifies this decision to the *C* when he instructs him to submit quotations.
61.5
Does the *PM* decide the *C* did not give such an early warning?
NO
YES
EARLY WARNING DECISION
61.5
The *PM* notifies this decision to the *C* when he instructs him to submit quotations.
FC 13
Notification of decision
FC 13
Instruction to submit quotations
Return

Flow chart 61 Sheet 4 of 4
Notifying compensation events

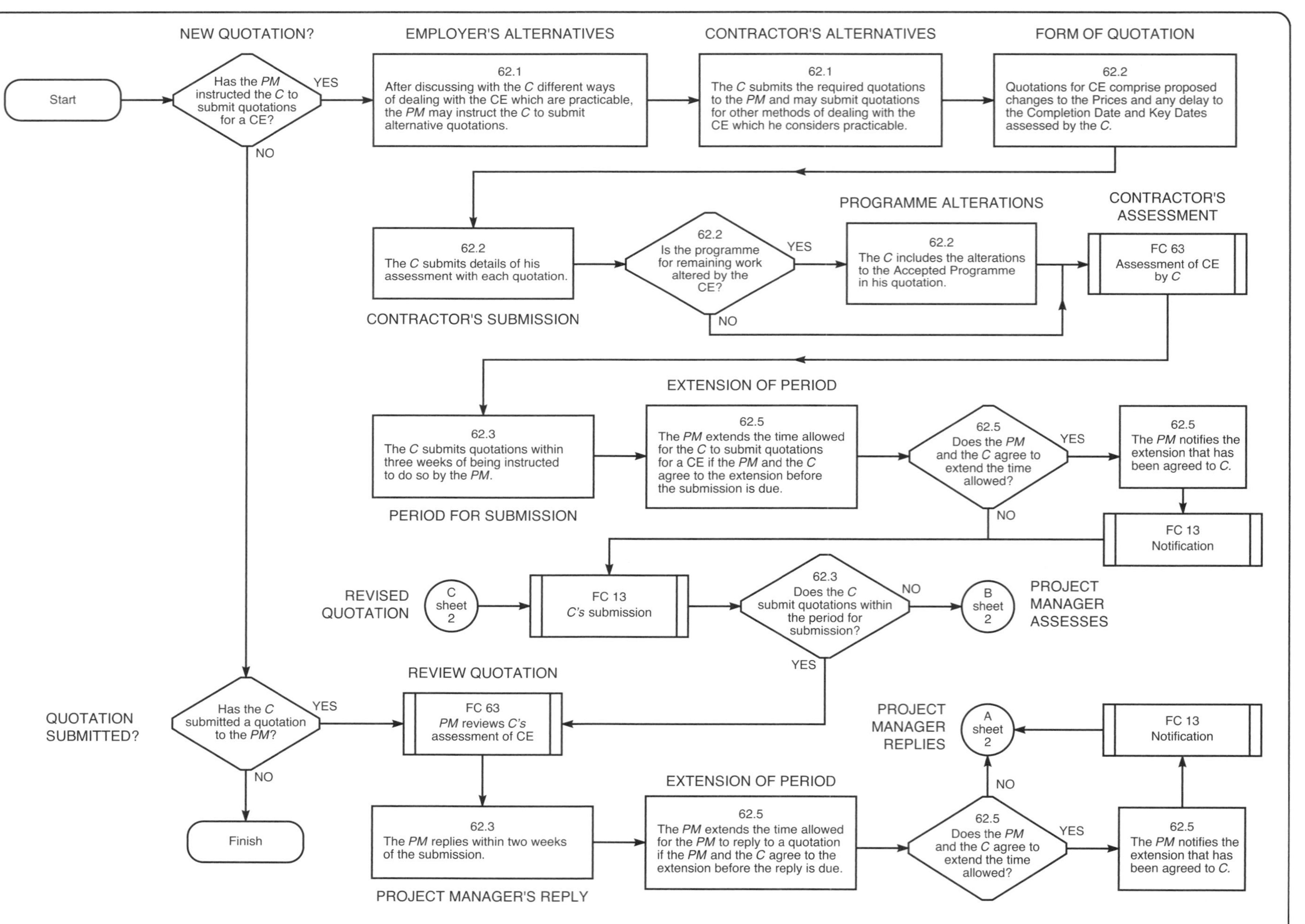

NEW QUOTATION?
Start
Has the PM instructed the C to submit quotations for a CE?
YES
NO
EMPLOYER'S ALTERNATIVES
62.1 After discussing with the C different ways of dealing with the CE which are practicable, the PM may instruct the C to submit alternative quotations.
CONTRACTOR'S ALTERNATIVES
62.1 The C submits the required quotations to the PM and may submit quotations for other methods of dealing with the CE which he considers practicable.
FORM OF QUOTATION
62.2 Quotations for CE comprise proposed changes to the Prices and any delay to the Completion Date and Key Dates assessed by the C.
62.2 The C submits details of his assessment with each quotation.
CONTRACTOR'S SUBMISSION
62.2 Is the programme for remaining work altered by the CE?
YES
NO
PROGRAMME ALTERATIONS
62.2 The C includes the alterations to the Accepted Programme in his quotation.
CONTRACTOR'S ASSESSMENT
FC 63 Assessment of CE by C
62.3 The C submits quotations within three weeks of being instructed to do so by the PM.
PERIOD FOR SUBMISSION
EXTENSION OF PERIOD
62.5 The PM extends the time allowed for the C to submit quotations for a CE if the PM and the C agree to the extension before the submission is due.
62.5 Does the PM and the C agree to extend the time allowed?
YES
NO
62.5 The PM notifies the extension that has been agreed to C.
FC 13 Notification
REVISED QUOTATION
C sheet 2
FC 13 C's submission
62.3 Does the C submit quotations within the period for submission?
NO
YES
B sheet 2
PROJECT MANAGER ASSESSES
QUOTATION SUBMITTED?
Has the C submitted a quotation to the PM?
YES
NO
Finish
REVIEW QUOTATION
FC 63 PM reviews C's assessment of CE
PROJECT MANAGER REPLIES
A sheet 2
FC 13 Notification
62.3 The PM replies within two weeks of the submission.
PROJECT MANAGER'S REPLY
EXTENSION OF PERIOD
62.5 The PM extends the time allowed for the PM to reply to a quotation if the PM and the C agree to the extension before the reply is due.
62.5 Does the PM and the C agree to extend the time allowed?
NO
YES
62.5 The PM notifies the extension that has been agreed to C.

Flow chart 62 Sheet 1 of 2
Quotations for compensation events

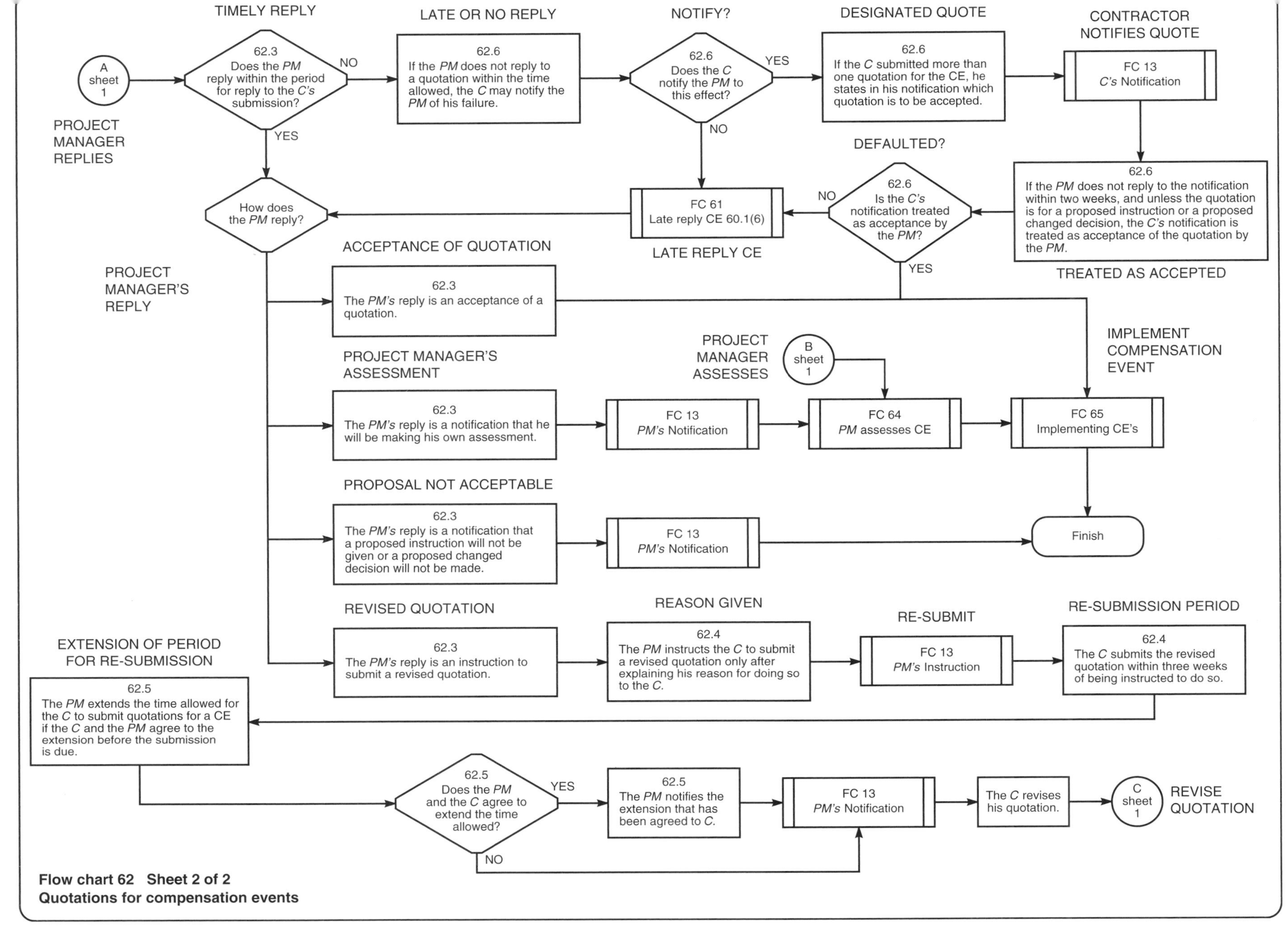

A sheet 1
PROJECT MANAGER REPLIES
TIMELY REPLY
62.3 Does the PM reply within the period for reply to the C's submission?
NO
YES
LATE OR NO REPLY
62.6 If the PM does not reply to a quotation within the time allowed, the C may notify the PM of his failure.
NOTIFY?
62.6 Does the C notify the PM to this effect?
YES
NO
DESIGNATED QUOTE
62.6 If the C submitted more than one quotation for the CE, he states in his notification which quotation is to be accepted.
CONTRACTOR NOTIFIES QUOTE
FC 13 C's Notification
DEFAULTED?
62.6 If the PM does not reply to the notification within two weeks, and unless the quotation is for a proposed instruction or a proposed changed decision, the C's notification is treated as acceptance of the quotation by the PM.
TREATED AS ACCEPTED
62.6 Is the C's notification treated as acceptance by the PM?
NO
YES
FC 61 Late reply CE 60.1(6)
LATE REPLY CE
How does the PM reply?
PROJECT MANAGER'S REPLY
ACCEPTANCE OF QUOTATION
62.3 The PM's reply is an acceptance of a quotation.
IMPLEMENT COMPENSATION EVENT
PROJECT MANAGER'S ASSESSMENT
62.3 The PM's reply is a notification that he will be making his own assessment.
FC 13 PM's Notification
PROJECT MANAGER ASSESSES
B sheet 1
FC 64 PM assesses CE
FC 65 Implementing CE's
PROPOSAL NOT ACCEPTABLE
62.3 The PM's reply is a notification that a proposed instruction will not be given or a proposed changed decision will not be made.
FC 13 PM's Notification
Finish
REVISED QUOTATION
62.3 The PM's reply is an instruction to submit a revised quotation.
REASON GIVEN
62.4 The PM instructs the C to submit a revised quotation only after explaining his reason for doing so to the C.
RE-SUBMIT
FC 13 PM's Instruction
RE-SUBMISSION PERIOD
62.4 The C submits the revised quotation within three weeks of being instructed to do so.
EXTENSION OF PERIOD FOR RE-SUBMISSION
62.5 The PM extends the time allowed for the C to submit quotations for a CE if the C and the PM agree to the extension before the submission is due.
62.5 Does the PM and the C agree to extend the time allowed?
YES
NO
62.5 The PM notifies the extension that has been agreed to C.
FC 13 PM's Notification
The C revises his quotation.
C sheet 1
REVISE QUOTATION

Flow chart 62 Sheet 2 of 2
Quotations for compensation events

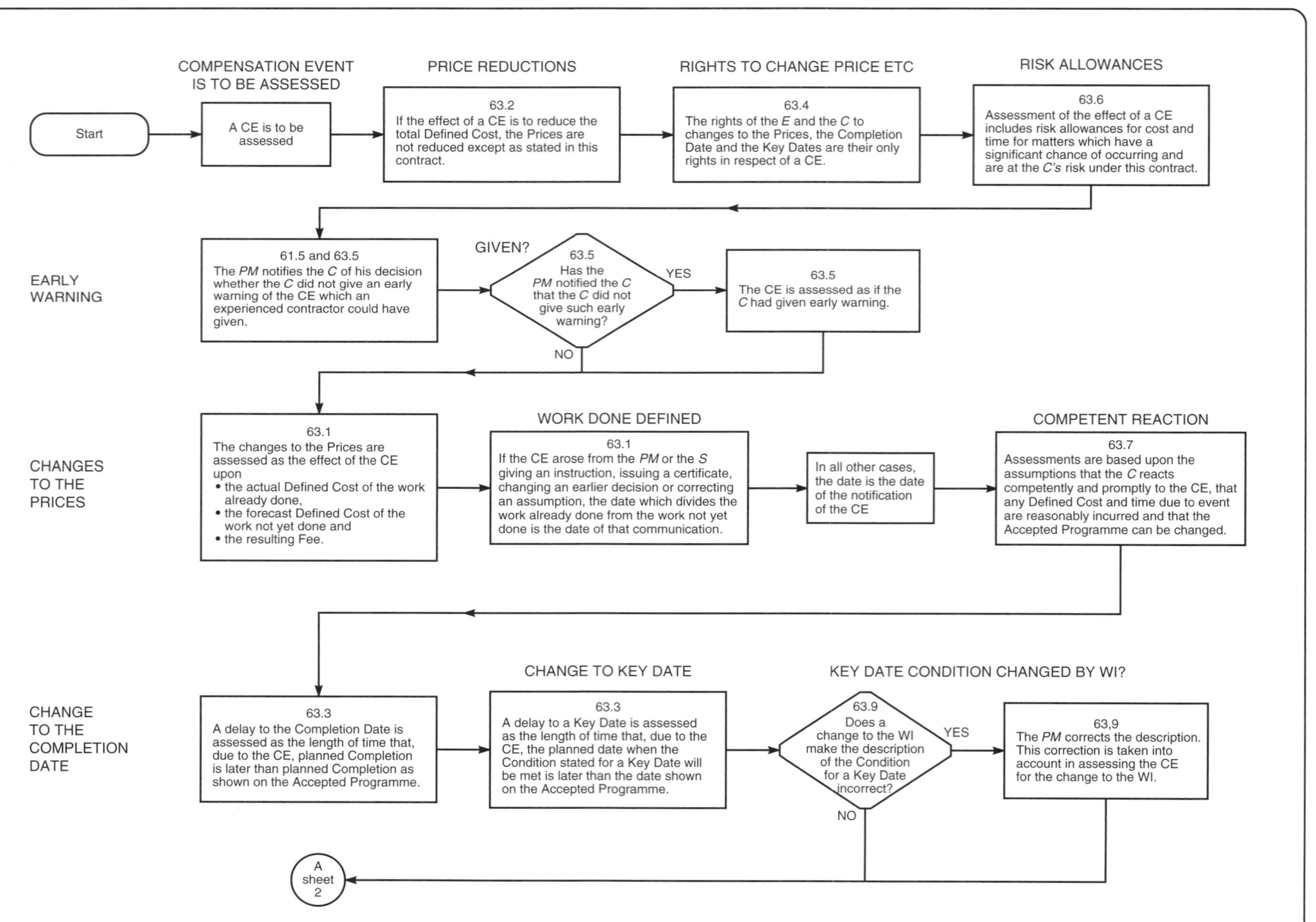
COMPENSATION EVENT IS TO BE ASSESSED
PRICE REDUCTIONS
RIGHTS TO CHANGE PRICE ETC
RISK ALLOWANCES
Start
A CE is to be assessed
63.2 If the effect of a CE is to reduce the total Defined Cost, the Prices are not reduced except as stated in this contract.
63.4 The rights of the E and the C to changes to the Prices, the Completion Date and the Key Dates are their only rights in respect of a CE.
63.6 Assessment of the effect of a CE includes risk allowances for cost and time for matters which have a significant chance of occurring and are at the C's risk under this contract.
EARLY WARNING
61.5 and 63.5 The PM notifies the C of his decision whether the C did not give an early warning of the CE which an experienced contractor could have given.
GIVEN?
63.5 Has the PM notified the C that the C did not give such early warning?
YES
NO
63.5 The CE is assessed as if the C had given early warning.
CHANGES TO THE PRICES
63.1 The changes to the Prices are assessed as the effect of the CE upon
• the actual Defined Cost of the work already done,
• the forecast Defined Cost of the work not yet done and
• the resulting Fee.
WORK DONE DEFINED
63.1 If the CE arose from the PM or the S giving an instruction, issuing a certificate, changing an earlier decision or correcting an assumption, the date which divides the work already done from the work not yet done is the date of that communication.
In all other cases, the date is the date of the notification of the CE
COMPETENT REACTION
63.7 Assessments are based upon the assumptions that the C reacts competently and promptly to the CE, that any Defined Cost and time due to event are reasonably incurred and that the Accepted Programme can be changed.
CHANGE TO THE COMPLETION DATE
63.3 A delay to the Completion Date is assessed as the length of time that, due to the CE, planned Completion is later than planned Completion as shown on the Accepted Programme.
CHANGE TO KEY DATE
63.3 A delay to a Key Date is assessed as the length of time that, due to the CE, the planned date when the Condition stated for a Key Date will be met is later than the date shown on the Accepted Programme.
KEY DATE CONDITION CHANGED BY WI?
63.9 Does a change to the WI make the description of the Condition for a Key Date incorrect?
YES
NO
63,9 The PM corrects the description. This correction is taken into account in assessing the CE for the change to the WI.
A sheet 2

Flow chart 63 Sheet 1 of 3
Assessing compensation events

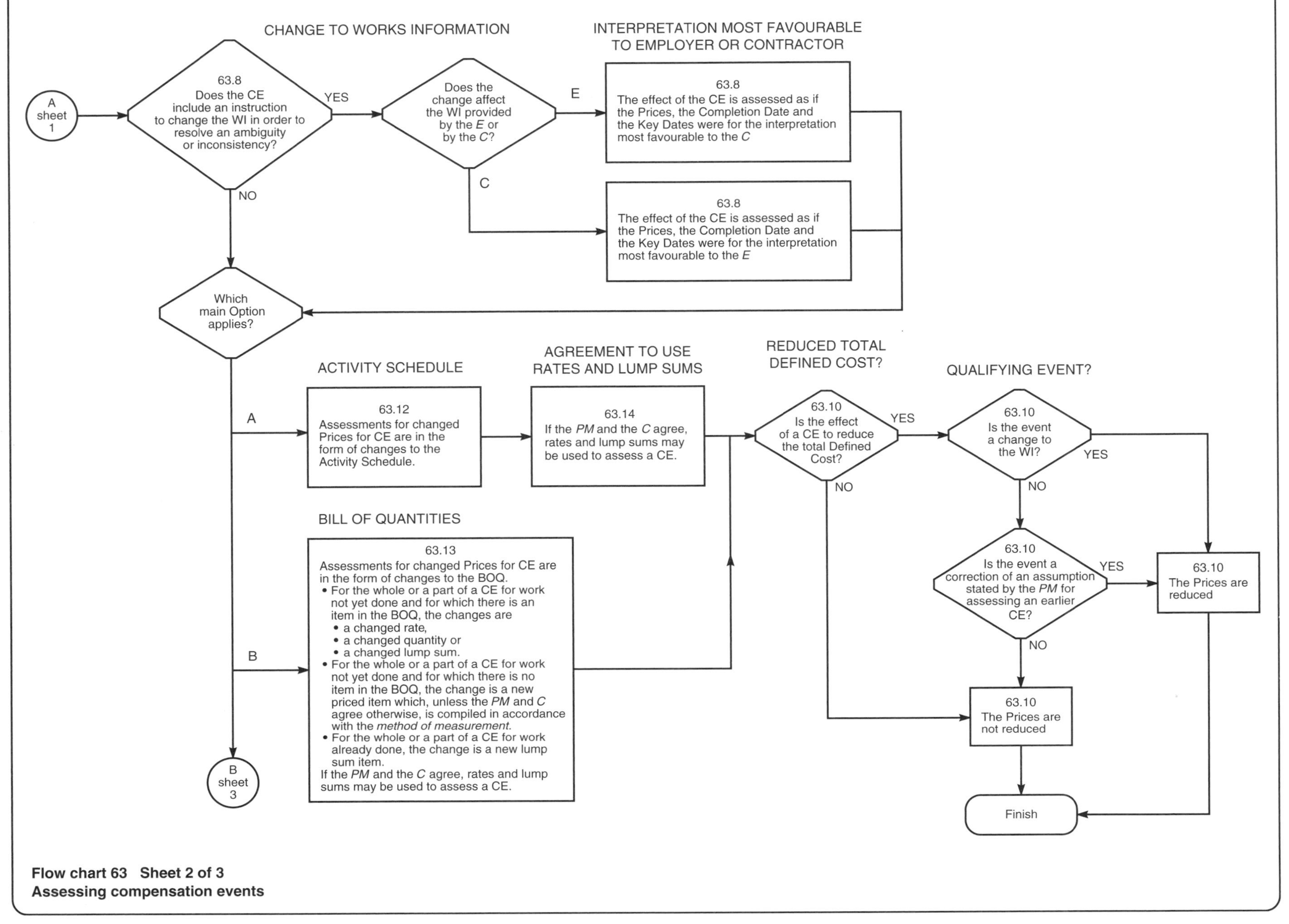
A sheet 1
CHANGE TO WORKS INFORMATION
63.8 Does the CE include an instruction to change the WI in order to resolve an ambiguity or inconsistency?
YES
NO
Does the change affect the WI provided by the E or by the C?
E
C
INTERPRETATION MOST FAVOURABLE TO EMPLOYER OR CONTRACTOR
63.8 The effect of the CE is assessed as if the Prices, the Completion Date and the Key Dates were for the interpretation most favourable to the C
63.8 The effect of the CE is assessed as if the Prices, the Completion Date and the Key Dates were for the interpretation most favourable to the E
Which main Option applies?
A
B
ACTIVITY SCHEDULE
63.12 Assessments for changed Prices for CE are in the form of changes to the Activity Schedule.
AGREEMENT TO USE RATES AND LUMP SUMS
63.14 If the PM and the C agree, rates and lump sums may be used to assess a CE.
BILL OF QUANTITIES
63.13 Assessments for changed Prices for CE are in the form of changes to the BOQ.
• For the whole or a part of a CE for work not yet done and for which there is an item in the BOQ, the changes are
• a changed rate,
• a changed quantity or
• a changed lump sum.
• For the whole or a part of a CE for work not yet done and for which there is no item in the BOQ, the change is a new priced item which, unless the PM and C agree otherwise, is compiled in accordance with the method of measurement.
• For the whole or a part of a CE for work already done, the change is a new lump sum item.
If the PM and the C agree, rates and lump sums may be used to assess a CE.
B sheet 3
REDUCED TOTAL DEFINED COST?
63.10 Is the effect of a CE to reduce the total Defined Cost?
YES
NO
QUALIFYING EVENT?
63.10 Is the event a change to the WI?
YES
NO
63.10 Is the event a correction of an assumption stated by the PM for assessing an earlier CE?
YES
NO
63.10 The Prices are reduced
63.10 The Prices are not reduced
Finish

Flow chart 63 Sheet 2 of 3
Assessing compensation events

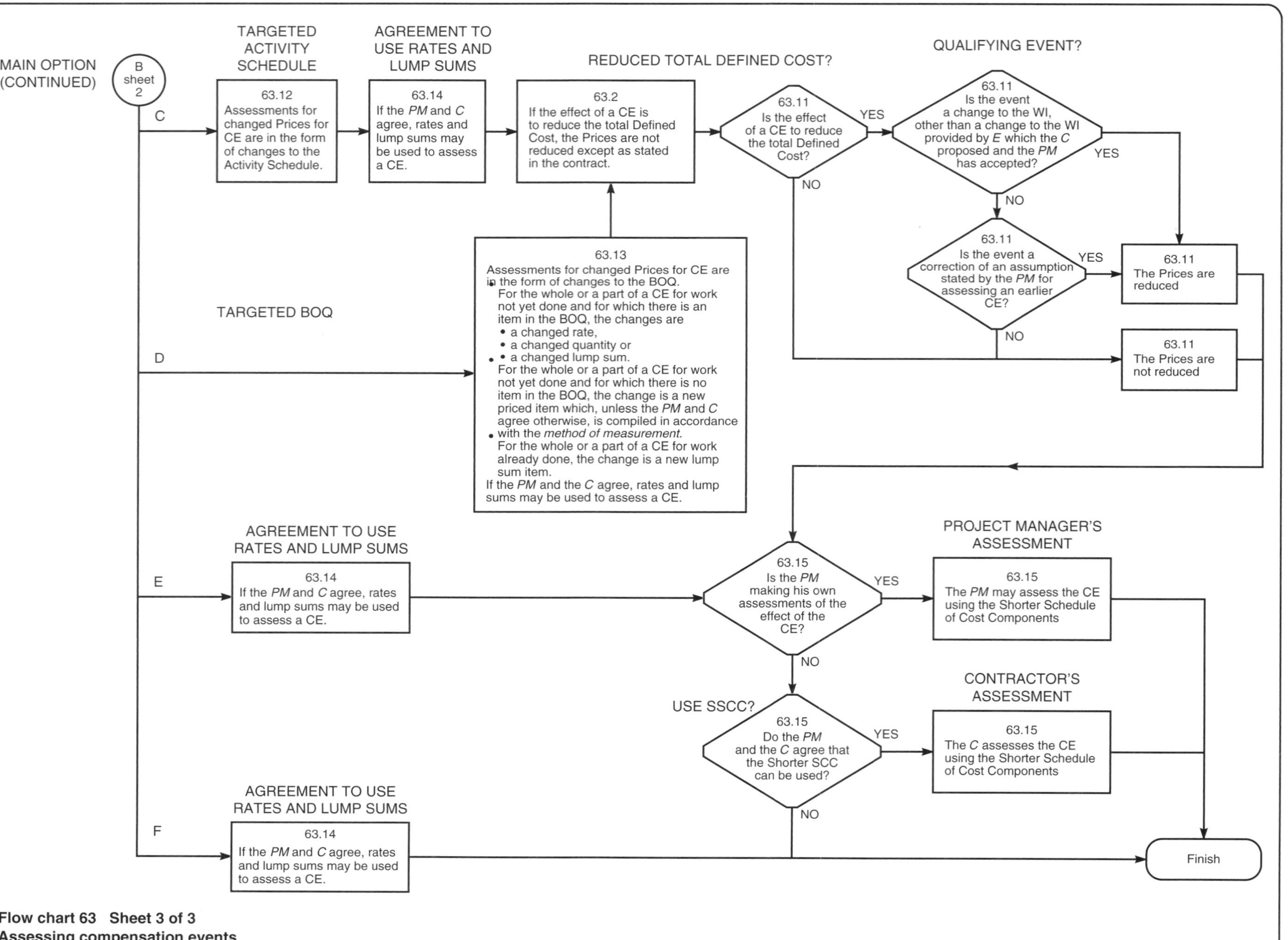
MAIN OPTION (CONTINUED)
B sheet 2
C
TARGETED ACTIVITY SCHEDULE
63.12 Assessments for changed Prices for CE are in the form of changes to the Activity Schedule.
AGREEMENT TO USE RATES AND LUMP SUMS
63.14 If the PM and C agree, rates and lump sums may be used to assess a CE.
REDUCED TOTAL DEFINED COST?
63.2 If the effect of a CE is to reduce the total Defined Cost, the Prices are not reduced except as stated in the contract.
63.11 Is the effect of a CE to reduce the total Defined Cost?
YES
NO
QUALIFYING EVENT?
63.11 Is the event a change to the WI, other than a change to the WI provided by E which the C proposed and the PM has accepted?
YES
NO
63.11 Is the event a correction of an assumption stated by the PM for assessing an earlier CE?
YES
NO
63.11 The Prices are reduced
63.11 The Prices are not reduced
D
TARGETED BOQ
63.13 Assessments for changed Prices for CE are in the form of changes to the BOQ.
• For the whole or a part of a CE for work not yet done and for which there is an item in the BOQ, the changes are
• a changed rate,
• a changed quantity or
• a changed lump sum.
• For the whole or a part of a CE for work not yet done and for which there is no item in the BOQ, the change is a new priced item which, unless the PM and C agree otherwise, is compiled in accordance with the method of measurement.
• For the whole or a part of a CE for work already done, the change is a new lump sum item.
If the PM and the C agree, rates and lump sums may be used to assess a CE.
E
AGREEMENT TO USE RATES AND LUMP SUMS
63.14 If the PM and C agree, rates and lump sums may be used to assess a CE.
63.15 Is the PM making his own assessments of the effect of the CE?
YES
NO
PROJECT MANAGER'S ASSESSMENT
63.15 The PM may assess the CE using the Shorter Schedule of Cost Components
USE SSCC?
63.15 Do the PM and the C agree that the Shorter SCC can be used?
YES
NO
CONTRACTOR'S ASSESSMENT
63.15 The C assesses the CE using the Shorter Schedule of Cost Components
F
AGREEMENT TO USE RATES AND LUMP SUMS
63.14 If the PM and C agree, rates and lump sums may be used to assess a CE.
Finish

Flow chart 63 Sheet 3 of 3
Assessing compensation events

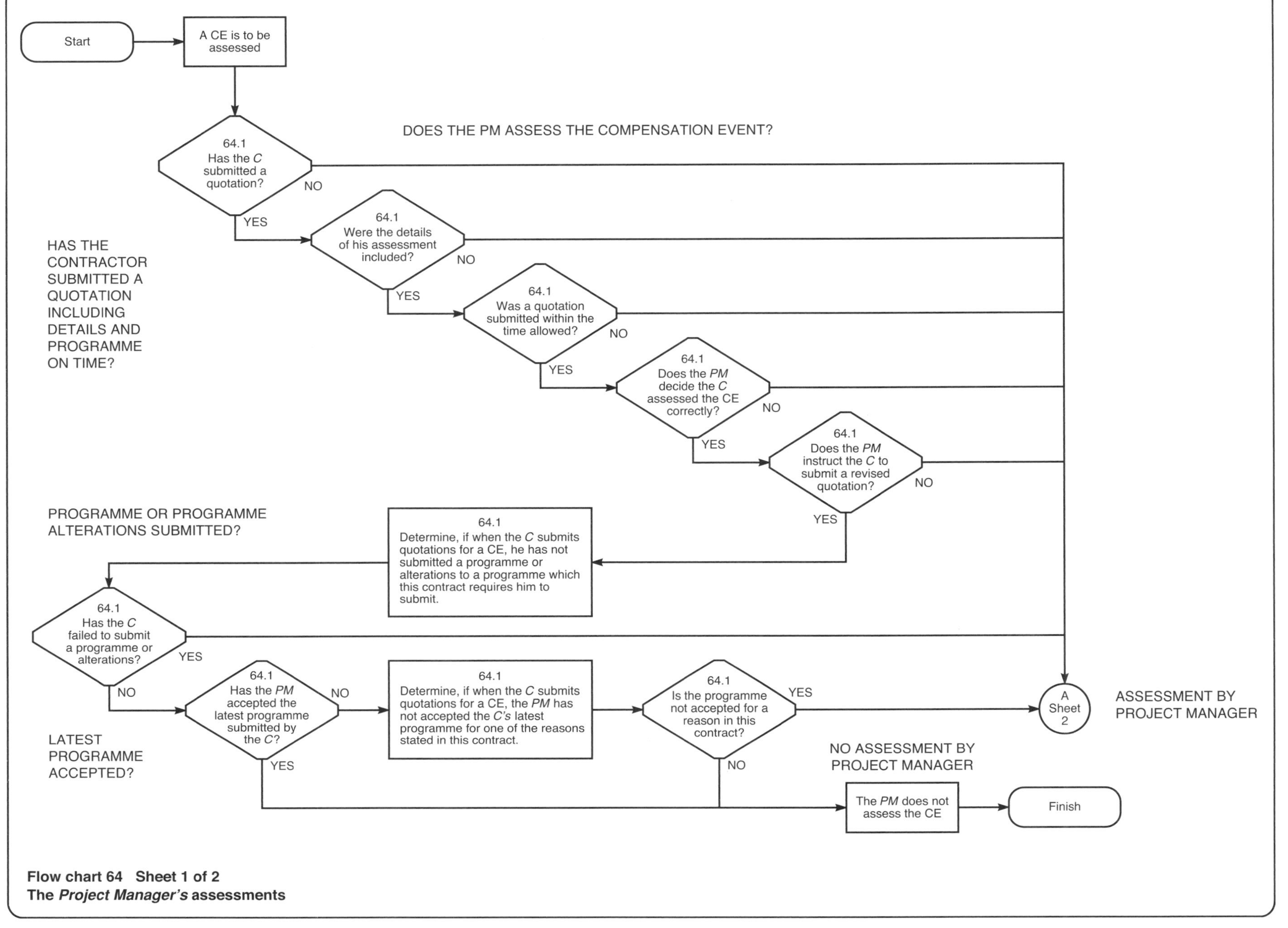

Start
A CE is to be assessed
DOES THE PM ASSESS THE COMPENSATION EVENT?
HAS THE CONTRACTOR SUBMITTED A QUOTATION INCLUDING DETAILS AND PROGRAMME ON TIME?
64.1 Has the C submitted a quotation?
NO
YES
64.1 Were the details of his assessment included?
NO
YES
64.1 Was a quotation submitted within the time allowed?
NO
YES
64.1 Does the PM decide the C assessed the CE correctly?
NO
YES
64.1 Does the PM instruct the C to submit a revised quotation?
NO
YES
PROGRAMME OR PROGRAMME ALTERATIONS SUBMITTED?
64.1 Determine, if when the C submits quotations for a CE, he has not submitted a programme or alterations to a programme which this contract requires him to submit.
64.1 Has the C failed to submit a programme or alterations?
YES
NO
LATEST PROGRAMME ACCEPTED?
64.1 Has the PM accepted the latest programme submitted by the C?
NO
YES
64.1 Determine, if when the C submits quotations for a CE, the PM has not accepted the C's latest programme for one of the reasons stated in this contract.
64.1 Is the programme not accepted for a reason in this contract?
YES
NO
A Sheet 2
ASSESSMENT BY PROJECT MANAGER
NO ASSESSMENT BY PROJECT MANAGER
The PM does not assess the CE
Finish

Flow chart 64 Sheet 1 of 2
The *Project Manager's* assessments

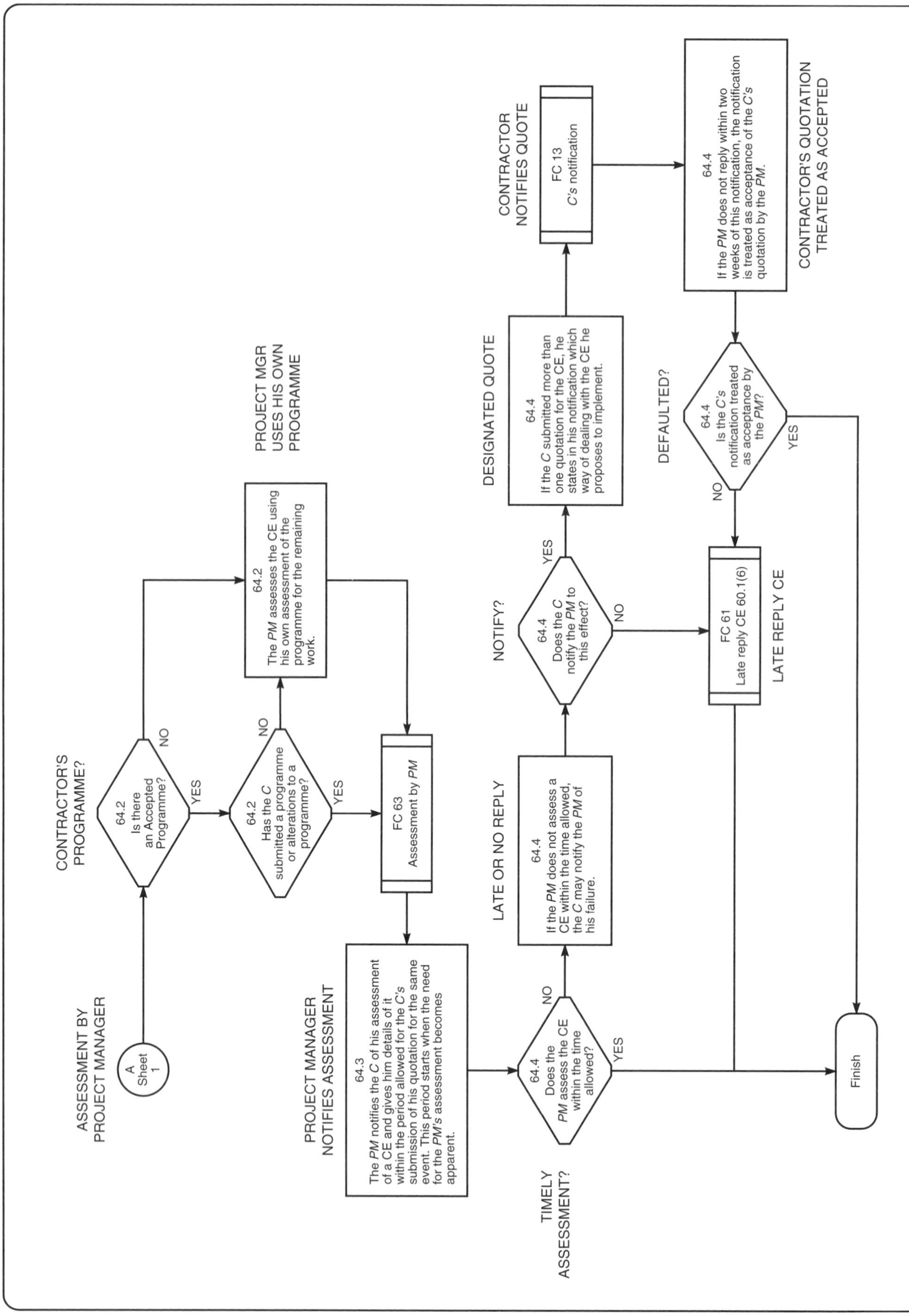

ASSESSMENT BY PROJECT MANAGER

A Sheet 1

CONTRACTOR'S PROGRAMME?

64.2 Is there an Accepted Programme?

NO

YES

64.2 Has the *C* submitted a programme or alterations to a programme?

NO

YES

64.2 The *PM* assesses the CE using his own assessment of the programme for the remaining work.

PROJECT MGR USES HIS OWN PROGRAMME

FC 63 Assessment by *PM*

PROJECT MANAGER NOTIFIES ASSESSMENT

64.3 The *PM* notifies the *C* of his assessment of a CE and gives him details of it within the period allowed for the *C's* submission of his quotation for the same event. This period starts when the need for the *PM's* assessment becomes apparent.

TIMELY ASSESSMENT?

64.4 Does the *PM* assess the CE within the time allowed?

NO

YES

LATE OR NO REPLY

64.4 If the *PM* does not assess a CE within the time allowed, the *C* may notify the *PM* of his failure.

NOTIFY?

64.4 Does the *C* notify the *PM* to this effect?

YES

NO

DESIGNATED QUOTE

64.4 If the *C* submitted more than one quotation for the CE, he states in his notification which way of dealing with the CE he proposes to implement.

CONTRACTOR NOTIFIES QUOTE

FC 13 *C's* notification

64.4 If the *PM* does not reply within two weeks of this notification, the notification is treated as acceptance of the *C's* quotation by the *PM*.

CONTRACTOR'S QUOTATION TREATED AS ACCEPTED

DEFAULTED?

64.4 Is the *C's* notification treated as acceptance by the *PM*?

NO

YES

FC 61 Late reply CE 60.1(6)

LATE REPLY CE

Finish

Flow chart 64 Sheet 2 of 2
The *Project Manager's* assessments

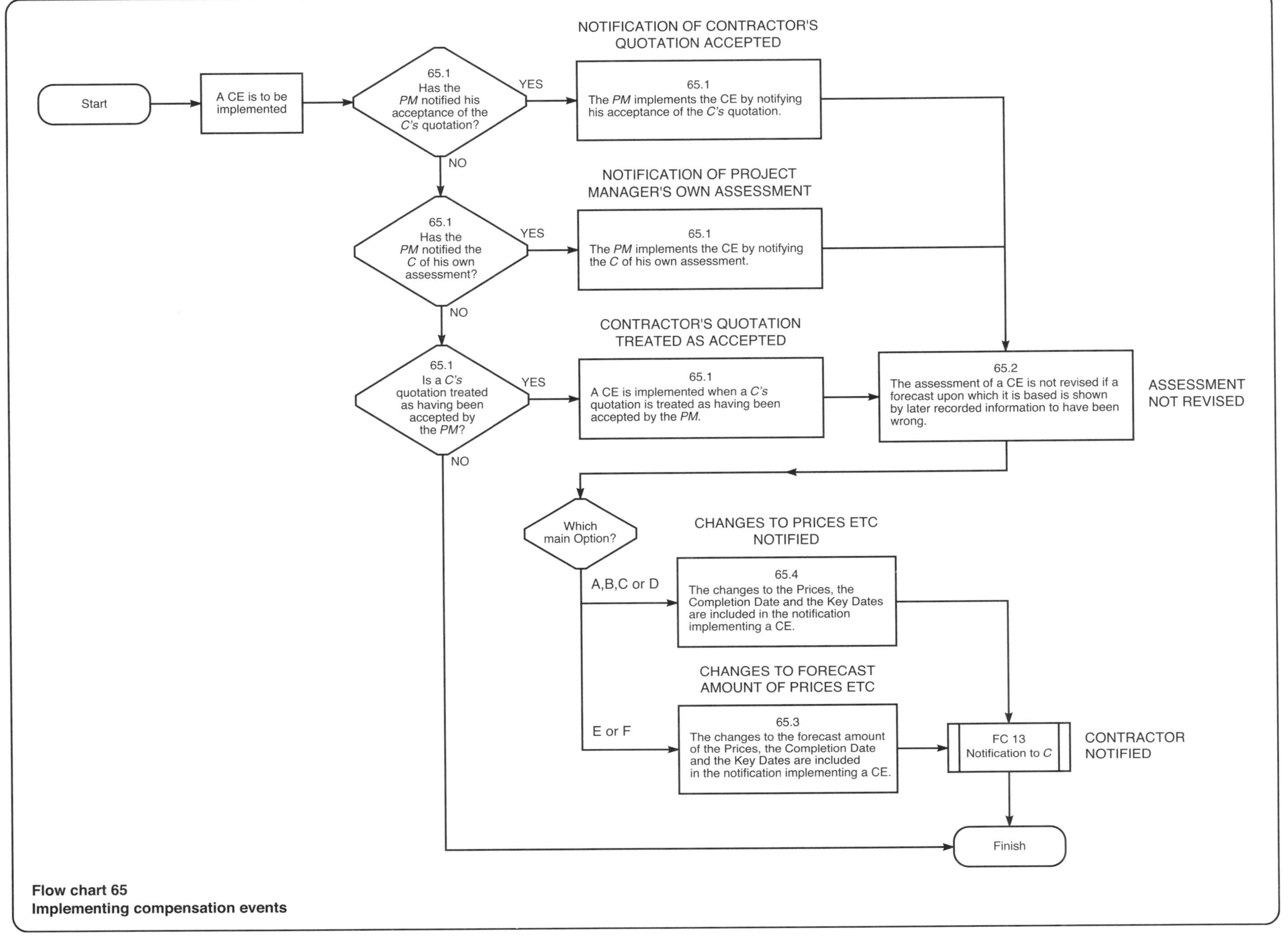

Start
A CE is to be implemented
65.1 Has the PM notified his acceptance of the C's quotation?
YES
NO
NOTIFICATION OF CONTRACTOR'S QUOTATION ACCEPTED
65.1 The PM implements the CE by notifying his acceptance of the C's quotation.
65.1 Has the PM notified the C of his own assessment?
YES
NO
NOTIFICATION OF PROJECT MANAGER'S OWN ASSESSMENT
65.1 The PM implements the CE by notifying the C of his own assessment.
65.1 Is a C's quotation treated as having been accepted by the PM?
YES
NO
CONTRACTOR'S QUOTATION TREATED AS ACCEPTED
65.1 A CE is implemented when a C's quotation is treated as having been accepted by the PM.
65.2 The assessment of a CE is not revised if a forecast upon which it is based is shown by later recorded information to have been wrong.
ASSESSMENT NOT REVISED
Which main Option?
A,B,C or D
E or F
CHANGES TO PRICES ETC NOTIFIED
65.4 The changes to the Prices, the Completion Date and the Key Dates are included in the notification implementing a CE.
CHANGES TO FORECAST AMOUNT OF PRICES ETC
65.3 The changes to the forecast amount of the Prices, the Completion Date and the Key Dates are included in the notification implementing a CE.
FC 13 Notification to C
CONTRACTOR NOTIFIED
Finish

Flow chart 65
Implementing compensation events

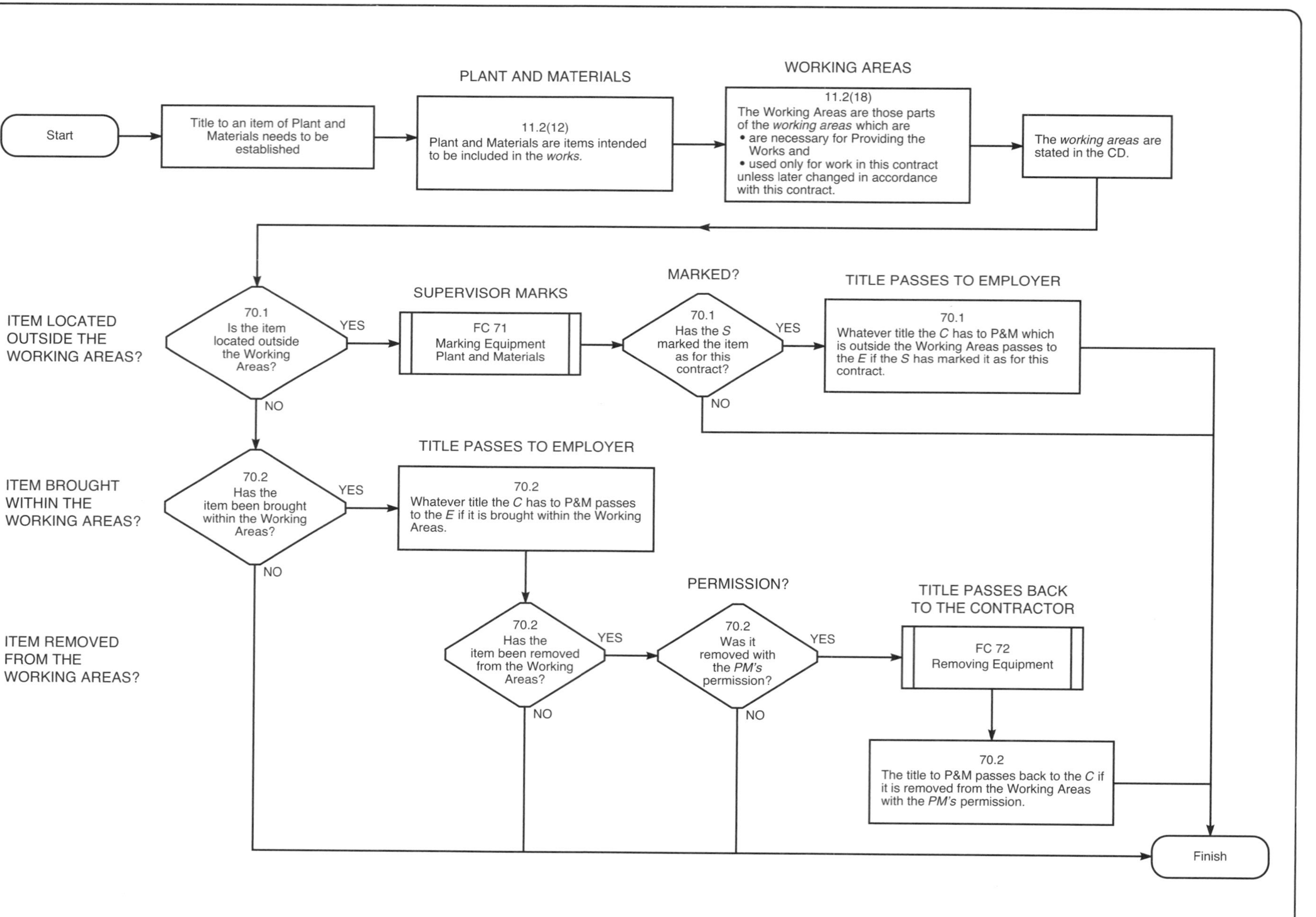
Start
Title to an item of Plant and Materials needs to be established
PLANT AND MATERIALS
11.2(12)
Plant and Materials are items intended to be included in the *works*.
WORKING AREAS
11.2(18)
The Working Areas are those parts of the *working areas* which are
• are necessary for Providing the Works and
• used only for work in this contract unless later changed in accordance with this contract.
The *working areas* are stated in the CD.
ITEM LOCATED OUTSIDE THE WORKING AREAS?
70.1
Is the item located outside the Working Areas?
YES
NO
SUPERVISOR MARKS
FC 71
Marking Equipment Plant and Materials
MARKED?
70.1
Has the *S* marked the item as for this contract?
YES
NO
TITLE PASSES TO EMPLOYER
70.1
Whatever title the *C* has to P&M which is outside the Working Areas passes to the *E* if the *S* has marked it as for this contract.
ITEM BROUGHT WITHIN THE WORKING AREAS?
70.2
Has the item been brought within the Working Areas?
YES
NO
TITLE PASSES TO EMPLOYER
70.2
Whatever title the *C* has to P&M passes to the *E* if it is brought within the Working Areas.
ITEM REMOVED FROM THE WORKING AREAS?
70.2
Has the item been removed from the Working Areas?
YES
NO
PERMISSION?
70.2
Was it removed with the *PM's* permission?
YES
NO
TITLE PASSES BACK TO THE CONTRACTOR
FC 72
Removing Equipment
70.2
The title to P&M passes back to the *C* if it is removed from the Working Areas with the *PM's* permission.
Finish

Flow chart 70
The *Employer's* title to Plant and Materials

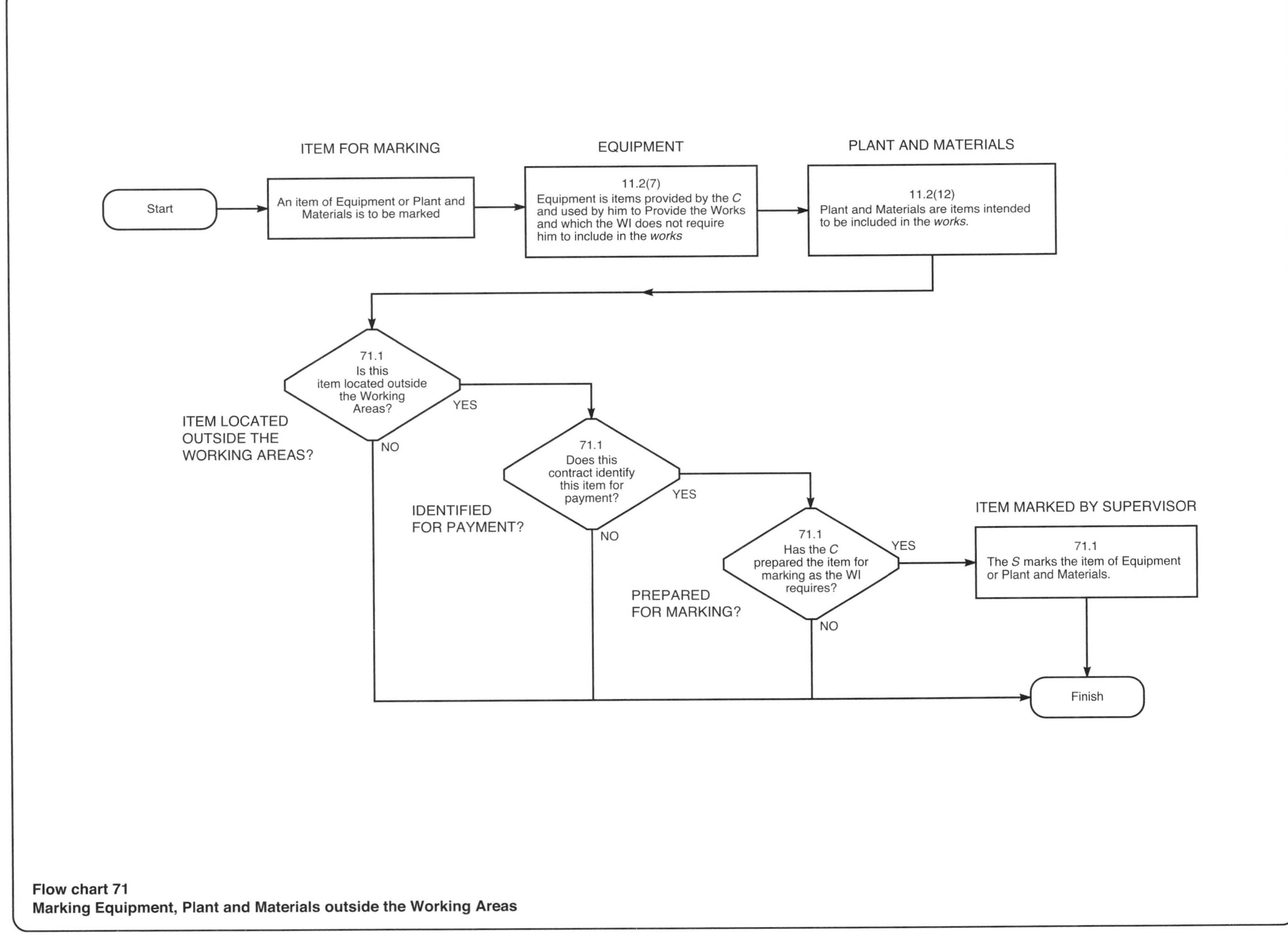
ITEM FOR MARKING
EQUIPMENT
PLANT AND MATERIALS
Start
An item of Equipment or Plant and Materials is to be marked
11.2(7)
Equipment is items provided by the C and used by him to Provide the Works and which the WI does not require him to include in the works
11.2(12)
Plant and Materials are items intended to be included in the works.
71.1
Is this item located outside the Working Areas?
ITEM LOCATED OUTSIDE THE WORKING AREAS?
YES
NO
71.1
Does this contract identify this item for payment?
IDENTIFIED FOR PAYMENT?
YES
NO
71.1
Has the C prepared the item for marking as the WI requires?
PREPARED FOR MARKING?
YES
NO
ITEM MARKED BY SUPERVISOR
71.1
The S marks the item of Equipment or Plant and Materials.
Finish

Flow chart 71
Marking Equipment, Plant and Materials outside the Working Areas

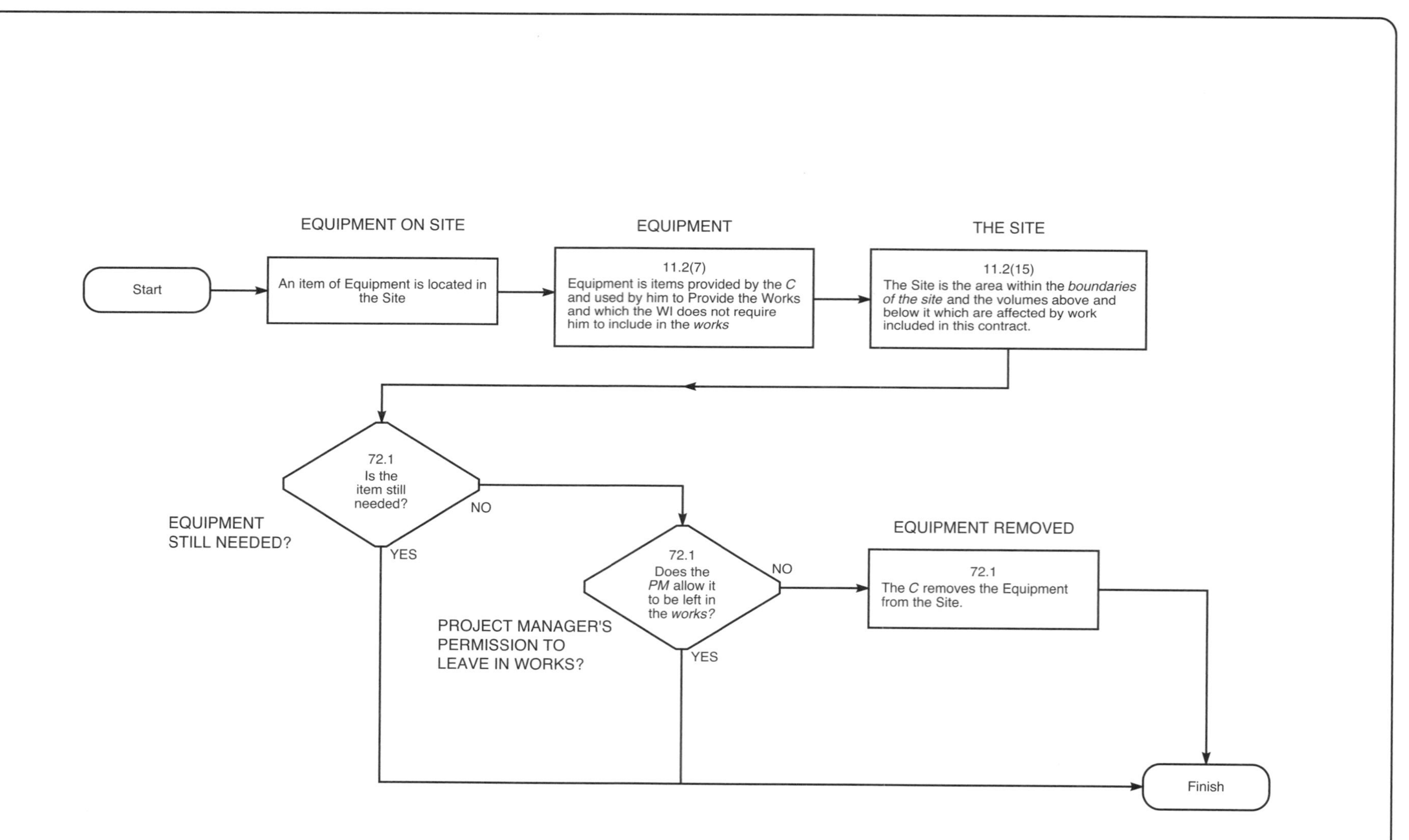
EQUIPMENT ON SITE
Start
An item of Equipment is located in the Site
EQUIPMENT
11.2(7)
Equipment is items provided by the *C* and used by him to Provide the Works and which the WI does not require him to include in the *works*
THE SITE
11.2(15)
The Site is the area within the *boundaries of the site* and the volumes above and below it which are affected by work included in this contract.
72.1
Is the item still needed?
EQUIPMENT STILL NEEDED?
NO
YES
72.1
Does the *PM* allow it to be left in the *works?*
PROJECT MANAGER'S PERMISSION TO LEAVE IN WORKS?
NO
YES
EQUIPMENT REMOVED
72.1
The *C* removes the Equipment from the Site.
Finish

Flow chart 72
Removing Equipment

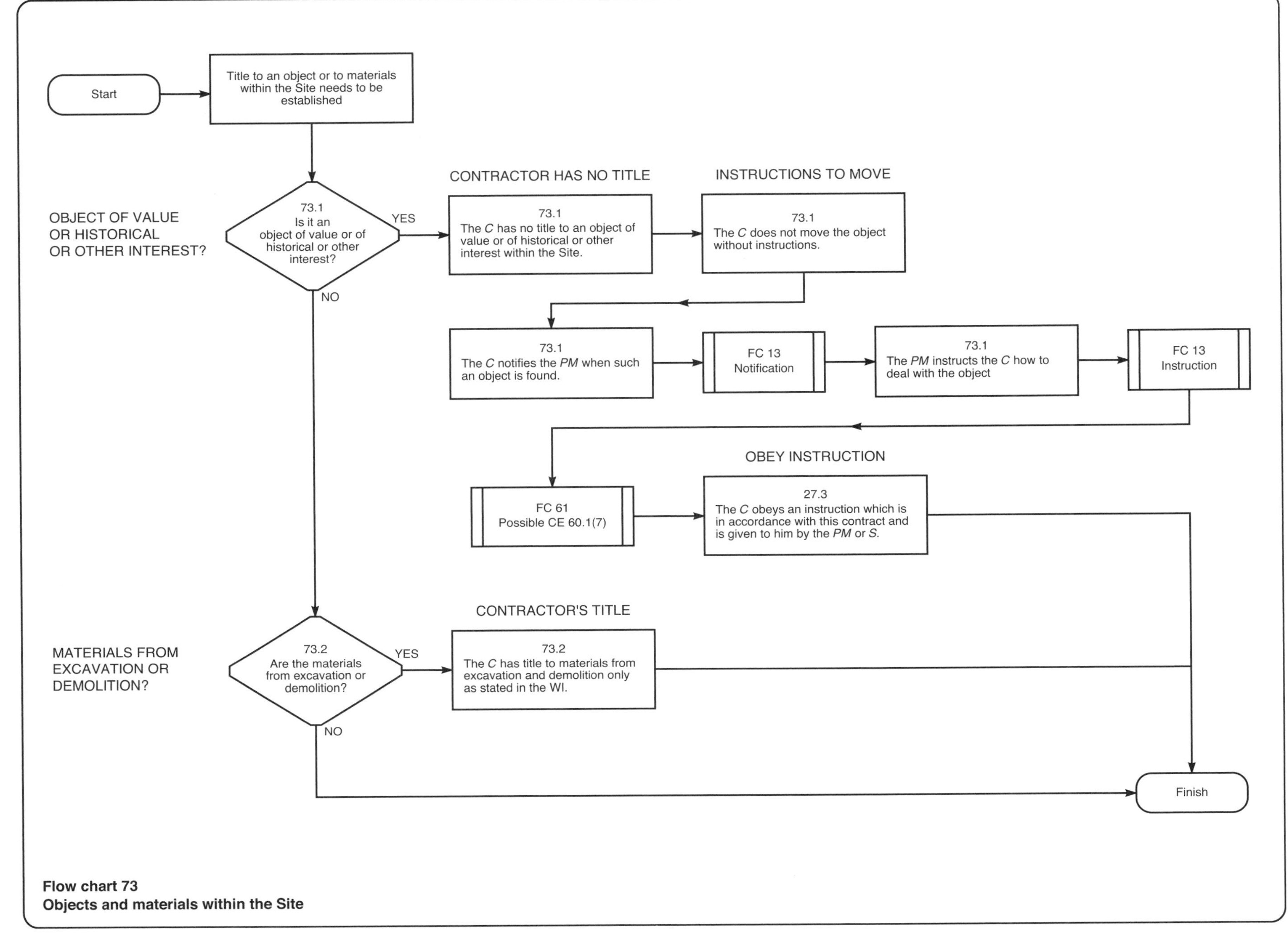
Start
Title to an object or to materials within the Site needs to be established
OBJECT OF VALUE OR HISTORICAL OR OTHER INTEREST?
73.1 Is it an object of value or of historical or other interest?
YES
NO
CONTRACTOR HAS NO TITLE
73.1 The C has no title to an object of value or of historical or other interest within the Site.
INSTRUCTIONS TO MOVE
73.1 The C does not move the object without instructions.
73.1 The C notifies the PM when such an object is found.
FC 13 Notification
73.1 The PM instructs the C how to deal with the object
FC 13 Instruction
OBEY INSTRUCTION
FC 61 Possible CE 60.1(7)
27.3 The C obeys an instruction which is in accordance with this contract and is given to him by the PM or S.
MATERIALS FROM EXCAVATION OR DEMOLITION?
73.2 Are the materials from excavation or demolition?
YES
NO
CONTRACTOR'S TITLE
73.2 The C has title to materials from excavation and demolition only as stated in the WI.
Finish

Flow chart 73
Objects and materials within the Site

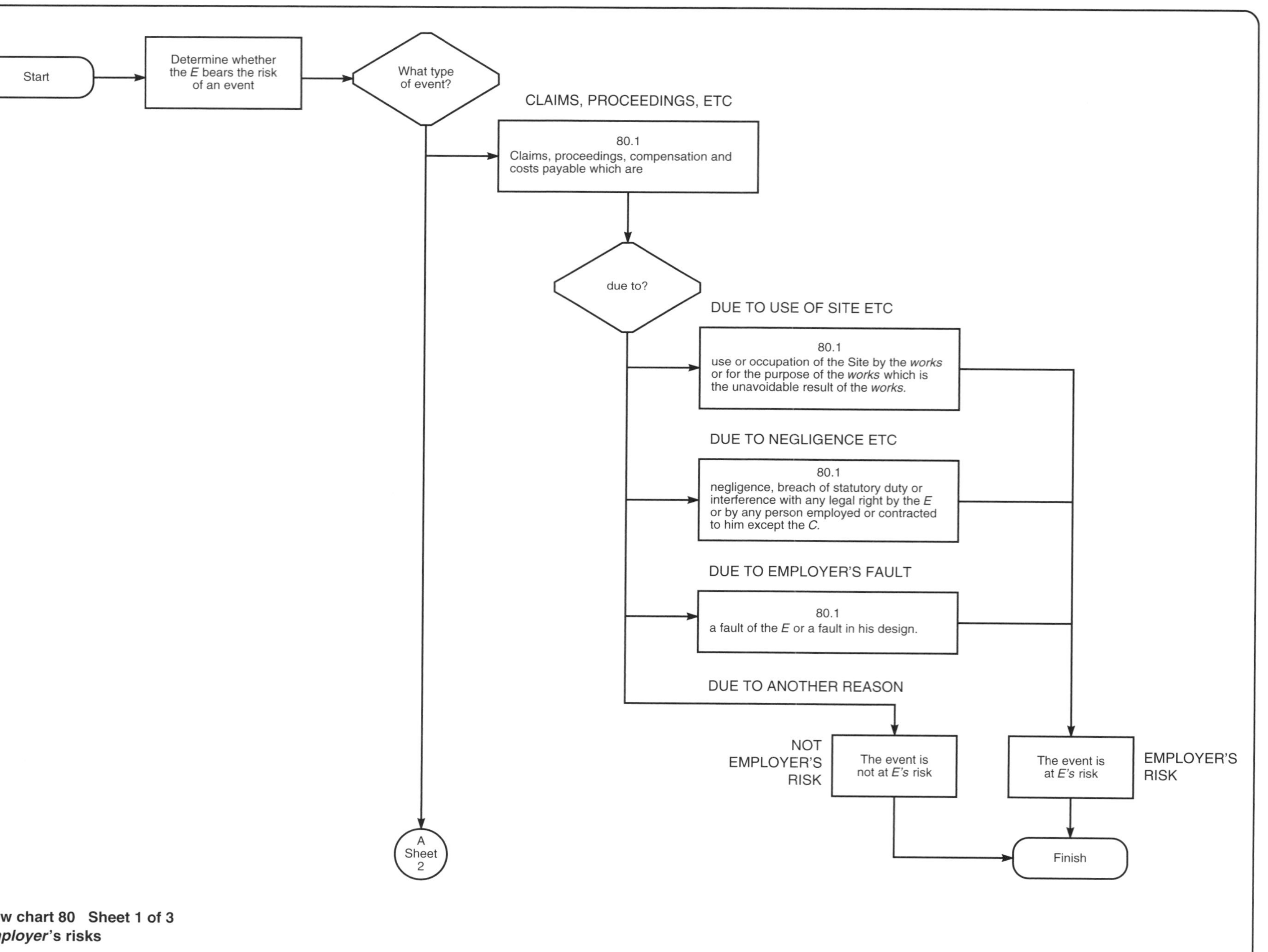
Start
Determine whether the *E* bears the risk of an event
What type of event?
CLAIMS, PROCEEDINGS, ETC
80.1 Claims, proceedings, compensation and costs payable which are
due to?
DUE TO USE OF SITE ETC
80.1 use or occupation of the Site by the *works* or for the purpose of the *works* which is the unavoidable result of the *works*.
DUE TO NEGLIGENCE ETC
80.1 negligence, breach of statutory duty or interference with any legal right by the *E* or by any person employed or contracted to him except the *C*.
DUE TO EMPLOYER'S FAULT
80.1 a fault of the *E* or a fault in his design.
DUE TO ANOTHER REASON
NOT EMPLOYER'S RISK
The event is not at *E's* risk
The event is at *E's* risk
EMPLOYER'S RISK
A Sheet 2
Finish

Flow chart 80 Sheet 1 of 3
***Employer*'s risks**

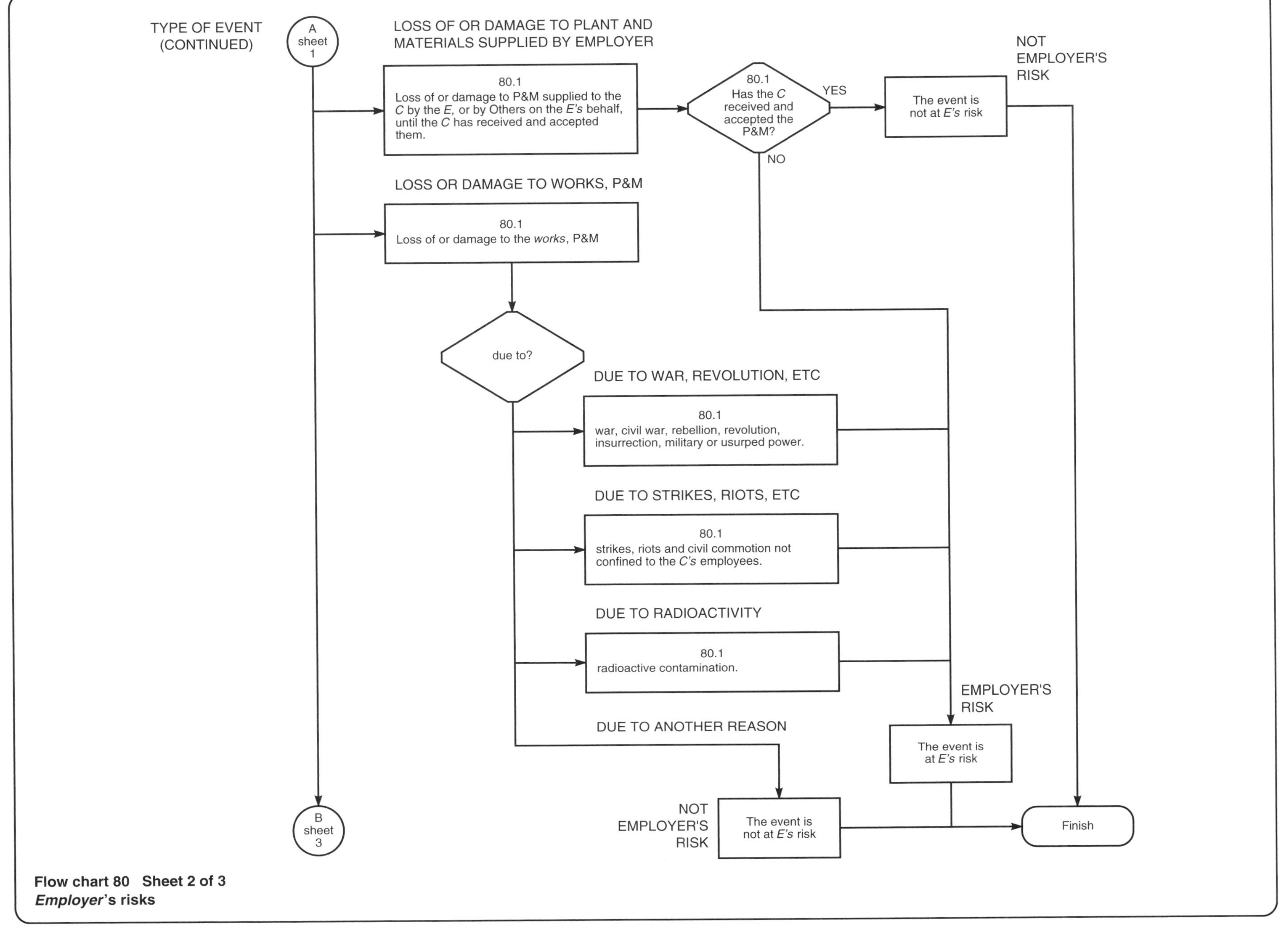
TYPE OF EVENT (CONTINUED)
A sheet 1
LOSS OF OR DAMAGE TO PLANT AND MATERIALS SUPPLIED BY EMPLOYER
80.1 Loss of or damage to P&M supplied to the C by the E, or by Others on the E's behalf, until the C has received and accepted them.
80.1 Has the C received and accepted the P&M?
YES
The event is not at E's risk
NOT EMPLOYER'S RISK
NO
LOSS OR DAMAGE TO WORKS, P&M
80.1 Loss of or damage to the works, P&M
due to?
DUE TO WAR, REVOLUTION, ETC
80.1 war, civil war, rebellion, revolution, insurrection, military or usurped power.
DUE TO STRIKES, RIOTS, ETC
80.1 strikes, riots and civil commotion not confined to the C's employees.
DUE TO RADIOACTIVITY
80.1 radioactive contamination.
EMPLOYER'S RISK
The event is at E's risk
DUE TO ANOTHER REASON
NOT EMPLOYER'S RISK
The event is not at E's risk
Finish
B sheet 3
Flow chart 80 Sheet 2 of 3
***Employer*'s risks**

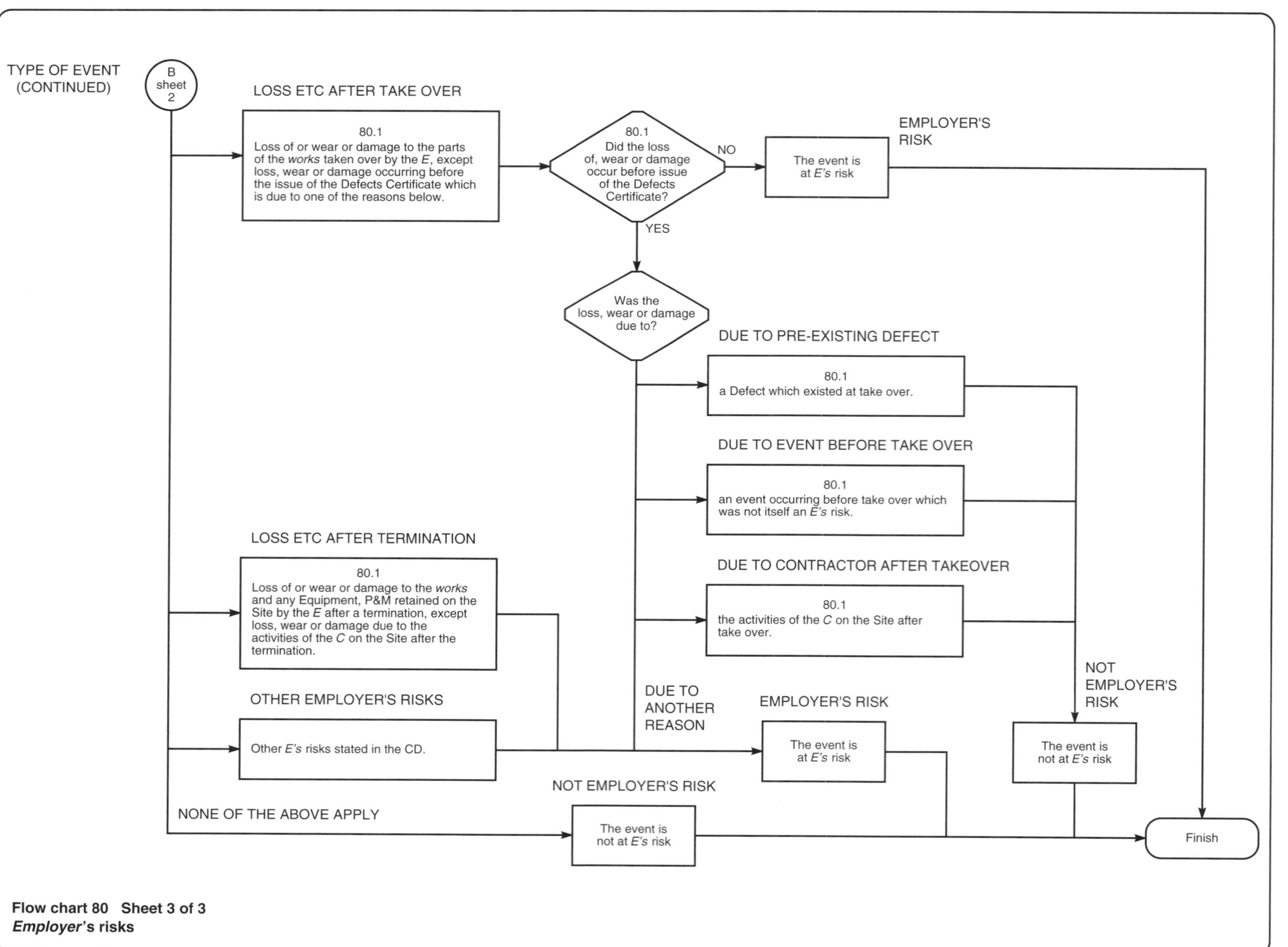
TYPE OF EVENT (CONTINUED)
B sheet 2
LOSS ETC AFTER TAKE OVER
80.1 Loss of or wear or damage to the parts of the *works* taken over by the *E*, except loss, wear or damage occurring before the issue of the Defects Certificate which is due to one of the reasons below.
80.1 Did the loss of, wear or damage occur before issue of the Defects Certificate?
NO
YES
The event is at *E's* risk
EMPLOYER'S RISK
Was the loss, wear or damage due to?
DUE TO PRE-EXISTING DEFECT
80.1 a Defect which existed at take over.
DUE TO EVENT BEFORE TAKE OVER
80.1 an event occurring before take over which was not itself an *E's* risk.
DUE TO CONTRACTOR AFTER TAKEOVER
80.1 the activities of the *C* on the Site after take over.
NOT EMPLOYER'S RISK
The event is not at *E's* risk
LOSS ETC AFTER TERMINATION
80.1 Loss of or wear or damage to the *works* and any Equipment, P&M retained on the Site by the *E* after a termination, except loss, wear or damage due to the activities of the *C* on the Site after the termination.
OTHER EMPLOYER'S RISKS
Other *E's* risks stated in the CD.
DUE TO ANOTHER REASON
EMPLOYER'S RISK
The event is at *E's* risk
NONE OF THE ABOVE APPLY
NOT EMPLOYER'S RISK
The event is not at *E's* risk
Finish

Flow chart 80 Sheet 3 of 3
***Employer*'s risks**

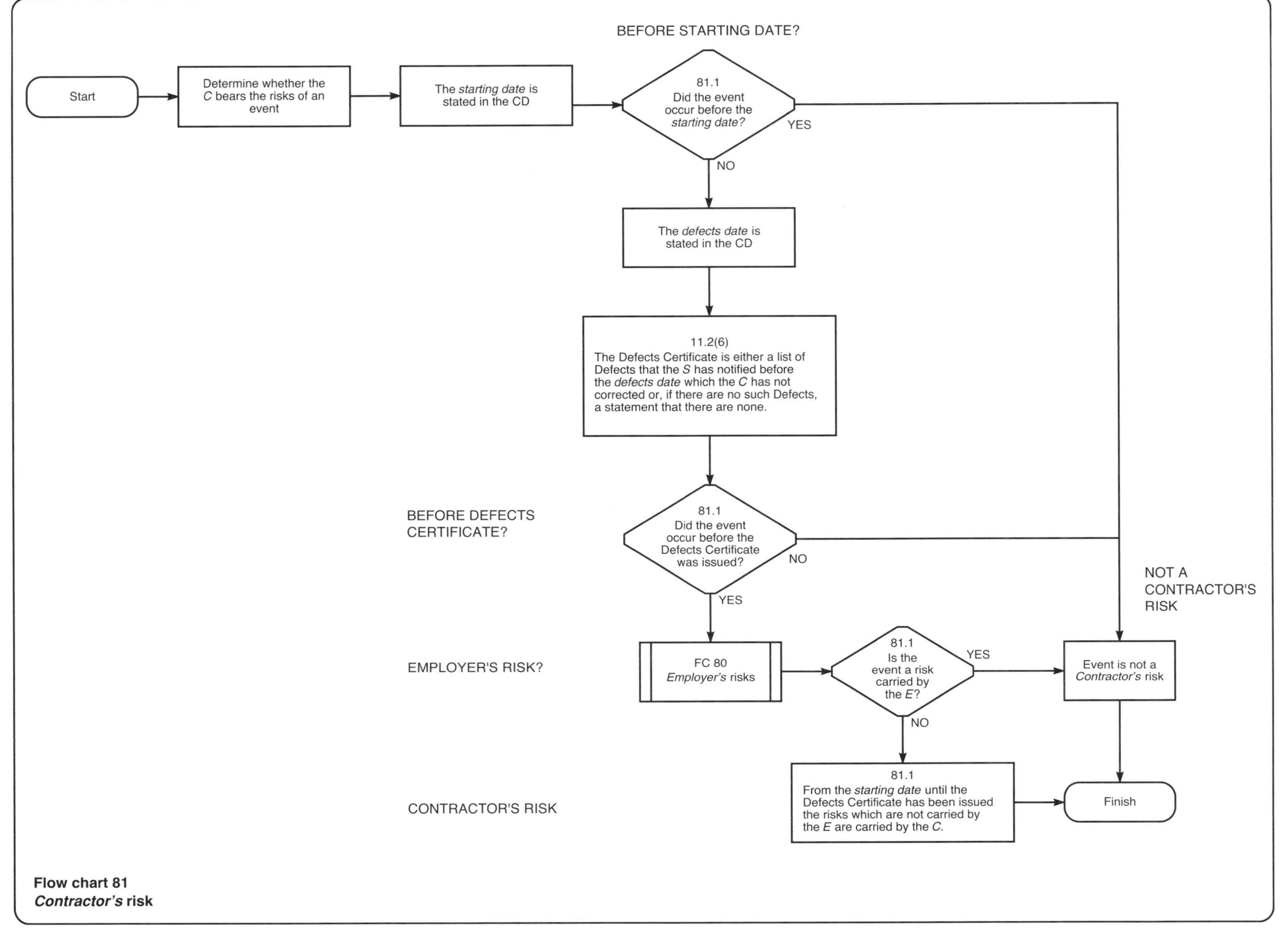

BEFORE STARTING DATE?
Start
Determine whether the C bears the risks of an event
The starting date is stated in the CD
81.1 Did the event occur before the starting date?
YES
NO
The defects date is stated in the CD
11.2(6) The Defects Certificate is either a list of Defects that the S has notified before the defects date which the C has not corrected or, if there are no such Defects, a statement that there are none.
BEFORE DEFECTS CERTIFICATE?
81.1 Did the event occur before the Defects Certificate was issued?
NO
YES
NOT A CONTRACTOR'S RISK
EMPLOYER'S RISK?
FC 80 Employer's risks
81.1 Is the event a risk carried by the E?
YES
NO
Event is not a Contractor's risk
CONTRACTOR'S RISK
81.1 From the starting date until the Defects Certificate has been issued the risks which are not carried by the E are carried by the C.
Finish

Flow chart 81
Contractor's risk

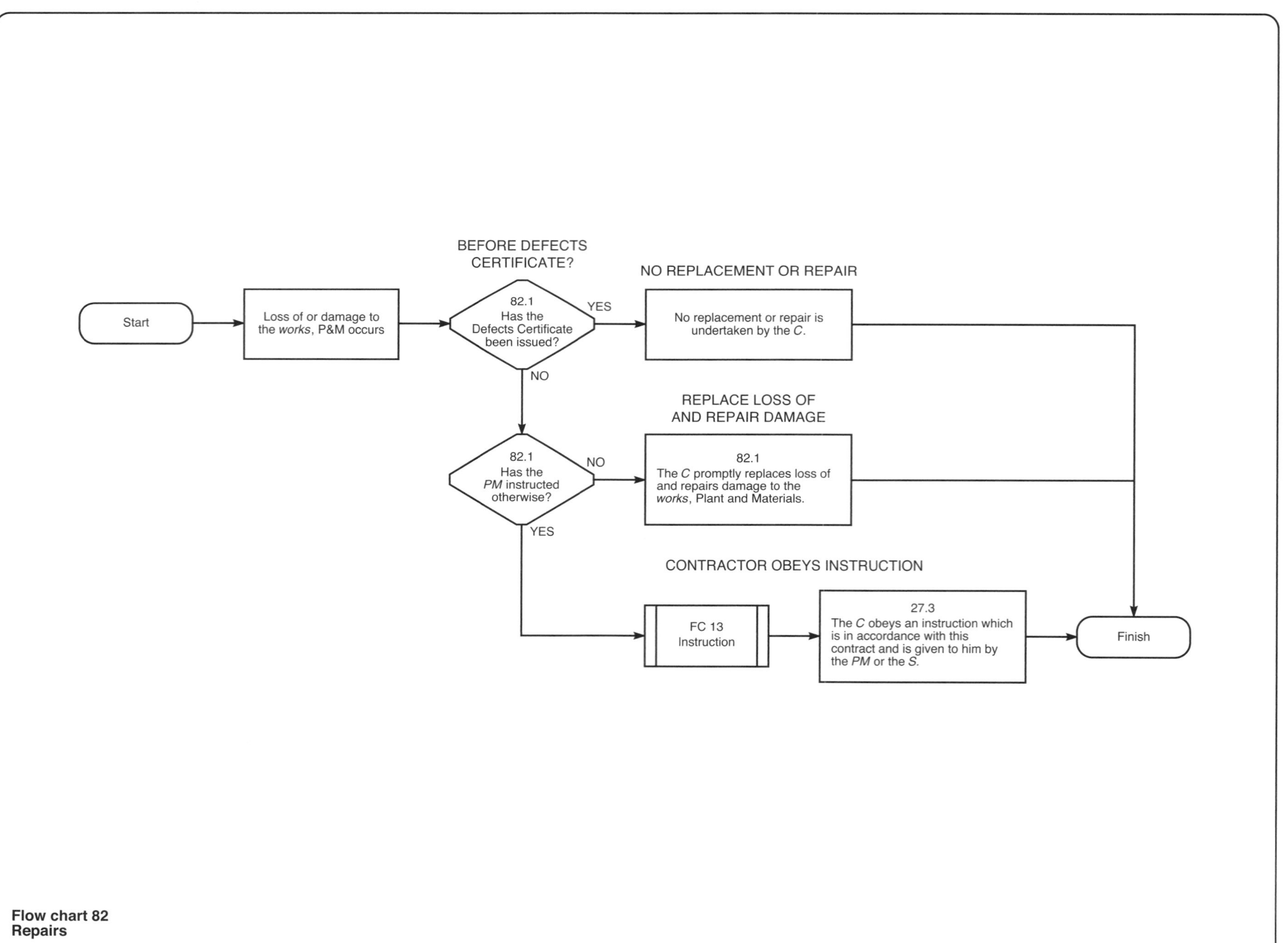
BEFORE DEFECTS CERTIFICATE?
NO REPLACEMENT OR REPAIR
Start
Loss of or damage to the *works*, P&M occurs
82.1 Has the Defects Certificate been issued?
YES
No replacement or repair is undertaken by the *C*.
NO
REPLACE LOSS OF AND REPAIR DAMAGE
82.1 Has the *PM* instructed otherwise?
NO
82.1 The *C* promptly replaces loss of and repairs damage to the *works*, Plant and Materials.
YES
CONTRACTOR OBEYS INSTRUCTION
FC 13 Instruction
27.3 The *C* obeys an instruction which is in accordance with this contract and is given to him by the *PM* or the *S*.
Finish

Flow chart 82
Repairs

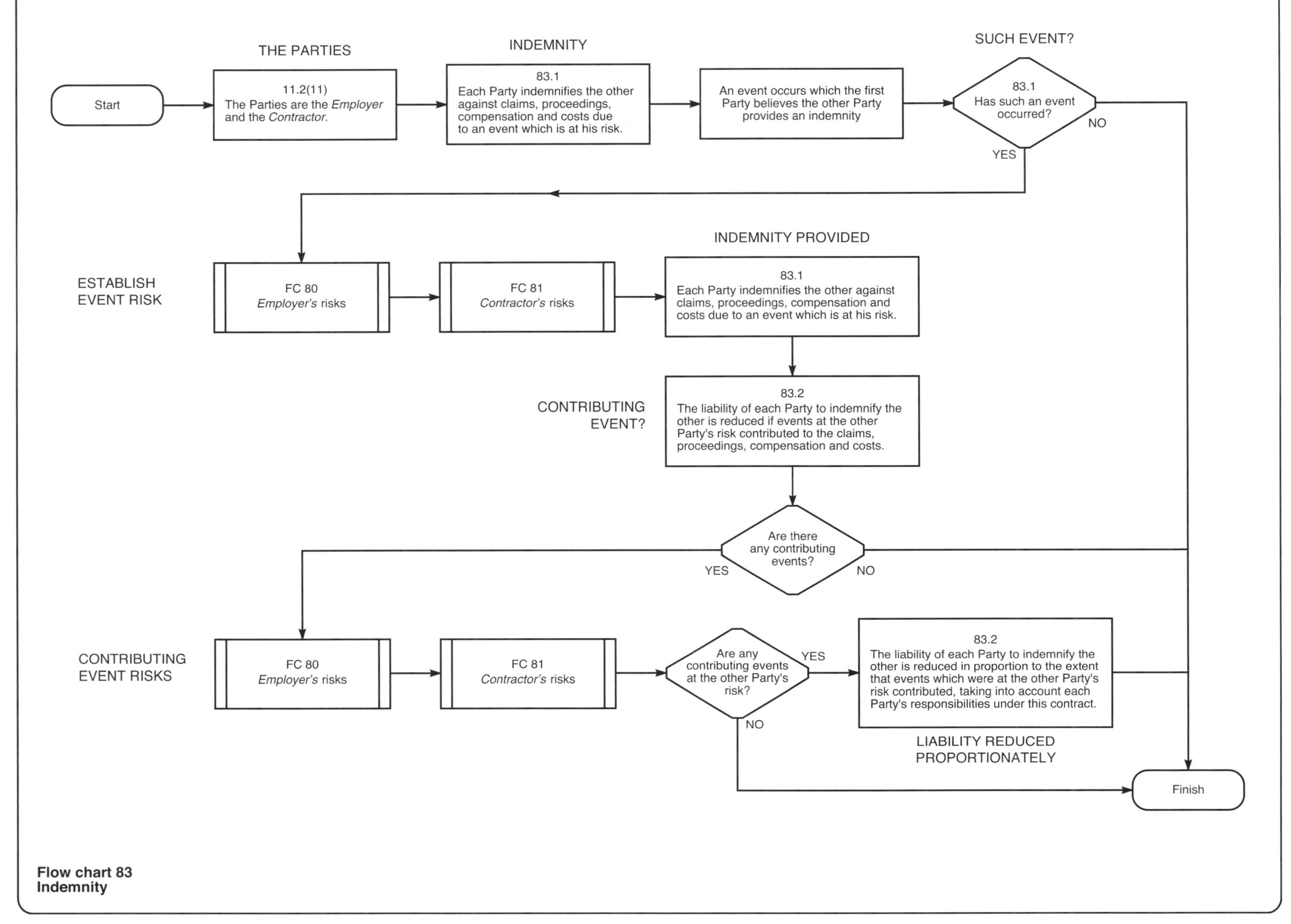
THE PARTIES
INDEMNITY
SUCH EVENT?
Start
11.2(11)
The Parties are the *Employer* and the *Contractor*.
83.1
Each Party indemnifies the other against claims, proceedings, compensation and costs due to an event which is at his risk.
An event occurs which the first Party believes the other Party provides an indemnity
83.1
Has such an event occurred?
NO
YES
INDEMNITY PROVIDED
ESTABLISH EVENT RISK
FC 80
Employer's risks
FC 81
Contractor's risks
83.1
Each Party indemnifies the other against claims, proceedings, compensation and costs due to an event which is at his risk.
CONTRIBUTING EVENT?
83.2
The liability of each Party to indemnify the other is reduced if events at the other Party's risk contributed to the claims, proceedings, compensation and costs.
Are there any contributing events?
YES
NO
CONTRIBUTING EVENT RISKS
FC 80
Employer's risks
FC 81
Contractor's risks
Are any contributing events at the other Party's risk?
YES
NO
83.2
The liability of each Party to indemnify the other is reduced in proportion to the extent that events which were at the other Party's risk contributed, taking into account each Party's responsibilities under this contract.
LIABILITY REDUCED PROPORTIONATELY
Finish

Flow chart 83
Indemnity

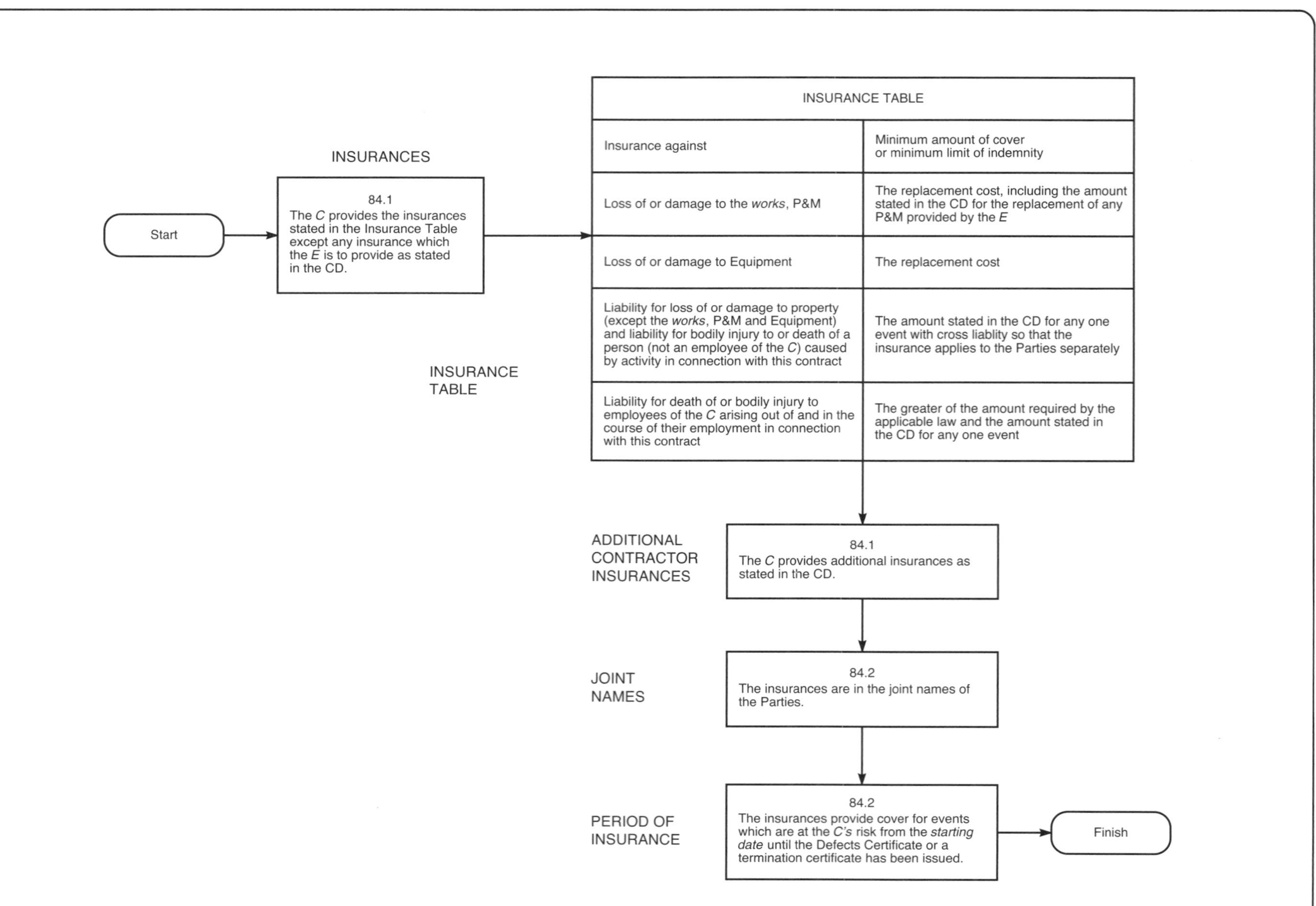
INSURANCES
Start
84.1
The C provides the insurances stated in the Insurance Table except any insurance which the E is to provide as stated in the CD.
INSURANCE TABLE
INSURANCE TABLE
Insurance against
Minimum amount of cover or minimum limit of indemnity
Loss of or damage to the works, P&M
The replacement cost, including the amount stated in the CD for the replacement of any P&M provided by the E
Loss of or damage to Equipment
The replacement cost
Liability for loss of or damage to property (except the works, P&M and Equipment) and liability for bodily injury to or death of a person (not an employee of the C) caused by activity in connection with this contract
The amount stated in the CD for any one event with cross liablity so that the insurance applies to the Parties separately
Liability for death of or bodily injury to employees of the C arising out of and in the course of their employment in connection with this contract
The greater of the amount required by the applicable law and the amount stated in the CD for any one event
ADDITIONAL CONTRACTOR INSURANCES
84.1
The C provides additional insurances as stated in the CD.
JOINT NAMES
84.2
The insurances are in the joint names of the Parties.
PERIOD OF INSURANCE
84.2
The insurances provide cover for events which are at the C's risk from the starting date until the Defects Certificate or a termination certificate has been issued.
Finish

Flow chart 84
Insurance cover

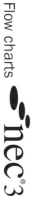

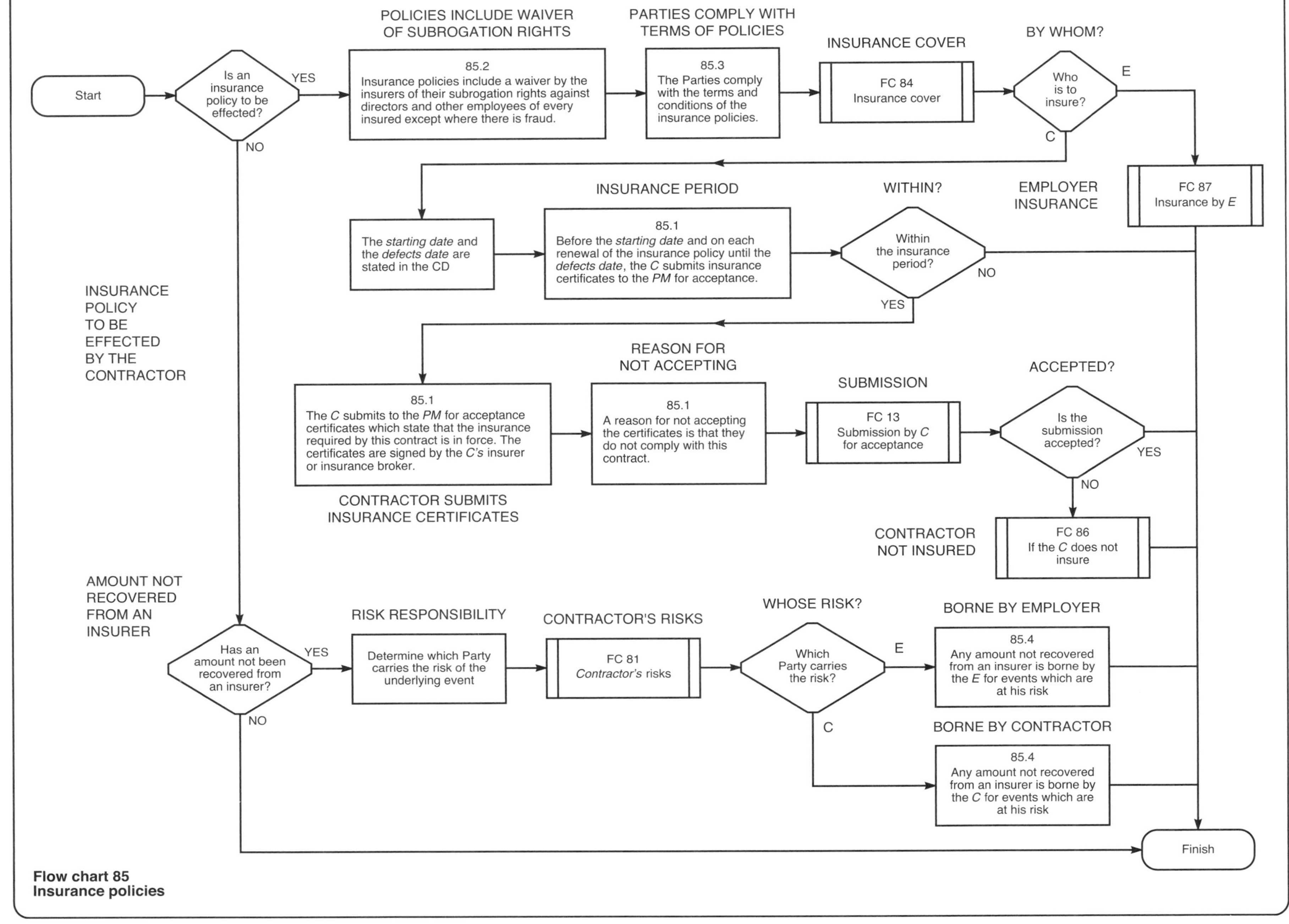
Start
Is an insurance policy to be effected?
YES
NO
POLICIES INCLUDE WAIVER OF SUBROGATION RIGHTS
85.2
Insurance policies include a waiver by the insurers of their subrogation rights against directors and other employees of every insured except where there is fraud.
PARTIES COMPLY WITH TERMS OF POLICIES
85.3
The Parties comply with the terms and conditions of the insurance policies.
INSURANCE COVER
FC 84
Insurance cover
BY WHOM?
Who is to insure?
E
C
FC 87
Insurance by E
EMPLOYER INSURANCE
INSURANCE POLICY TO BE EFFECTED BY THE CONTRACTOR
The starting date and the defects date are stated in the CD
INSURANCE PERIOD
85.1
Before the starting date and on each renewal of the insurance policy until the defects date, the C submits insurance certificates to the PM for acceptance.
WITHIN?
Within the insurance period?
NO
YES
85.1
The C submits to the PM for acceptance certificates which state that the insurance required by this contract is in force. The certificates are signed by the C's insurer or insurance broker.
CONTRACTOR SUBMITS INSURANCE CERTIFICATES
REASON FOR NOT ACCEPTING
85.1
A reason for not accepting the certificates is that they do not comply with this contract.
SUBMISSION
FC 13
Submission by C for acceptance
ACCEPTED?
Is the submission accepted?
YES
NO
CONTRACTOR NOT INSURED
FC 86
If the C does not insure
AMOUNT NOT RECOVERED FROM AN INSURER
Has an amount not been recovered from an insurer?
YES
NO
RISK RESPONSIBILITY
Determine which Party carries the risk of the underlying event
CONTRACTOR'S RISKS
FC 81
Contractor's risks
WHOSE RISK?
Which Party carries the risk?
E
C
BORNE BY EMPLOYER
85.4
Any amount not recovered from an insurer is borne by the E for events which are at his risk
BORNE BY CONTRACTOR
85.4
Any amount not recovered from an insurer is borne by the C for events which are at his risk
Finish
Flow chart 85
Insurance policies

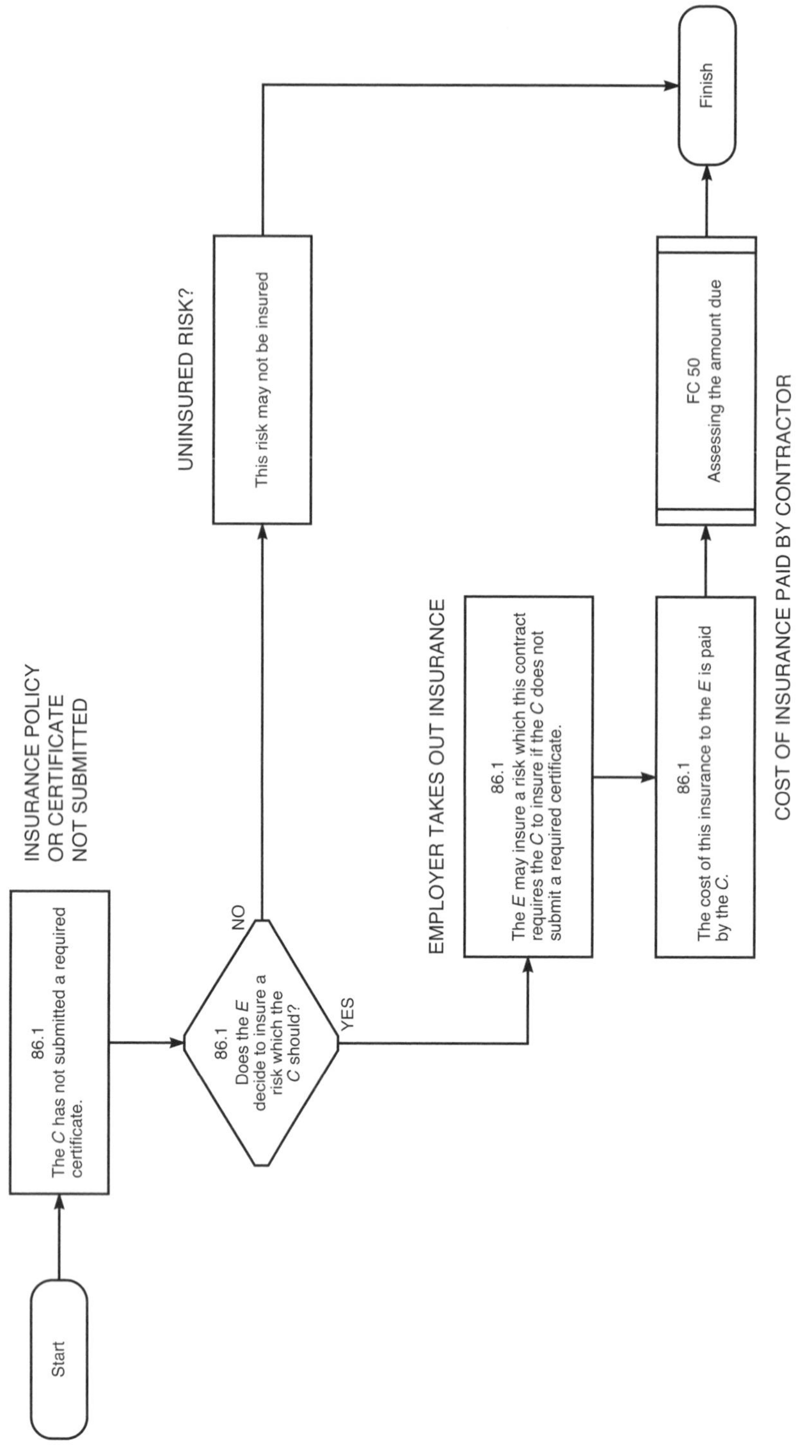

Start

86.1
The *C* has not submitted a required certificate.

INSURANCE POLICY
OR CERTIFICATE
NOT SUBMITTED

86.1
Does the *E* decide to insure a risk which the *C* should?

NO

UNINSURED RISK?

This risk may not be insured

YES

EMPLOYER TAKES OUT INSURANCE

86.1
The *E* may insure a risk which this contract requires the *C* to insure if the *C* does not submit a required certificate.

86.1
The cost of this insurance to the *E* is paid by the *C*.

FC 50
Assessing the amount due

Finish

COST OF INSURANCE PAID BY CONTRACTOR

Flow chart 86
If the *Contractor* does not insure

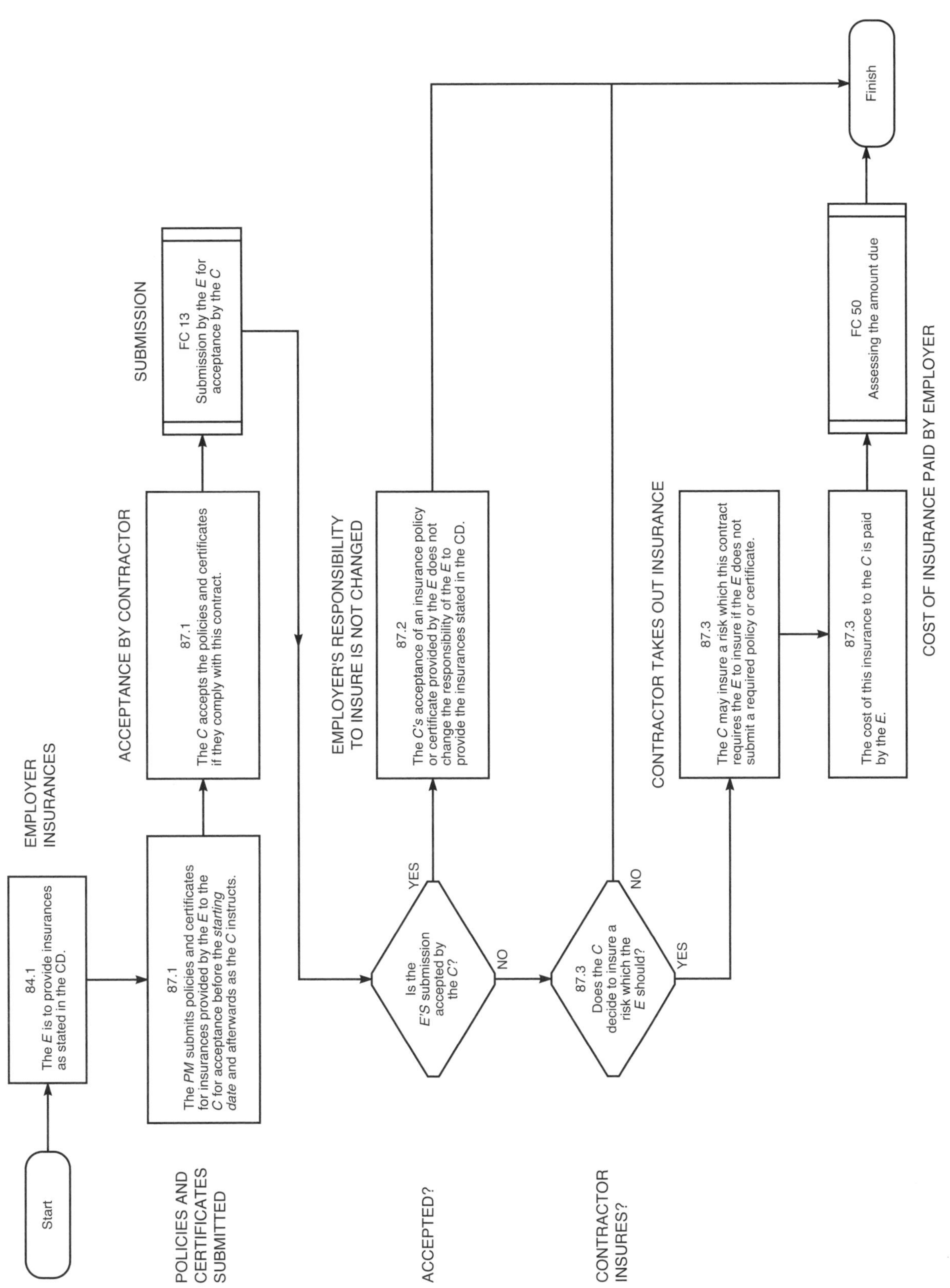

Start

EMPLOYER INSURANCES

84.1
The *E* is to provide insurances as stated in the CD.

POLICIES AND CERTIFICATES SUBMITTED

87.1
The *PM* submits policies and certificates for insurances provided by the *E* to the *C* for acceptance before the *starting date* and afterwards as the *C* instructs.

ACCEPTANCE BY CONTRACTOR

87.1
The *C* accepts the policies and certificates if they comply with this contract.

SUBMISSION

FC 13
Submission by the *E* for acceptance by the *C*

ACCEPTED?

Is the *E'S* submission accepted by the *C*?

YES

EMPLOYER'S RESPONSIBILITY TO INSURE IS NOT CHANGED

87.2
The *C's* acceptance of an insurance policy or certificate provided by the *E* does not change the responsibility of the *E* to provide the insurances stated in the CD.

NO

CONTRACTOR INSURES?

87.3
Does the *C* decide to insure a risk which the *E* should?

NO

YES

CONTRACTOR TAKES OUT INSURANCE

87.3
The *C* may insure a risk which this contract requires the *E* to insure if the *E* does not submit a required policy or certificate.

COST OF INSURANCE PAID BY EMPLOYER

87.3
The cost of this insurance to the *C* is paid by the *E*.

FC 50
Assessing the amount due

Finish

Flow chart 87
Insurance by the *Employer*

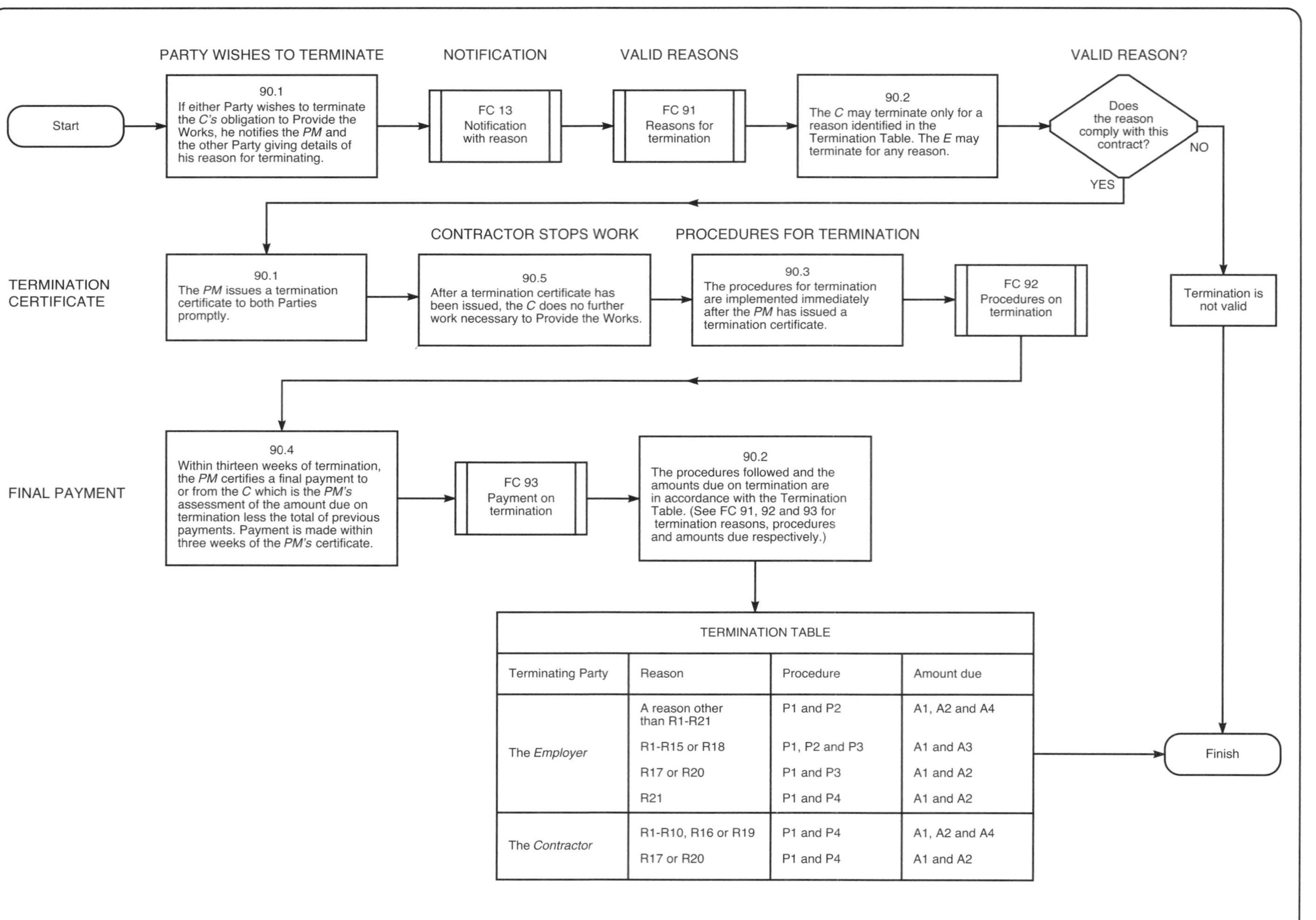
PARTY WISHES TO TERMINATE
NOTIFICATION
VALID REASONS
VALID REASON?
Start
90.1 If either Party wishes to terminate the *C's* obligation to Provide the Works, he notifies the *PM* and the other Party giving details of his reason for terminating.
FC 13 Notification with reason
FC 91 Reasons for termination
90.2 The *C* may terminate only for a reason identified in the Termination Table. The *E* may terminate for any reason.
Does the reason comply with this contract?
NO
YES
TERMINATION CERTIFICATE
CONTRACTOR STOPS WORK
PROCEDURES FOR TERMINATION
90.1 The *PM* issues a termination certificate to both Parties promptly.
90.5 After a termination certificate has been issued, the *C* does no further work necessary to Provide the Works.
90.3 The procedures for termination are implemented immediately after the *PM* has issued a termination certificate.
FC 92 Procedures on termination
Termination is not valid
FINAL PAYMENT
90.4 Within thirteen weeks of termination, the *PM* certifies a final payment to or from the *C* which is the *PM's* assessment of the amount due on termination less the total of previous payments. Payment is made within three weeks of the *PM's* certificate.
FC 93 Payment on termination
90.2 The procedures followed and the amounts due on termination are in accordance with the Termination Table. (See FC 91, 92 and 93 for termination reasons, procedures and amounts due respectively.)
TERMINATION TABLE
Finish

Terminating Party	Reason	Procedure	Amount due
The *Employer*	A reason other than R1-R21	P1 and P2	A1, A2 and A4
	R1-R15 or R18	P1, P2 and P3	A1 and A3
	R17 or R20	P1 and P3	A1 and A2
	R21	P1 and P4	A1 and A2
The *Contractor*	R1-R10, R16 or R19	P1 and P4	A1, A2 and A4
	R17 or R20	P1 and P4	A1 and A2

Flow chart 90
Termination

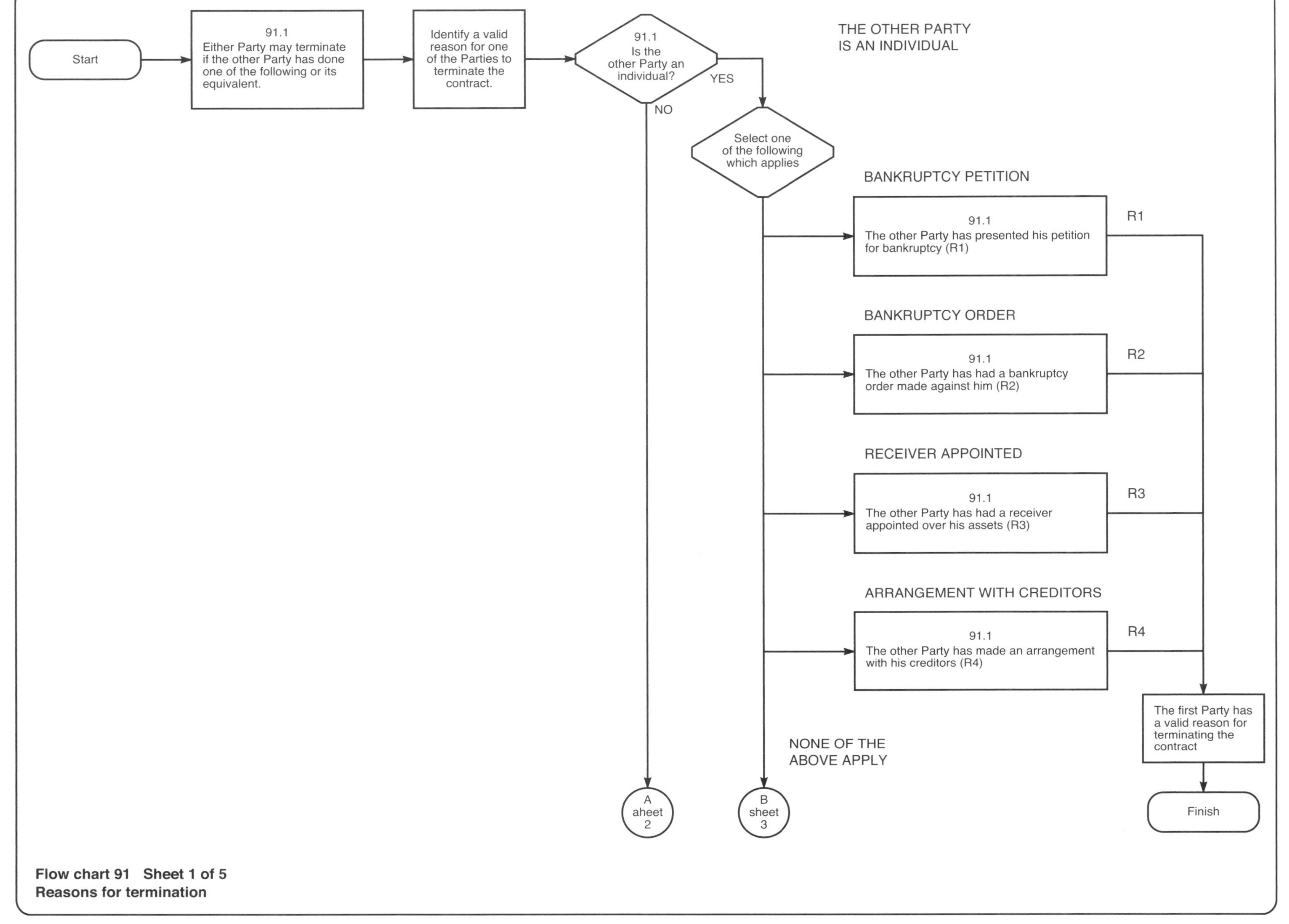
Start
91.1
Either Party may terminate if the other Party has done one of the following or its equivalent.
Identify a valid reason for one of the Parties to terminate the contract.
91.1
Is the other Party an individual?
YES
NO
THE OTHER PARTY IS AN INDIVIDUAL
Select one of the following which applies
BANKRUPTCY PETITION
91.1
The other Party has presented his petition for bankruptcy (R1)
R1
BANKRUPTCY ORDER
91.1
The other Party has had a bankruptcy order made against him (R2)
R2
RECEIVER APPOINTED
91.1
The other Party has had a receiver appointed over his assets (R3)
R3
ARRANGEMENT WITH CREDITORS
91.1
The other Party has made an arrangement with his creditors (R4)
R4
The first Party has a valid reason for terminating the contract
NONE OF THE ABOVE APPLY
A
aheet
2
B
sheet
3
Finish

Flow chart 91 Sheet 1 of 5
Reasons for termination

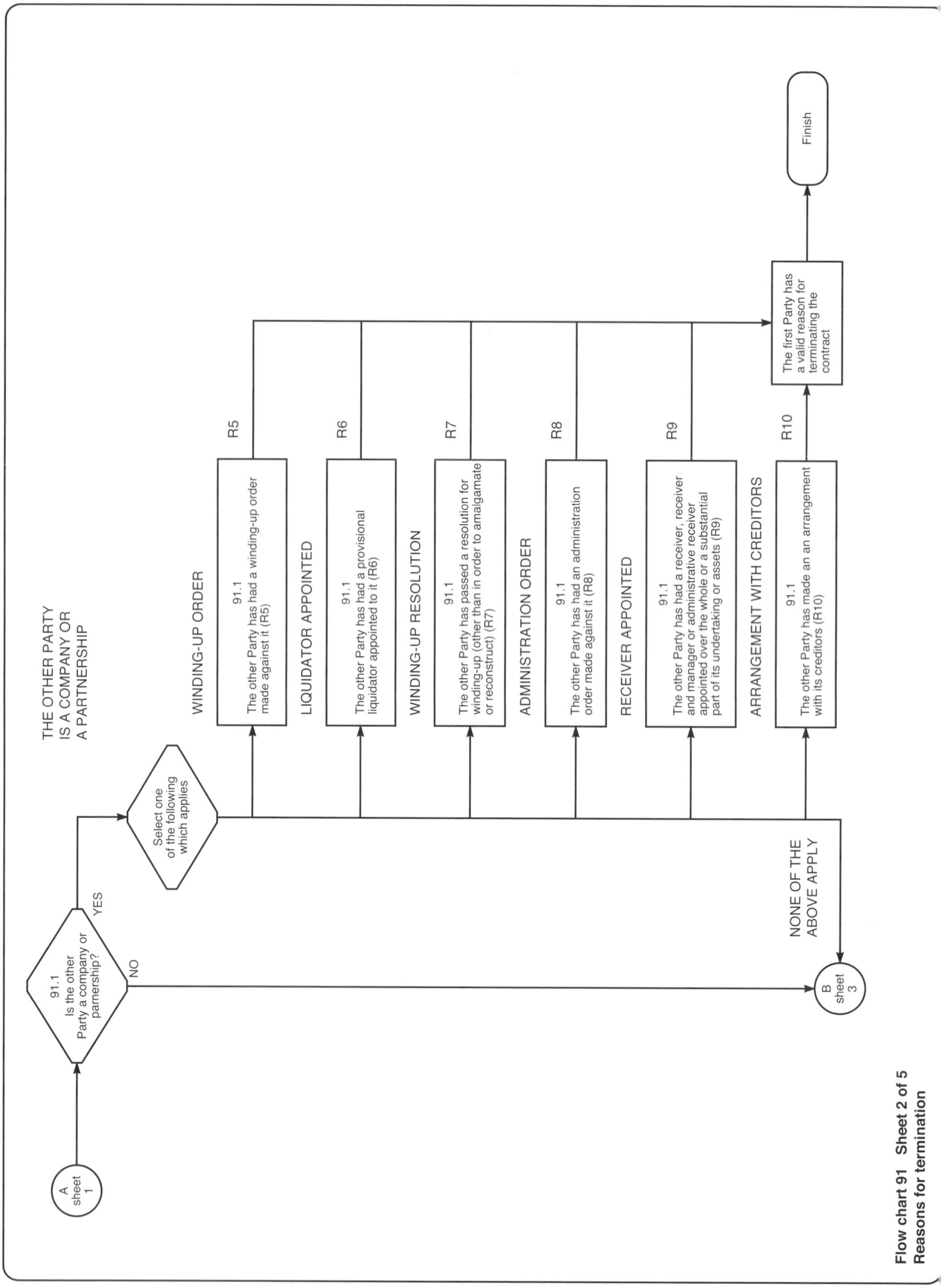

A sheet 1

91.1
Is the other Party a company or parnership?

YES

NO

THE OTHER PARTY IS A COMPANY OR A PARTNERSHIP

Select one of the following which applies

WINDING-UP ORDER

91.1
The other Party has had a winding-up order made against it (R5)

R5

LIQUIDATOR APPOINTED

91.1
The other Party has had a provisional liquidator appointed to it (R6)

R6

WINDING-UP RESOLUTION

91.1
The other Party has passed a resolution for winding-up (other than in order to amalgamate or reconstruct) (R7)

R7

ADMINISTRATION ORDER

91.1
The other Party has had an administration order made against it (R8)

R8

RECEIVER APPOINTED

91.1
The other Party has had a receiver, receiver and manager or administrative receiver appointed over the whole or a substantial part of its undertaking or assets (R9)

R9

ARRANGEMENT WITH CREDITORS

91.1
The other Party has made an an arrangement with its creditors (R10)

R10

The first Party has a valid reason for terminating the contract

Finish

NONE OF THE ABOVE APPLY

B sheet 3

Flow chart 91 Sheet 2 of 5
Reasons for termination

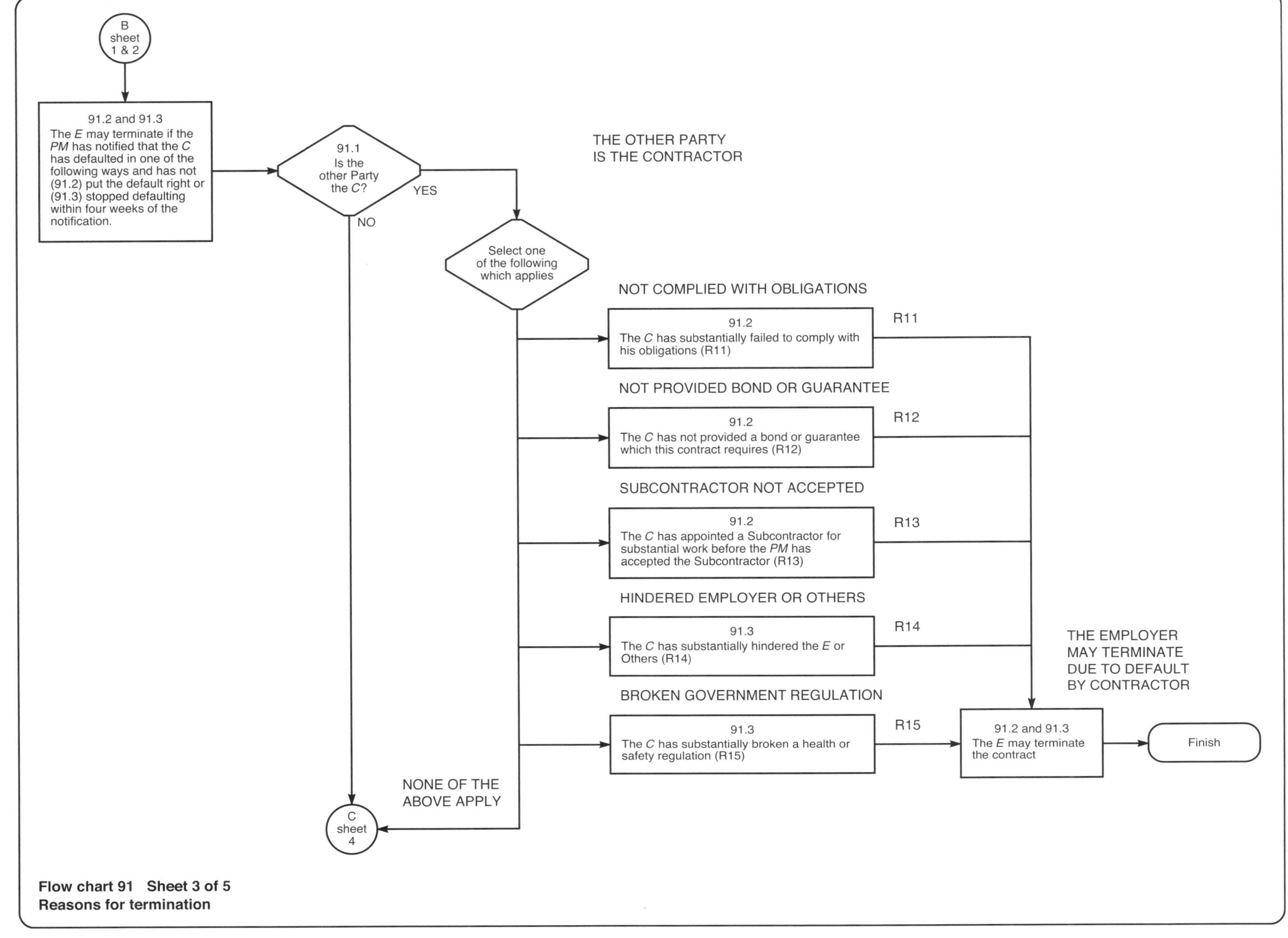
B sheet 1 & 2
91.2 and 91.3 The E may terminate if the PM has notified that the C has defaulted in one of the following ways and has not (91.2) put the default right or (91.3) stopped defaulting within four weeks of the notification.
91.1 Is the other Party the C?
YES
NO
THE OTHER PARTY IS THE CONTRACTOR
Select one of the following which applies
NOT COMPLIED WITH OBLIGATIONS
91.2 The C has substantially failed to comply with his obligations (R11)
R11
NOT PROVIDED BOND OR GUARANTEE
91.2 The C has not provided a bond or guarantee which this contract requires (R12)
R12
SUBCONTRACTOR NOT ACCEPTED
91.2 The C has appointed a Subcontractor for substantial work before the PM has accepted the Subcontractor (R13)
R13
HINDERED EMPLOYER OR OTHERS
91.3 The C has substantially hindered the E or Others (R14)
R14
BROKEN GOVERNMENT REGULATION
91.3 The C has substantially broken a health or safety regulation (R15)
R15
THE EMPLOYER MAY TERMINATE DUE TO DEFAULT BY CONTRACTOR
91.2 and 91.3 The E may terminate the contract
Finish
NONE OF THE ABOVE APPLY
C sheet 4

Flow chart 91 Sheet 3 of 5
Reasons for termination

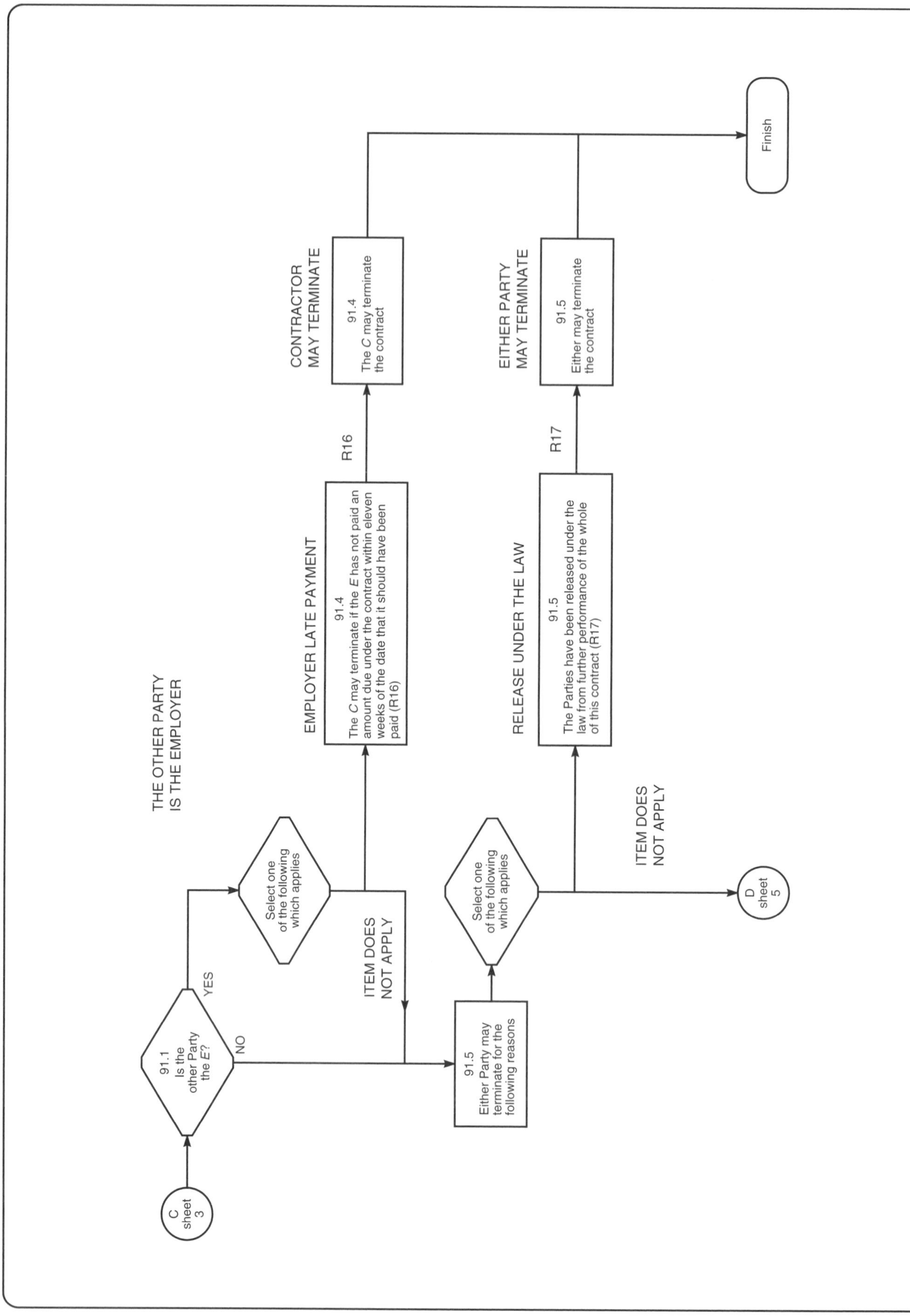

C sheet 3

91.1
Is the other Party the *E*?

YES

THE OTHER PARTY
IS THE EMPLOYER

Select one of the following which applies

EMPLOYER LATE PAYMENT

91.4
The *C* may terminate if the *E* has not paid an amount due under the contract within eleven weeks of the date that it should have been paid (R16)

R16

CONTRACTOR
MAY TERMINATE

91.4
The *C* may terminate the contract

ITEM DOES
NOT APPLY

NO

91.5
Either Party may terminate for the following reasons

Select one of the following which applies

RELEASE UNDER THE LAW

91.5
The Parties have been released under the law from further performance of the whole of this contract (R17)

R17

EITHER PARTY
MAY TERMINATE

91.5
Either may terminate the contract

ITEM DOES
NOT APPLY

D sheet 5

Finish

Flow chart 91 Sheet 4 of 5
Reasons for termination

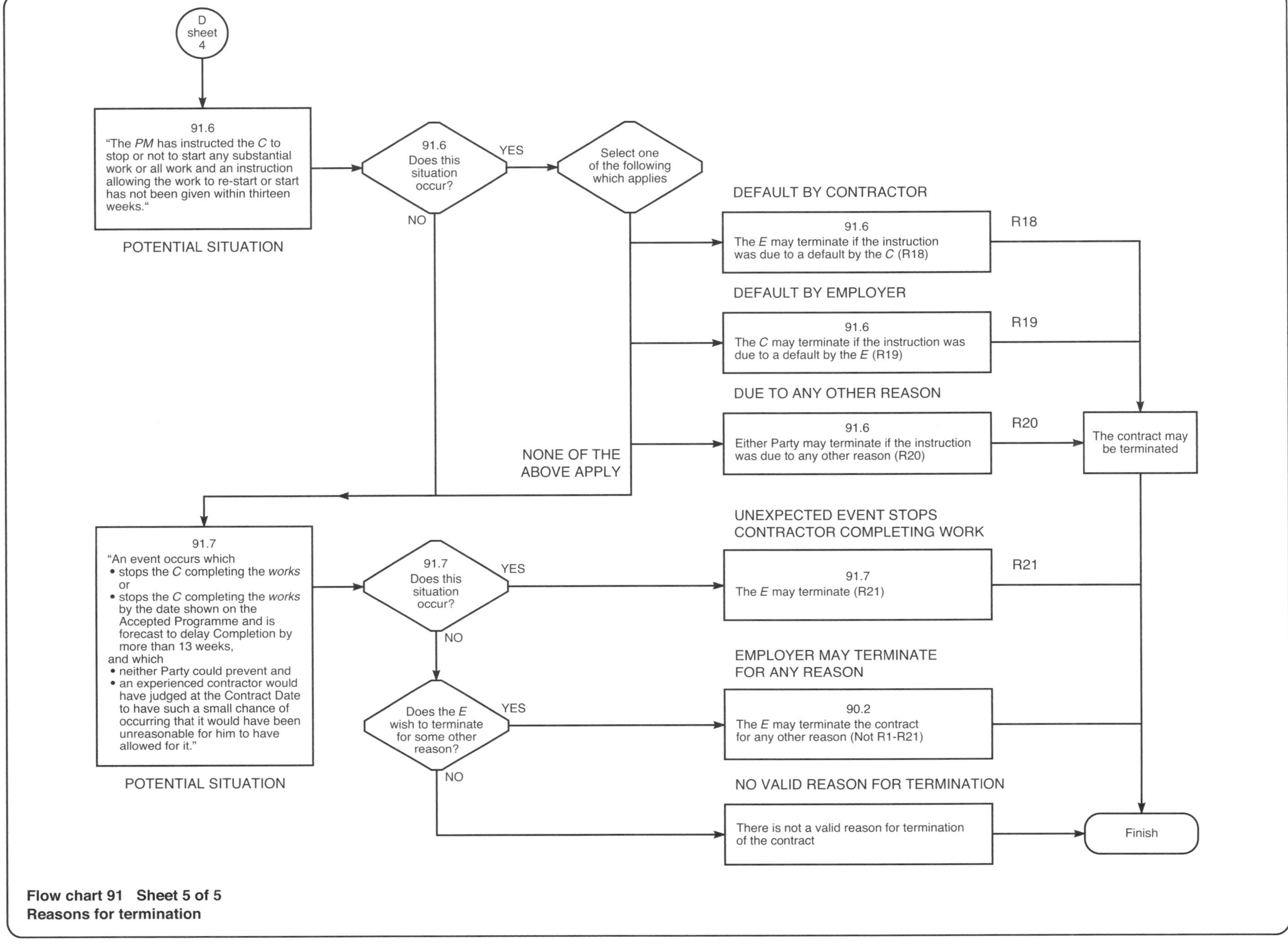
D sheet 4
91.6
"The *PM* has instructed the *C* to stop or not to start any substantial work or all work and an instruction allowing the work to re-start or start has not been given within thirteen weeks."
POTENTIAL SITUATION
91.6 Does this situation occur?
YES
NO
Select one of the following which applies
DEFAULT BY CONTRACTOR
91.6 The *E* may terminate if the instruction was due to a default by the *C* (R18)
R18
DEFAULT BY EMPLOYER
91.6 The *C* may terminate if the instruction was due to a default by the *E* (R19)
R19
DUE TO ANY OTHER REASON
91.6 Either Party may terminate if the instruction was due to any other reason (R20)
R20
NONE OF THE ABOVE APPLY
The contract may be terminated
91.7
"An event occurs which
• stops the *C* completing the *works*
or
• stops the *C* completing the *works* by the date shown on the Accepted Programme and is forecast to delay Completion by more than 13 weeks,
and which
• neither Party could prevent and
• an experienced contractor would have judged at the Contract Date to have such a small chance of occurring that it would have been unreasonable for him to have allowed for it."
POTENTIAL SITUATION
91.7 Does this situation occur?
YES
NO
UNEXPECTED EVENT STOPS CONTRACTOR COMPLETING WORK
91.7 The *E* may terminate (R21)
R21
Does the *E* wish to terminate for some other reason?
YES
NO
EMPLOYER MAY TERMINATE FOR ANY REASON
90.2 The *E* may terminate the contract for any other reason (Not R1-R21)
NO VALID REASON FOR TERMINATION
There is not a valid reason for termination of the contract
Finish

Flow chart 91 Sheet 5 of 5
Reasons for termination

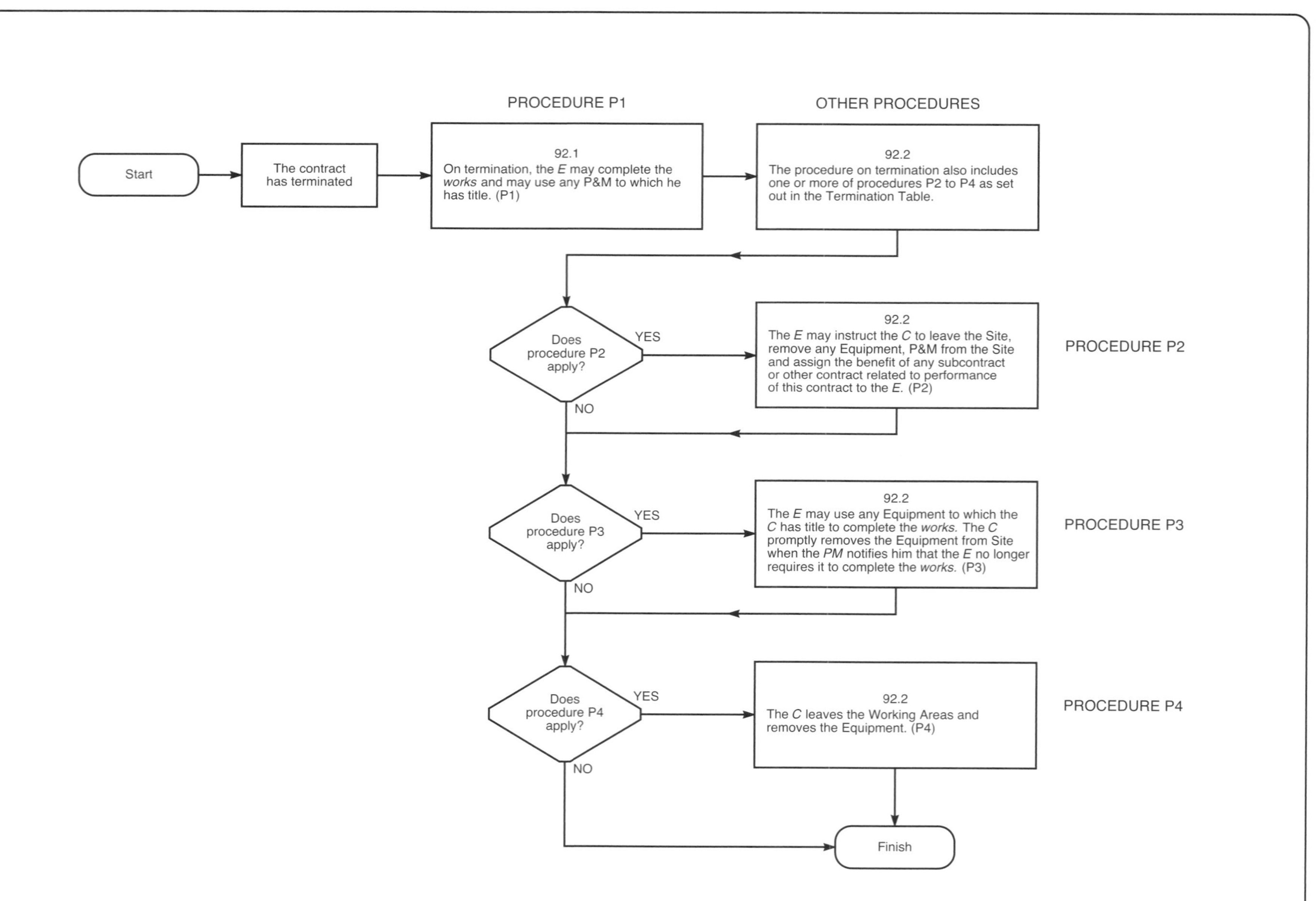
PROCEDURE P1
OTHER PROCEDURES
Start
The contract has terminated
92.1 On termination, the *E* may complete the *works* and may use any P&M to which he has title. (P1)
92.2 The procedure on termination also includes one or more of procedures P2 to P4 as set out in the Termination Table.
Does procedure P2 apply?
YES
NO
92.2 The *E* may instruct the *C* to leave the Site, remove any Equipment, P&M from the Site and assign the benefit of any subcontract or other contract related to performance of this contract to the *E*. (P2)
PROCEDURE P2
Does procedure P3 apply?
YES
NO
92.2 The *E* may use any Equipment to which the *C* has title to complete the *works*. The *C* promptly removes the Equipment from Site when the *PM* notifies him that the *E* no longer requires it to complete the *works*. (P3)
PROCEDURE P3
Does procedure P4 apply?
YES
NO
92.2 The *C* leaves the Working Areas and removes the Equipment. (P4)
PROCEDURE P4
Finish

Flow chart 92
Procedures on termination

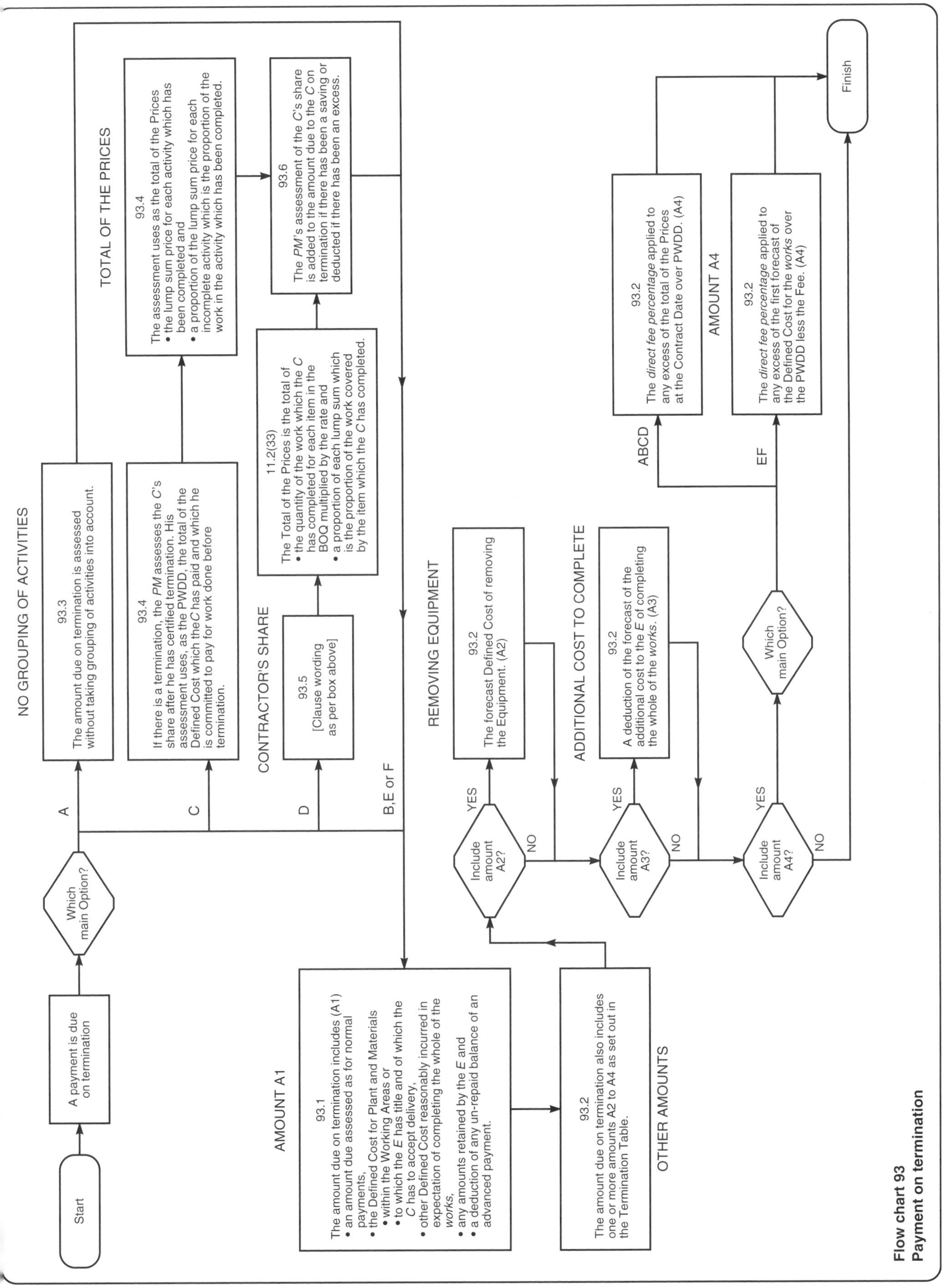

Flow chart 93
Payment on termination

Start

A payment is due on termination

Which main Option?

A

NO GROUPING OF ACTIVITIES

93.3
The amount due on termination is assessed without taking grouping of activities into account.

C

93.4
If there is a termination, the *PM* assesses the *C*'s share after he has certified termination. His assessment uses, as the PWDD, the total of the Defined Cost which the *C* has paid and which he is committed to pay for work done before termination.

TOTAL OF THE PRICES

93.4
The assessment uses as the total of the Prices
- the lump sum price for each activity which has been completed and
- a proportion of the lump sum price for each incomplete activity which is the proportion of the work in the activity which has been completed.

D

CONTRACTOR'S SHARE

93.5
[Clause wording as per box above]

11.2(33)
The Total of the Prices is the total of
- the quantity of the work which the *C* has completed for each item in the BOQ multiplied by the rate and
- a proportion of each lump sum which is the proportion of the work covered by the item which the *C* has completed.

93.6
The *PM*'s assessment of the *C*'s share is added to the amount due to the *C* on termination if there has been a saving or deducted if there has been an excess.

B,E or F

AMOUNT A1

93.1
The amount due on termination includes (A1)
- an amount due assessed as for normal payments,
- the Defined Cost for Plant and Materials
  - within the Working Areas or
  - to which the *E* has title and of which the *C* has to accept delivery,
- other Defined Cost reasonably incurred in expectation of completing the whole of the *works*,
- any amounts retained by the *E* and
- a deduction of any un-repaid balance of an advanced payment.

OTHER AMOUNTS

93.2
The amount due on termination also includes one or more amounts A2 to A4 as set out in the Termination Table.

Include amount A2?

YES

REMOVING EQUIPMENT

93.2
The forecast Defined Cost of removing the Equipment. (A2)

NO

Include amount A3?

YES

ADDITIONAL COST TO COMPLETE

93.2
A deduction of the forecast of the additional cost to the *E* of completing the whole of the *works*. (A3)

NO

Include amount A4?

YES

Which main Option?

ABCD

93.2
The *direct fee percentage* applied to any excess of the total of the Prices at the Contract Date over PWDD. (A4)

AMOUNT A4

EF

93.2
The *direct fee percentage* applied to any excess of the first forecast of the Defined Cost for the *works* over the PWDD less the Fee. (A4)

NO

Finish

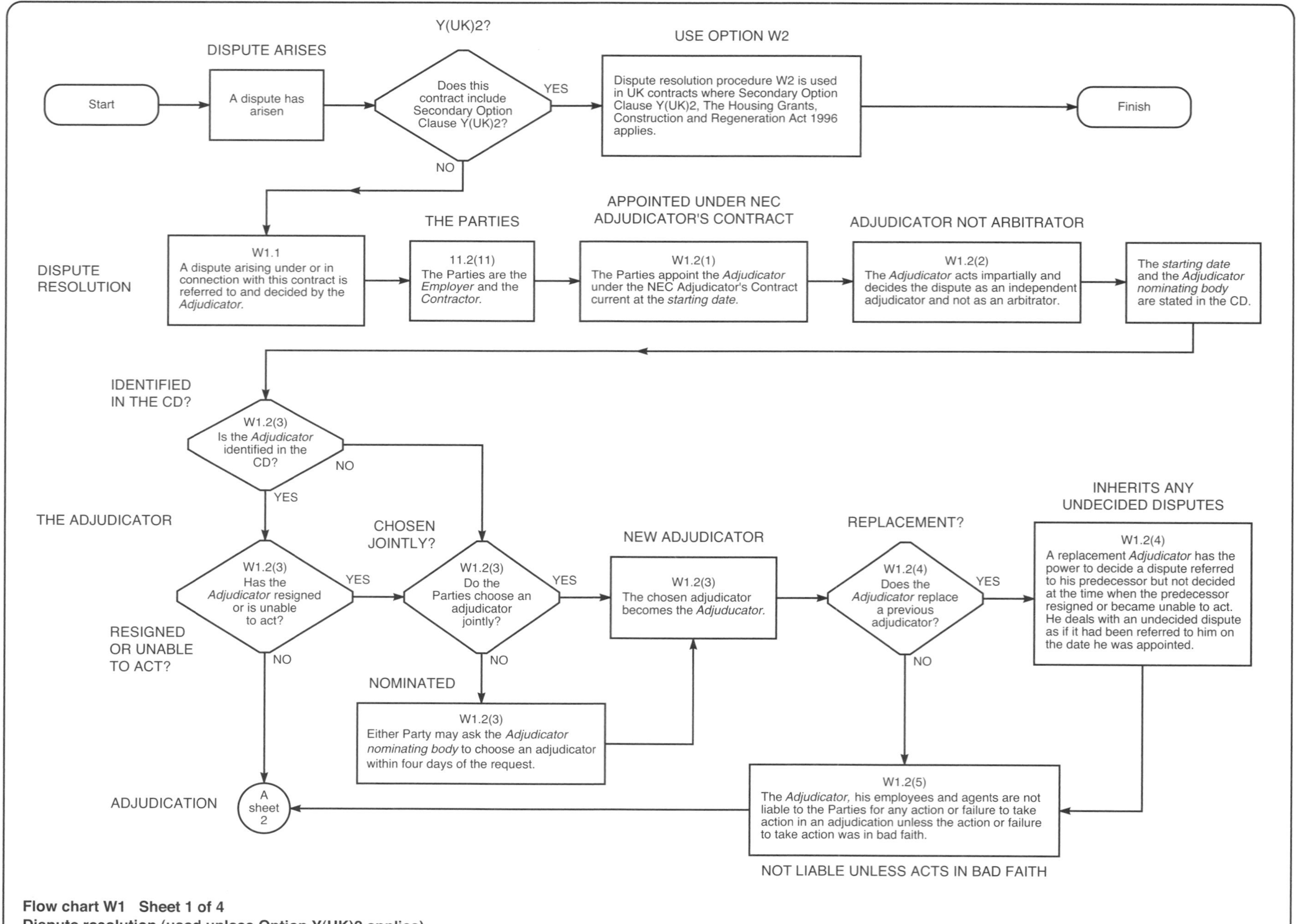

DISPUTE ARISES
Start
A dispute has arisen
Y(UK)2?
Does this contract include Secondary Option Clause Y(UK)2?
YES
NO
USE OPTION W2
Dispute resolution procedure W2 is used in UK contracts where Secondary Option Clause Y(UK)2, The Housing Grants, Construction and Regeneration Act 1996 applies.
Finish
DISPUTE RESOLUTION
W1.1
A dispute arising under or in connection with this contract is referred to and decided by the Adjudicator.
THE PARTIES
11.2(11)
The Parties are the Employer and the Contractor.
APPOINTED UNDER NEC ADJUDICATOR'S CONTRACT
W1.2(1)
The Parties appoint the Adjudicator under the NEC Adjudicator's Contract current at the starting date.
ADJUDICATOR NOT ARBITRATOR
W1.2(2)
The Adjudicator acts impartially and decides the dispute as an independent adjudicator and not as an arbitrator.
The starting date and the Adjudicator nominating body are stated in the CD.
IDENTIFIED IN THE CD?
W1.2(3)
Is the Adjudicator identified in the CD?
NO
YES
THE ADJUDICATOR
W1.2(3)
Has the Adjudicator resigned or is unable to act?
YES
NO
RESIGNED OR UNABLE TO ACT?
CHOSEN JOINTLY?
W1.2(3)
Do the Parties choose an adjudicator jointly?
YES
NO
NOMINATED
W1.2(3)
Either Party may ask the Adjudicator nominating body to choose an adjudicator within four days of the request.
NEW ADJUDICATOR
W1.2(3)
The chosen adjudicator becomes the Adjuducator.
REPLACEMENT?
W1.2(4)
Does the Adjudicator replace a previous adjudicator?
YES
NO
INHERITS ANY UNDECIDED DISPUTES
W1.2(4)
A replacement Adjudicator has the power to decide a dispute referred to his predecessor but not decided at the time when the predecessor resigned or became unable to act. He deals with an undecided dispute as if it had been referred to him on the date he was appointed.
ADJUDICATION
A sheet 2
W1.2(5)
The Adjudicator, his employees and agents are not liable to the Parties for any action or failure to take action in an adjudication unless the action or failure to take action was in bad faith.
NOT LIABLE UNLESS ACTS IN BAD FAITH

Flow chart W1 Sheet 1 of 4
Dispute resolution (used unless Option Y(UK)2 applies)

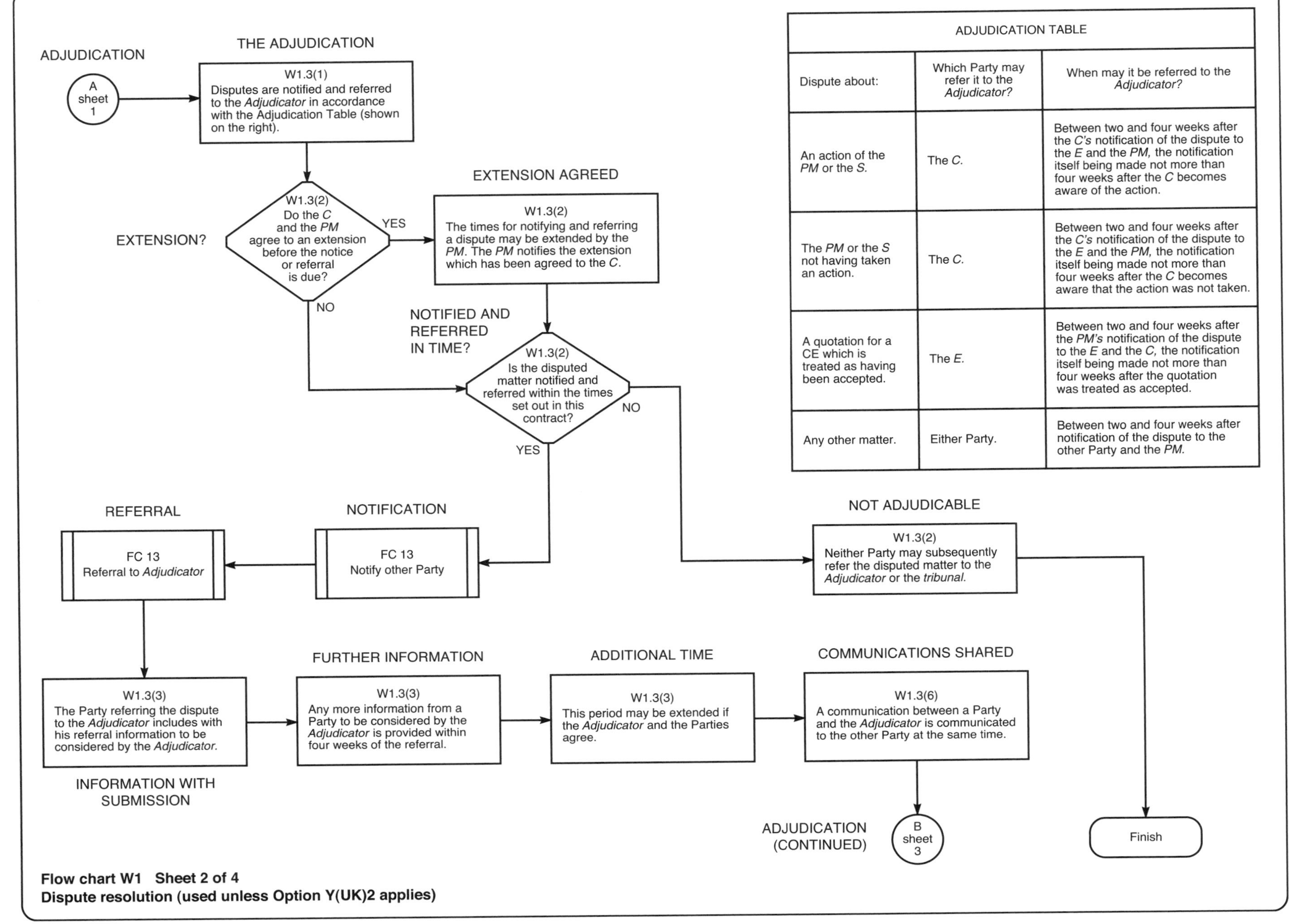
ADJUDICATION
A sheet 1
THE ADJUDICATION
W1.3(1)
Disputes are notified and referred to the Adjudicator in accordance with the Adjudication Table (shown on the right).
EXTENSION?
W1.3(2)
Do the C and the PM agree to an extension before the notice or referral is due?
YES
NO
EXTENSION AGREED
W1.3(2)
The times for notifying and referring a dispute may be extended by the PM. The PM notifies the extension which has been agreed to the C.
NOTIFIED AND REFERRED IN TIME?
W1.3(2)
Is the disputed matter notified and referred within the times set out in this contract?
NO
YES
REFERRAL
FC 13
Referral to Adjudicator
NOTIFICATION
FC 13
Notify other Party
NOT ADJUDICABLE
W1.3(2)
Neither Party may subsequently refer the disputed matter to the Adjudicator or the tribunal.
W1.3(3)
The Party referring the dispute to the Adjudicator includes with his referral information to be considered by the Adjudicator.
INFORMATION WITH SUBMISSION
FURTHER INFORMATION
W1.3(3)
Any more information from a Party to be considered by the Adjudicator is provided within four weeks of the referral.
ADDITIONAL TIME
W1.3(3)
This period may be extended if the Adjudicator and the Parties agree.
COMMUNICATIONS SHARED
W1.3(6)
A communication between a Party and the Adjudicator is communicated to the other Party at the same time.
ADJUDICATION (CONTINUED)
B sheet 3
Finish
ADJUDICATION TABLE

Dispute about:	Which Party may refer it to the *Adjudicator?*	When may it be referred to the *Adjudicator?*
An action of the *PM* or the *S*.	The *C*.	Between two and four weeks after the *C's* notification of the dispute to the *E* and the *PM*, the notification itself being made not more than four weeks after the *C* becomes aware of the action.
The *PM* or the *S* not having taken an action.	The *C*.	Between two and four weeks after the *C's* notification of the dispute to the *E* and the *PM*, the notification itself being made not more than four weeks after the *C* becomes aware that the action was not taken.
A quotation for a CE which is treated as having been accepted.	The *E*.	Between two and four weeks after the *PM's* notification of the dispute to the *E* and the *C*, the notification itself being made not more than four weeks after the quotation was treated as accepted.
Any other matter.	Either Party.	Between two and four weeks after notification of the dispute to the other Party and the *PM*.

Flow chart W1 Sheet 2 of 4
Dispute resolution (used unless Option Y(UK)2 applies)

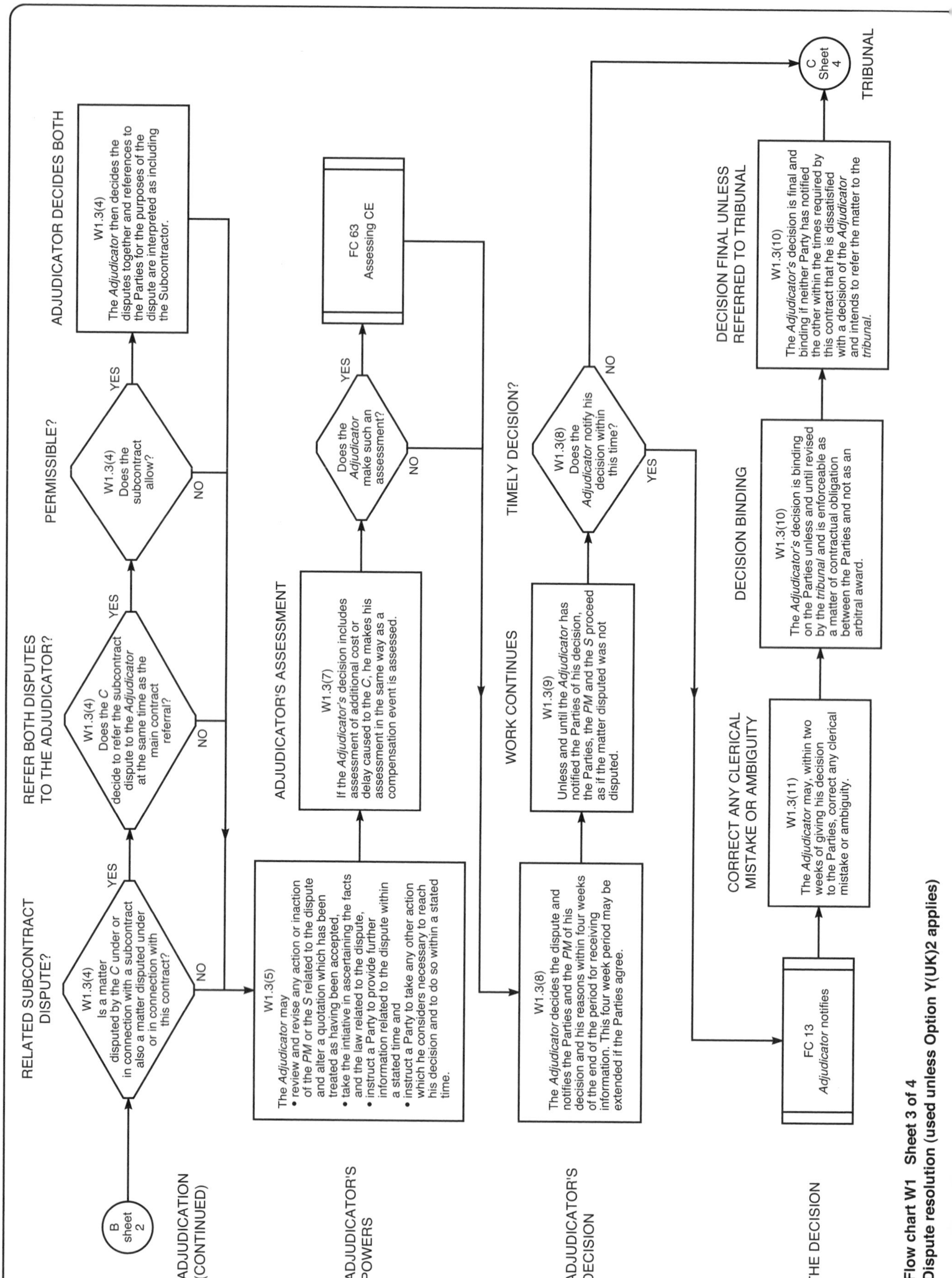

ADJUDICATION (CONTINUED)

B sheet 2

RELATED SUBCONTRACT DISPUTE?

W1.3(4)
Is a matter disputed by the *C* under or in connection with a subcontract also a matter disputed under or in connection with this contract?
YES / NO

REFER BOTH DISPUTES TO THE ADJUDICATOR?

W1.3(4)
Does the *C* decide to refer the subcontract dispute to the *Adjudicator* at the same time as the main contract referral?
YES / NO

PERMISSIBLE?

W1.3(4)
Does the subcontract allow?
YES / NO

ADJUDICATOR DECIDES BOTH

W1.3(4)
The *Adjudicator* then decides the disputes together and references to the Parties for the purposes of the dispute are interpreted as including the Subcontractor.

ADJUDICATOR'S POWERS

W1.3(5)
The *Adjudicator* may
- review and revise any action or inaction of the *PM* or the *S* related to the dispute and alter a quotation which has been treated as having been accepted,
- take the intiative in ascertaining the facts and the law related to the dispute,
- instruct a Party to provide further information related to the dispute within a stated time and
- instruct a Party to take any other action which he considers necessary to reach his decision and to do so within a stated time.

ADJUDICATOR'S ASSESSMENT

W1.3(7)
If the *Adjudicator's* decision includes assessment of additional cost or delay caused to the *C*, he makes his assessment in the same way as a compensation event is assessed.

Does the *Adjudicator* make such an assessment?
YES / NO

FC 63
Assessing CE

ADJUDICATOR'S DECISION

W1.3(8)
The *Adjudicator* decides the dispute and notifies the Parties and the *PM* of his decision and his reasons within four weeks of the end of the period for receiving information. This four week period may be extended if the Parties agree.

WORK CONTINUES

W1.3(9)
Unless and until the *Adjudicator* has notified the Parties of his decision, the Parties, the *PM* and the *S* proceed as if the matter disputed was not disputed.

TIMELY DECISION?

W1.3(8)
Does the *Adjudicator* notify his decision within this time?
YES / NO

THE DECISION

FC 13
Adjudicator notifies

CORRECT ANY CLERICAL MISTAKE OR AMBIGUITY

W1.3(11)
The *Adjudicator* may, within two weeks of giving his decision to the Parties, correct any clerical mistake or ambiguity.

DECISION BINDING

W1.3(10)
The *Adjudicator's* decision is binding on the Parties unless and until revised by the *tribunal* and is enforceable as a matter of contractual obligation between the Parties and not as an arbitral award.

DECISION FINAL UNLESS REFERRED TO TRIBUNAL

W1.3(10)
The *Adjudicator's* decision is final and binding if neither Party has notified the other within the times required by this contract that he is dissatisfied with a decision of the *Adjudicator* and intends to refer the matter to the *tribunal*.

C Sheet 4

TRIBUNAL

Flow chart W1 Sheet 3 of 4
Dispute resolution (used unless Option Y(UK)2 applies)

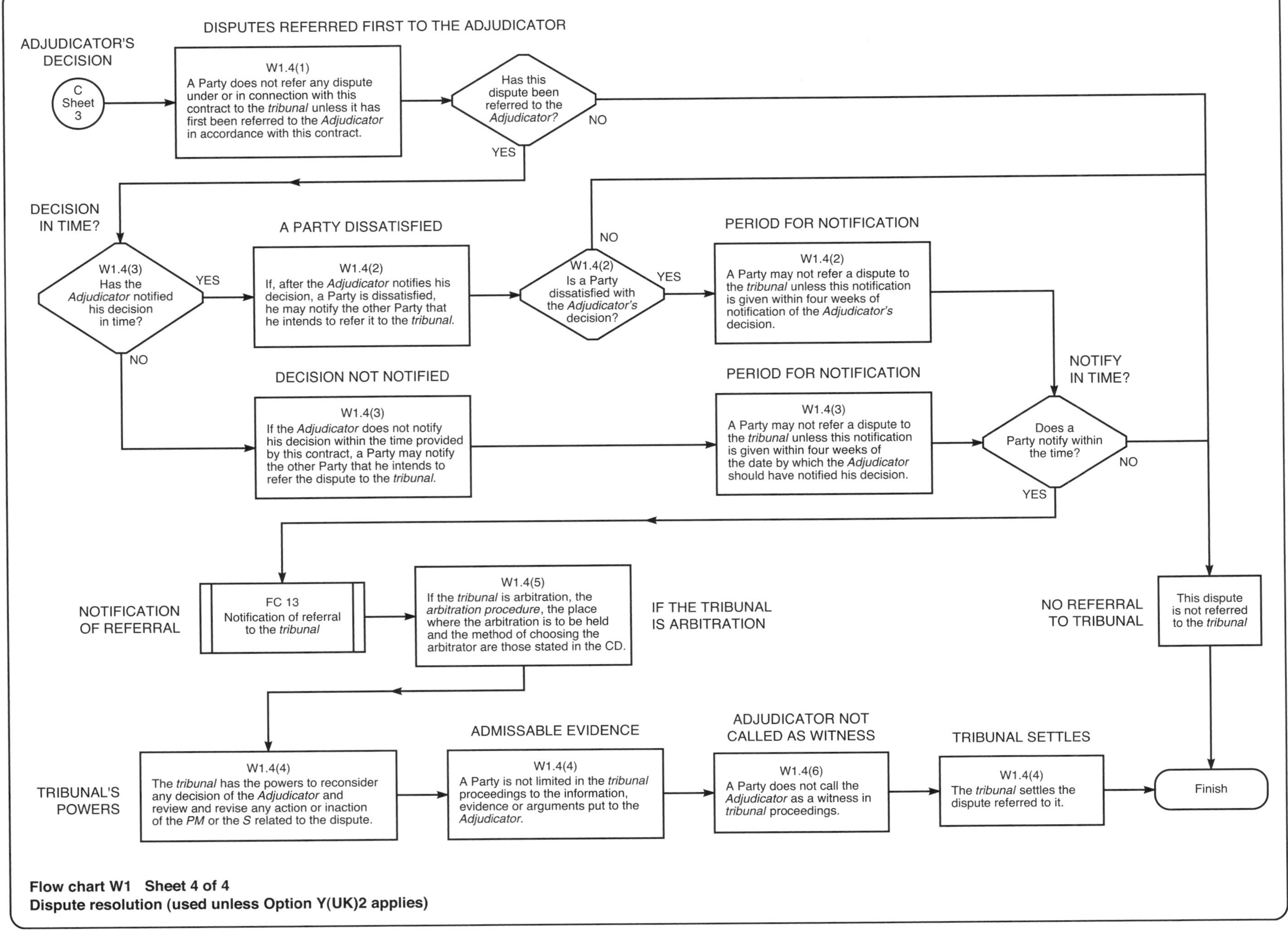
ADJUDICATOR'S DECISION
C Sheet 3
DISPUTES REFERRED FIRST TO THE ADJUDICATOR
W1.4(1)
A Party does not refer any dispute under or in connection with this contract to the tribunal unless it has first been referred to the Adjudicator in accordance with this contract.
Has this dispute been referred to the Adjudicator?
NO
YES
DECISION IN TIME?
W1.4(3) Has the Adjudicator notified his decision in time?
YES
NO
A PARTY DISSATISFIED
W1.4(2)
If, after the Adjudicator notifies his decision, a Party is dissatisfied, he may notify the other Party that he intends to refer it to the tribunal.
W1.4(2) Is a Party dissatisfied with the Adjudicator's decision?
NO
YES
PERIOD FOR NOTIFICATION
W1.4(2)
A Party may not refer a dispute to the tribunal unless this notification is given within four weeks of notification of the Adjudicator's decision.
DECISION NOT NOTIFIED
W1.4(3)
If the Adjudicator does not notify his decision within the time provided by this contract, a Party may notify the other Party that he intends to refer the dispute to the tribunal.
PERIOD FOR NOTIFICATION
W1.4(3)
A Party may not refer a dispute to the tribunal unless this notification is given within four weeks of the date by which the Adjudicator should have notified his decision.
NOTIFY IN TIME?
Does a Party notify within the time?
NO
YES
NOTIFICATION OF REFERRAL
FC 13
Notification of referral to the tribunal
W1.4(5)
If the tribunal is arbitration, the arbitration procedure, the place where the arbitration is to be held and the method of choosing the arbitrator are those stated in the CD.
IF THE TRIBUNAL IS ARBITRATION
NO REFERRAL TO TRIBUNAL
This dispute is not referred to the tribunal
TRIBUNAL'S POWERS
W1.4(4)
The tribunal has the powers to reconsider any decision of the Adjudicator and review and revise any action or inaction of the PM or the S related to the dispute.
ADMISSABLE EVIDENCE
W1.4(4)
A Party is not limited in the tribunal proceedings to the information, evidence or arguments put to the Adjudicator.
ADJUDICATOR NOT CALLED AS WITNESS
W1.4(6)
A Party does not call the Adjudicator as a witness in tribunal proceedings.
TRIBUNAL SETTLES
W1.4(4)
The tribunal settles the dispute referred to it.
Finish

Flow chart W1 Sheet 4 of 4
Dispute resolution (used unless Option Y(UK)2 applies)

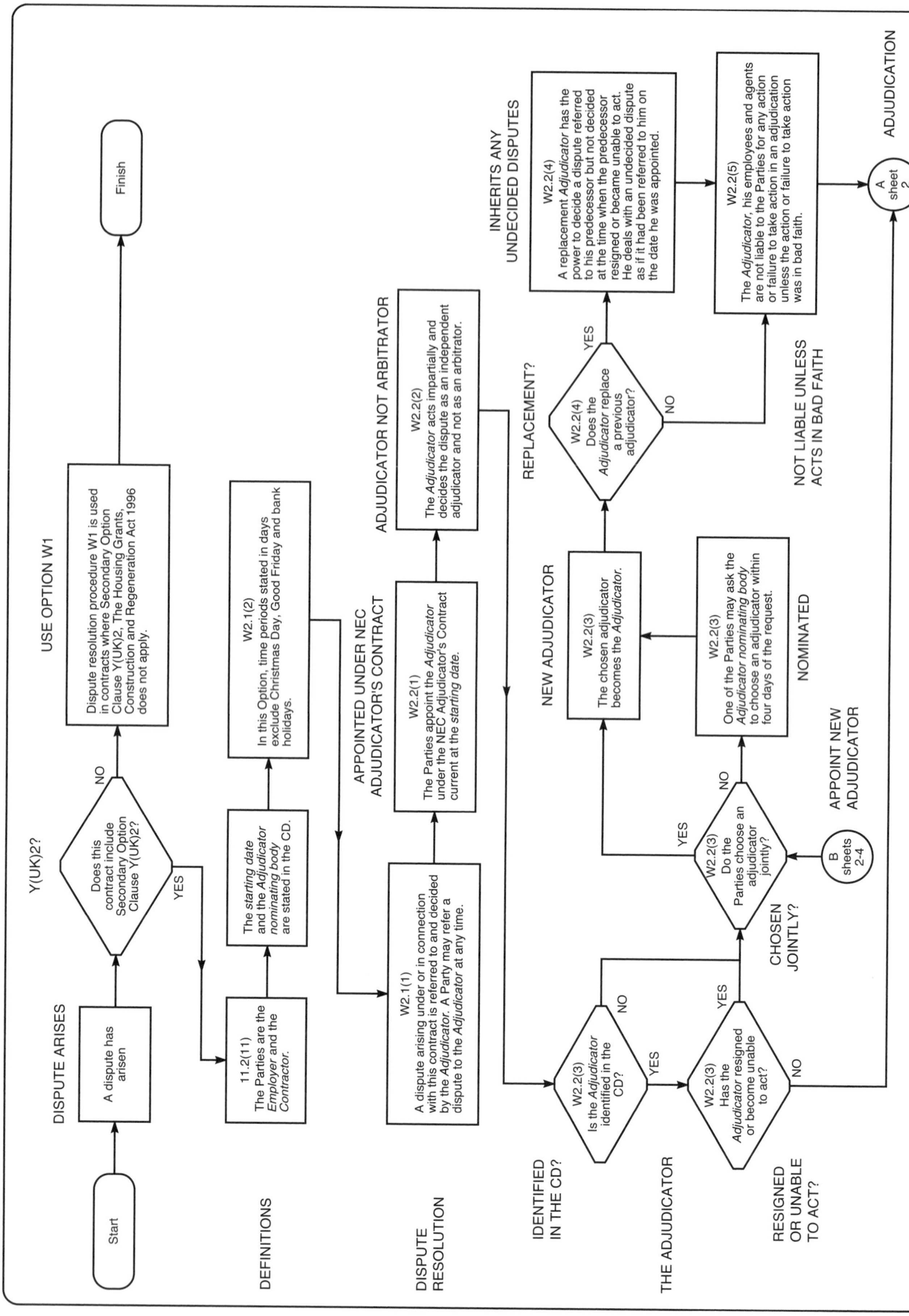

DISPUTE ARISES

Start

A dispute has arisen

Y(UK)2?

Does this contract include Secondary Option Clause Y(UK)2?

NO

USE OPTION W1

Dispute resolution procedure W1 is used in contracts where Secondary Option Clause Y(UK)2, The Housing Grants, Construction and Regeneration Act 1996 does not apply.

Finish

YES

DEFINITIONS

11.2(11)
The Parties are the *Employer* and the *Contractor.*

The *starting date* and the *Adjudicator nominating body* are stated in the CD.

W2.1(2)
In this Option, time periods stated in days exclude Christmas Day, Good Friday and bank holidays.

DISPUTE RESOLUTION

W2.1(1)
A dispute arising under or in connection with this contract is referred to and decided by the *Adjudicator.* A Party may refer a dispute to the *Adjudicator* at any time.

APPOINTED UNDER NEC ADJUDICATOR'S CONTRACT

W2.2(1)
The Parties appoint the *Adjudicator* under the NEC Adjudicator's Contract current at the *starting date.*

ADJUDICATOR NOT ARBITRATOR

W2.2(2)
The *Adjudicator* acts impartially and decides the dispute as an independent adjudicator and not as an arbitrator.

IDENTIFIED IN THE CD?

W2.2(3)
Is the *Adjudicator* identified in the CD?

NO

YES

THE ADJUDICATOR

RESIGNED OR UNABLE TO ACT?

W2.2(3)
Has the *Adjudicator* resigned or become unable to act?

YES

NO

CHOSEN JOINTLY?

W2.2(3)
Do the Parties choose an adjudicator jointly?

YES

NO

B sheets 2-4

APPOINT NEW ADJUDICATOR

NEW ADJUDICATOR

W2.2(3)
The chosen adjudicator becomes the *Adjudicator.*

NOMINATED

W2.2(3)
One of the Parties may ask the *Adjudicator nominating body* to choose an adjudicator within four days of the request.

REPLACEMENT?

W2.2(4)
Does the *Adjudicator* replace a previous adjudicator?

YES

NO

INHERITS ANY UNDECIDED DISPUTES

W2.2(4)
A replacement *Adjudicator* has the power to decide a dispute referred to his predecessor but not decided at the time when the predecessor resigned or became unable to act. He deals with an undecided dispute as if it had been referred to him on the date he was appointed.

NOT LIABLE UNLESS ACTS IN BAD FAITH

W2.2(5)
The *Adjudicator,* his employees and agents are not liable to the Parties for any action or failure to take action in an adjudication unless the action or failure to take action was in bad faith.

A sheet 2

ADJUDICATION

Flow chart W2 Sheet 1 of 5
Dispute resolution (used when Option Y(UK)2 applies)

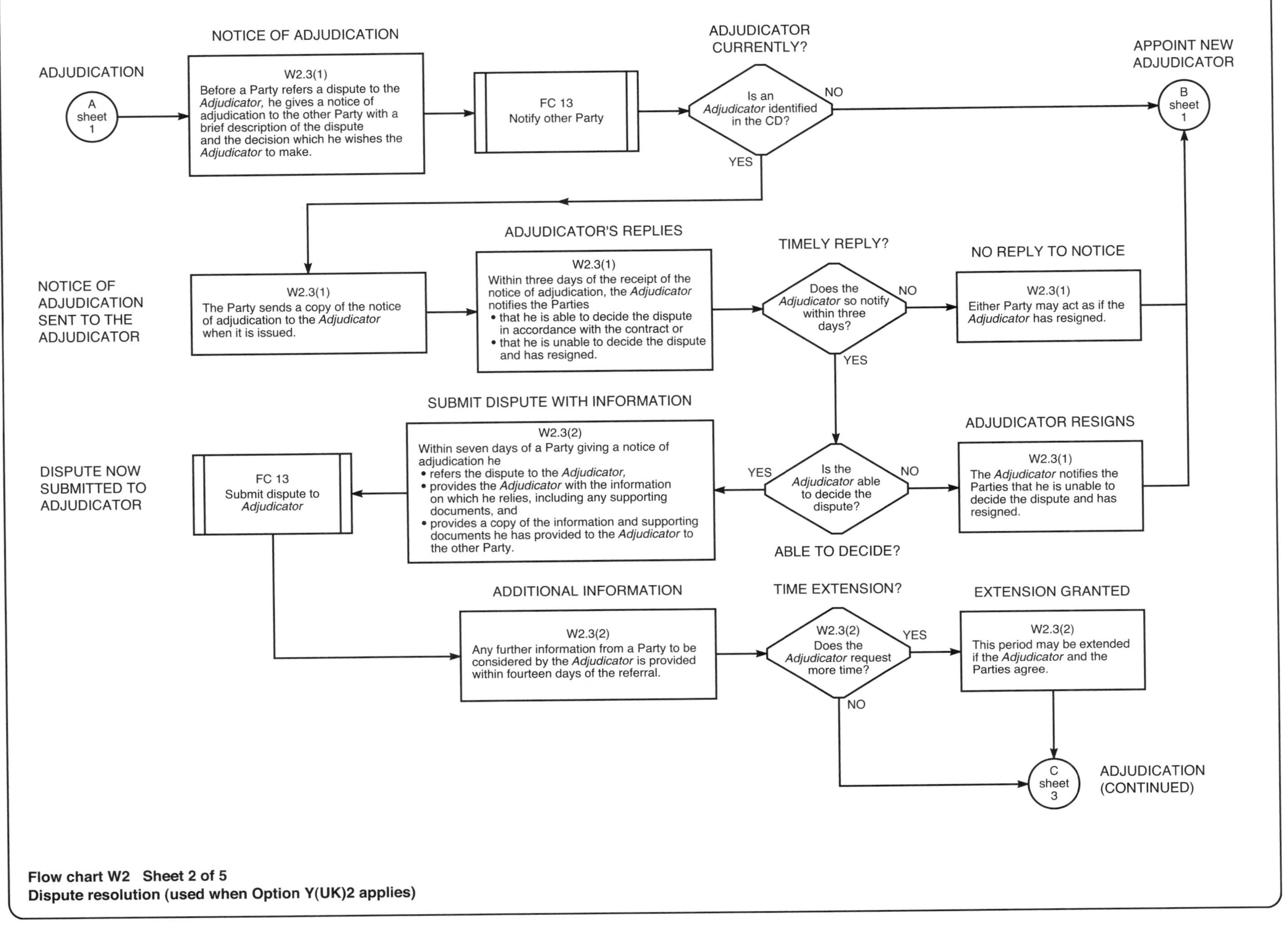
ADJUDICATION
A sheet 1
NOTICE OF ADJUDICATION
W2.3(1)
Before a Party refers a dispute to the Adjudicator, he gives a notice of adjudication to the other Party with a brief description of the dispute and the decision which he wishes the Adjudicator to make.
FC 13
Notify other Party
ADJUDICATOR CURRENTLY?
Is an Adjudicator identified in the CD?
NO
YES
APPOINT NEW ADJUDICATOR
B sheet 1
NOTICE OF ADJUDICATION SENT TO THE ADJUDICATOR
W2.3(1)
The Party sends a copy of the notice of adjudication to the Adjudicator when it is issued.
ADJUDICATOR'S REPLIES
W2.3(1)
Within three days of the receipt of the notice of adjudication, the Adjudicator notifies the Parties
• that he is able to decide the dispute in accordance with the contract or
• that he is unable to decide the dispute and has resigned.
TIMELY REPLY?
Does the Adjudicator so notify within three days?
NO
YES
NO REPLY TO NOTICE
W2.3(1)
Either Party may act as if the Adjudicator has resigned.
SUBMIT DISPUTE WITH INFORMATION
W2.3(2)
Within seven days of a Party giving a notice of adjudication he
• refers the dispute to the Adjudicator,
• provides the Adjudicator with the information on which he relies, including any supporting documents, and
• provides a copy of the information and supporting documents he has provided to the Adjudicator to the other Party.
DISPUTE NOW SUBMITTED TO ADJUDICATOR
FC 13
Submit dispute to Adjudicator
YES
Is the Adjudicator able to decide the dispute?
NO
ABLE TO DECIDE?
ADJUDICATOR RESIGNS
W2.3(1)
The Adjudicator notifies the Parties that he is unable to decide the dispute and has resigned.
ADDITIONAL INFORMATION
W2.3(2)
Any further information from a Party to be considered by the Adjudicator is provided within fourteen days of the referral.
TIME EXTENSION?
W2.3(2)
Does the Adjudicator request more time?
YES
NO
EXTENSION GRANTED
W2.3(2)
This period may be extended if the Adjudicator and the Parties agree.
C sheet 3
ADJUDICATION (CONTINUED)

Flow chart W2 Sheet 2 of 5
Dispute resolution (used when Option Y(UK)2 applies)

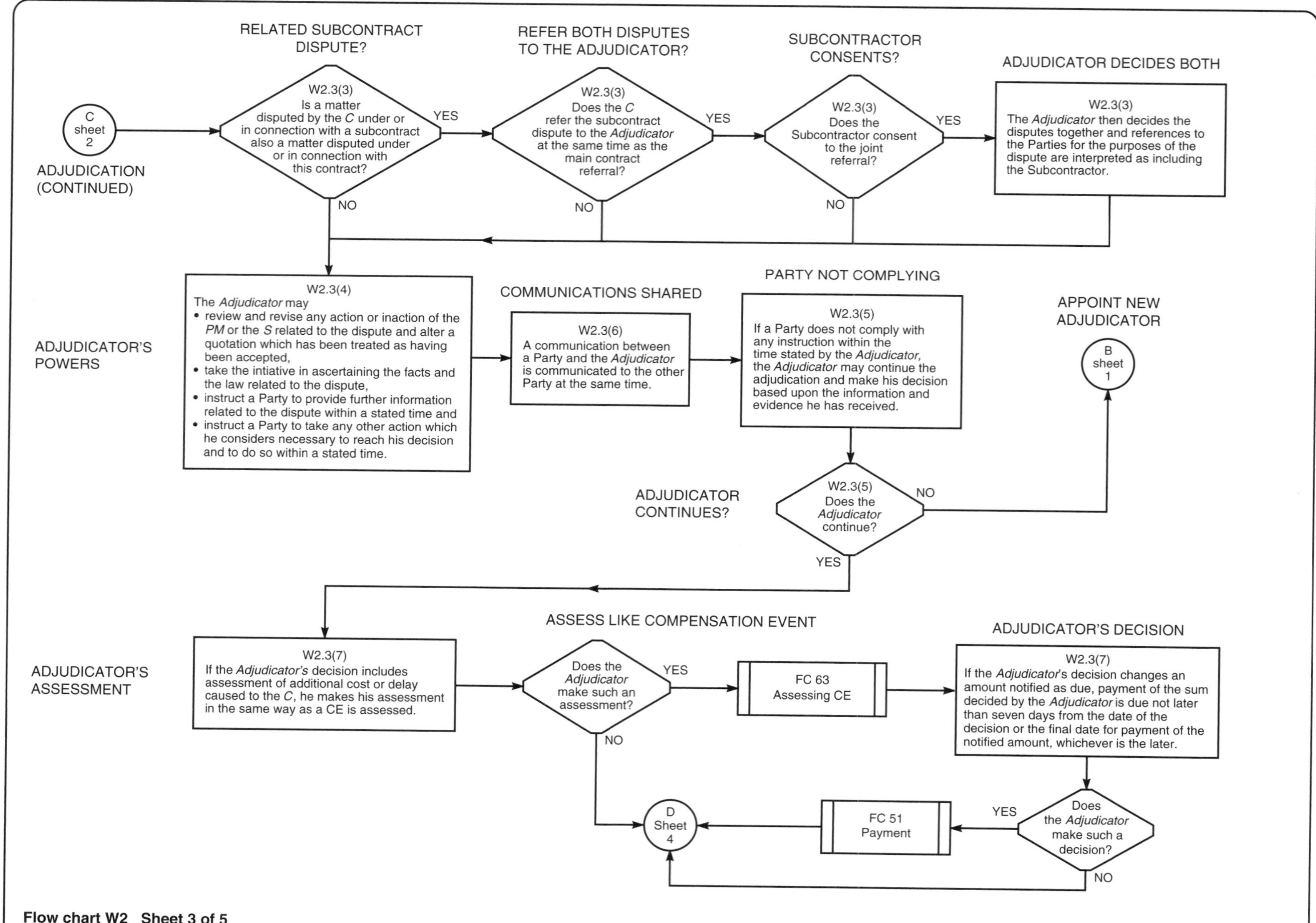
RELATED SUBCONTRACT DISPUTE?
REFER BOTH DISPUTES TO THE ADJUDICATOR?
SUBCONTRACTOR CONSENTS?
ADJUDICATOR DECIDES BOTH
C sheet 2
ADJUDICATION (CONTINUED)
W2.3(3) Is a matter disputed by the C under or in connection with a subcontract also a matter disputed under or in connection with this contract?
YES
NO
W2.3(3) Does the C refer the subcontract dispute to the Adjudicator at the same time as the main contract referral?
YES
NO
W2.3(3) Does the Subcontractor consent to the joint referral?
YES
NO
W2.3(3) The Adjudicator then decides the disputes together and references to the Parties for the purposes of the dispute are interpreted as including the Subcontractor.
ADJUDICATOR'S POWERS
W2.3(4) The Adjudicator may
• review and revise any action or inaction of the PM or the S related to the dispute and alter a quotation which has been treated as having been accepted,
• take the intiative in ascertaining the facts and the law related to the dispute,
• instruct a Party to provide further information related to the dispute within a stated time and
• instruct a Party to take any other action which he considers necessary to reach his decision and to do so within a stated time.
COMMUNICATIONS SHARED
W2.3(6) A communication between a Party and the Adjudicator is communicated to the other Party at the same time.
PARTY NOT COMPLYING
W2.3(5) If a Party does not comply with any instruction within the time stated by the Adjudicator, the Adjudicator may continue the adjudication and make his decision based upon the information and evidence he has received.
APPOINT NEW ADJUDICATOR
B sheet 1
ADJUDICATOR CONTINUES?
W2.3(5) Does the Adjudicator continue?
NO
YES
ASSESS LIKE COMPENSATION EVENT
ADJUDICATOR'S DECISION
ADJUDICATOR'S ASSESSMENT
W2.3(7) If the Adjudicator's decision includes assessment of additional cost or delay caused to the C, he makes his assessment in the same way as a CE is assessed.
Does the Adjudicator make such an assessment?
YES
NO
FC 63 Assessing CE
W2.3(7) If the Adjudicator's decision changes an amount notified as due, payment of the sum decided by the Adjudicator is due not later than seven days from the date of the decision or the final date for payment of the notified amount, whichever is the later.
D Sheet 4
FC 51 Payment
YES
Does the Adjudicator make such a decision?
NO

Flow chart W2 Sheet 3 of 5
Dispute resolution (used when Option Y(UK)2 applies)

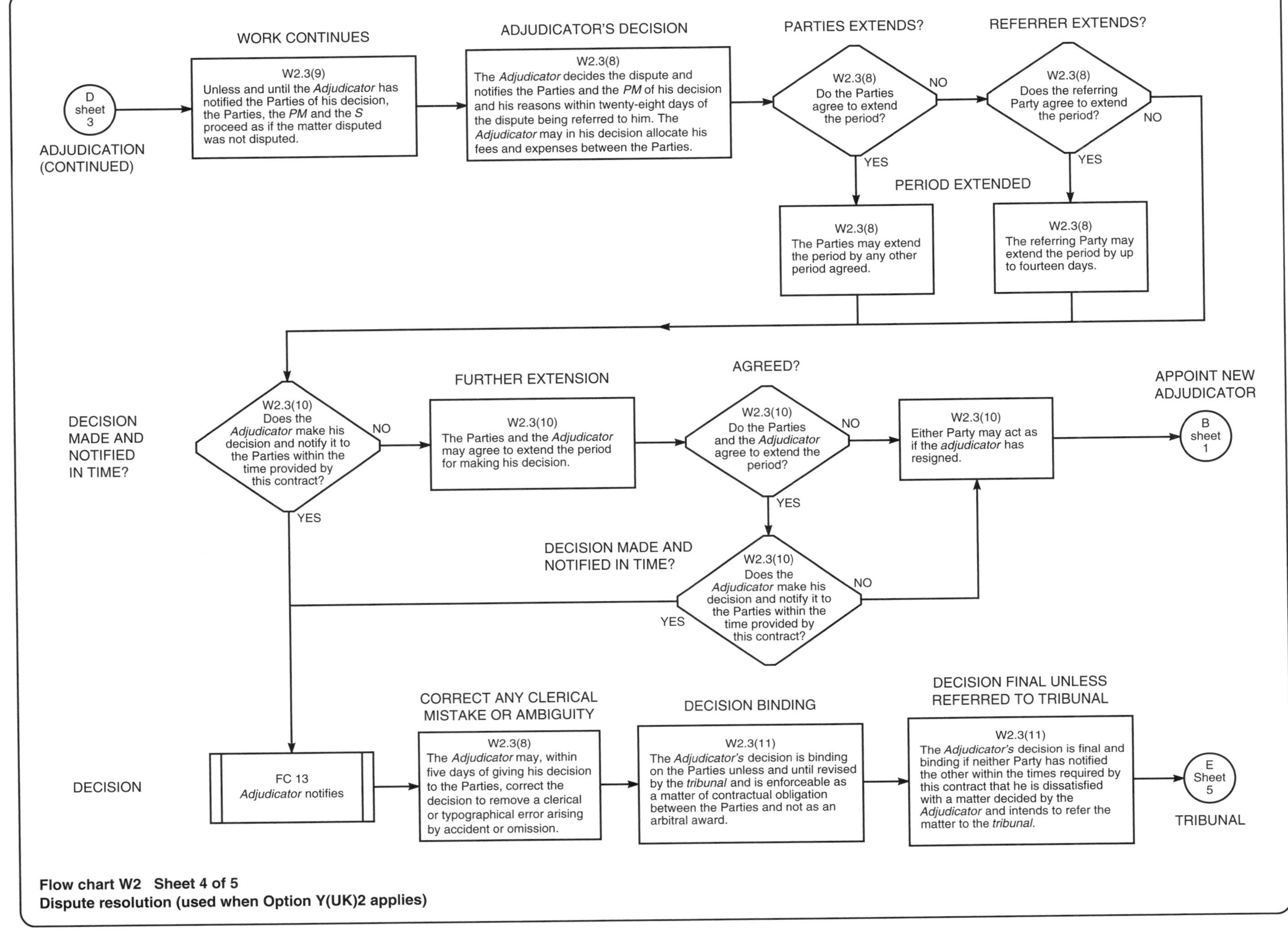
ADJUDICATION (CONTINUED)
D sheet 3
WORK CONTINUES
W2.3(9)
Unless and until the *Adjudicator* has notified the Parties of his decision, the Parties, the *PM* and the *S* proceed as if the matter disputed was not disputed.
ADJUDICATOR'S DECISION
W2.3(8)
The *Adjudicator* decides the dispute and notifies the Parties and the *PM* of his decision and his reasons within twenty-eight days of the dispute being referred to him. The *Adjudicator* may in his decision allocate his fees and expenses between the Parties.
PARTIES EXTENDS?
W2.3(8)
Do the Parties agree to extend the period?
NO
YES
REFERRER EXTENDS?
W2.3(8)
Does the referring Party agree to extend the period?
NO
YES
PERIOD EXTENDED
W2.3(8)
The Parties may extend the period by any other period agreed.
W2.3(8)
The referring Party may extend the period by up to fourteen days.
DECISION MADE AND NOTIFIED IN TIME?
W2.3(10)
Does the *Adjudicator* make his decision and notify it to the Parties within the time provided by this contract?
NO
YES
FURTHER EXTENSION
W2.3(10)
The Parties and the *Adjudicator* may agree to extend the period for making his decision.
AGREED?
W2.3(10)
Do the Parties and the *Adjudicator* agree to extend the period?
NO
YES
W2.3(10)
Either Party may act as if the *adjudicator* has resigned.
APPOINT NEW ADJUDICATOR
B sheet 1
DECISION MADE AND NOTIFIED IN TIME?
W2.3(10)
Does the *Adjudicator* make his decision and notify it to the Parties within the time provided by this contract?
NO
YES
DECISION
FC 13
Adjudicator notifies
CORRECT ANY CLERICAL MISTAKE OR AMBIGUITY
W2.3(8)
The *Adjudicator* may, within five days of giving his decision to the Parties, correct the decision to remove a clerical or typographical error arising by accident or omission.
DECISION BINDING
W2.3(11)
The *Adjudicator's* decision is binding on the Parties unless and until revised by the *tribunal* and is enforceable as a matter of contractual obligation between the Parties and not as an arbitral award.
DECISION FINAL UNLESS REFERRED TO TRIBUNAL
W2.3(11)
The *Adjudicator's* decision is final and binding if neither Party has notified the other within the times required by this contract that he is dissatisfied with a matter decided by the *Adjudicator* and intends to refer the matter to the *tribunal*.
E Sheet 5
TRIBUNAL
Flow chart W2 Sheet 4 of 5
Dispute resolution (used when Option Y(UK)2 applies)

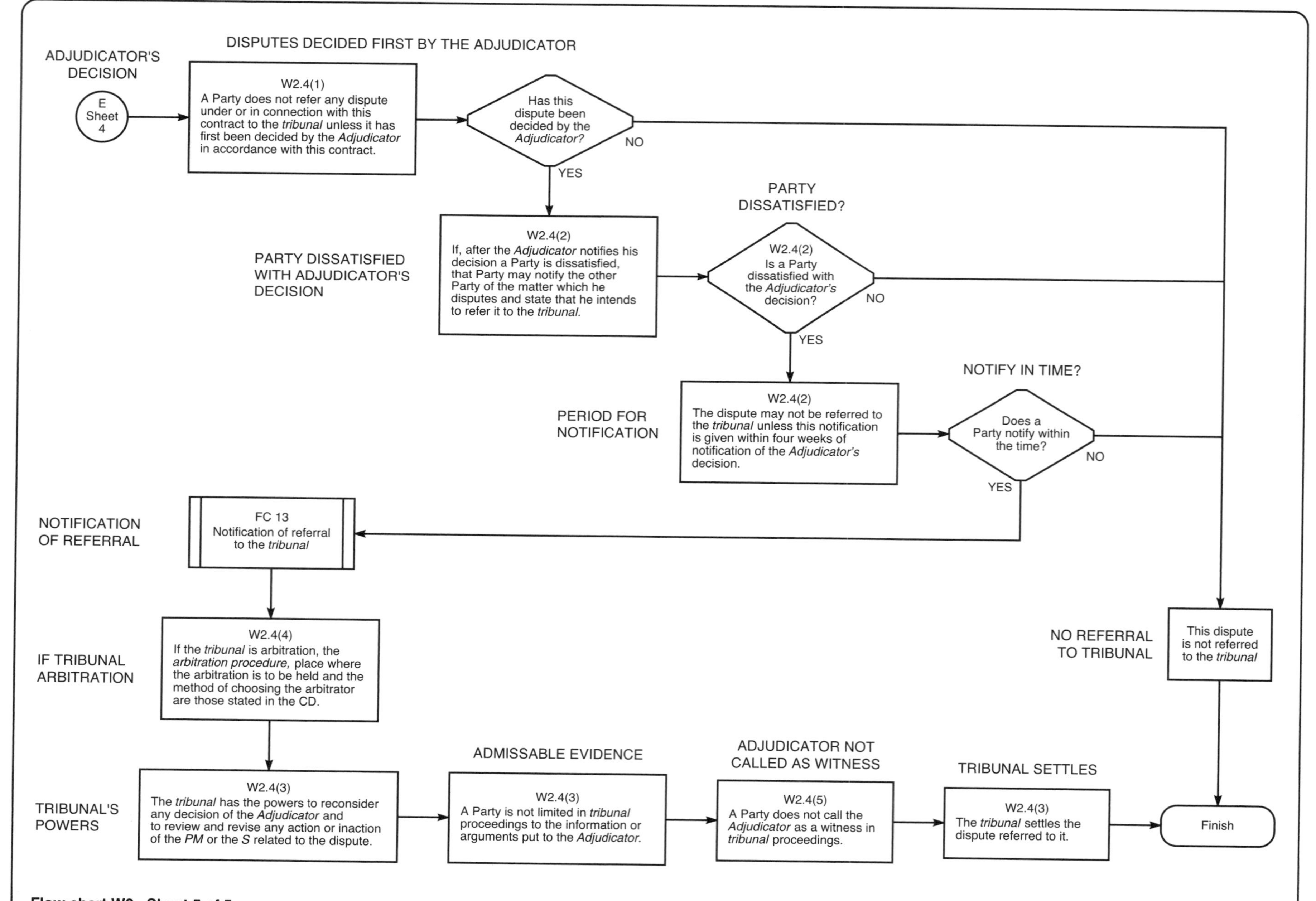
ADJUDICATOR'S DECISION
E Sheet 4
DISPUTES DECIDED FIRST BY THE ADJUDICATOR
W2.4(1) A Party does not refer any dispute under or in connection with this contract to the *tribunal* unless it has first been decided by the *Adjudicator* in accordance with this contract.
Has this dispute been decided by the *Adjudicator*?
NO
YES
PARTY DISSATISFIED WITH ADJUDICATOR'S DECISION
W2.4(2) If, after the *Adjudicator* notifies his decision a Party is dissatisfied, that Party may notify the other Party of the matter which he disputes and state that he intends to refer it to the *tribunal*.
PARTY DISSATISFIED?
W2.4(2) Is a Party dissatisfied with the *Adjudicator's* decision?
NO
YES
PERIOD FOR NOTIFICATION
W2.4(2) The dispute may not be referred to the *tribunal* unless this notification is given within four weeks of notification of the *Adjudicator's* decision.
NOTIFY IN TIME?
Does a Party notify within the time?
NO
YES
NOTIFICATION OF REFERRAL
FC 13 Notification of referral to the *tribunal*
IF TRIBUNAL ARBITRATION
W2.4(4) If the *tribunal* is arbitration, the *arbitration procedure,* place where the arbitration is to be held and the method of choosing the arbitrator are those stated in the CD.
NO REFERRAL TO TRIBUNAL
This dispute is not referred to the *tribunal*
TRIBUNAL'S POWERS
W2.4(3) The *tribunal* has the powers to reconsider any decision of the *Adjudicator* and to review and revise any action or inaction of the *PM* or the *S* related to the dispute.
ADMISSABLE EVIDENCE
W2.4(3) A Party is not limited in *tribunal* proceedings to the information or arguments put to the *Adjudicator*.
ADJUDICATOR NOT CALLED AS WITNESS
W2.4(5) A Party does not call the *Adjudicator* as a witness in *tribunal* proceedings.
TRIBUNAL SETTLES
W2.4(3) The *tribunal* settles the dispute referred to it.
Finish

Flow chart W2 Sheet 5 of 5
Dispute resolution (used when Option Y(UK)2 applies)

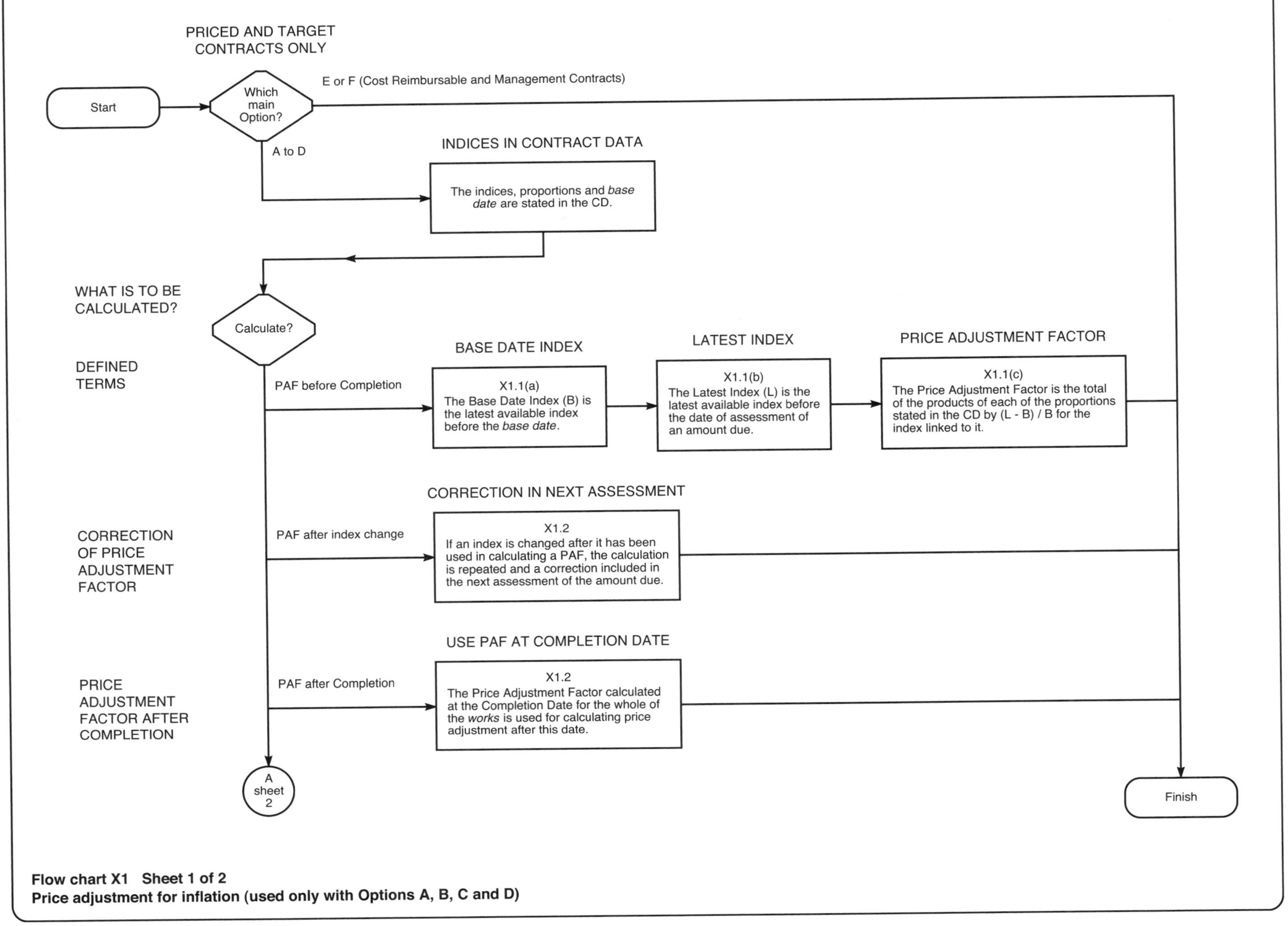
PRICED AND TARGET CONTRACTS ONLY
Start
Which main Option?
E or F (Cost Reimbursable and Management Contracts)
A to D
INDICES IN CONTRACT DATA
The indices, proportions and *base date* are stated in the CD.
WHAT IS TO BE CALCULATED?
Calculate?
DEFINED TERMS
PAF before Completion
BASE DATE INDEX
X1.1(a)
The Base Date Index (B) is the latest available index before the *base date*.
LATEST INDEX
X1.1(b)
The Latest Index (L) is the latest available index before the date of assessment of an amount due.
PRICE ADJUSTMENT FACTOR
X1.1(c)
The Price Adjustment Factor is the total of the products of each of the proportions stated in the CD by (L - B) / B for the index linked to it.
CORRECTION OF PRICE ADJUSTMENT FACTOR
PAF after index change
CORRECTION IN NEXT ASSESSMENT
X1.2
If an index is changed after it has been used in calculating a PAF, the calculation is repeated and a correction included in the next assessment of the amount due.
PRICE ADJUSTMENT FACTOR AFTER COMPLETION
PAF after Completion
USE PAF AT COMPLETION DATE
X1.2
The Price Adjustment Factor calculated at the Completion Date for the whole of the *works* is used for calculating price adjustment after this date.
A sheet 2
Finish

Flow chart X1 Sheet 1 of 2
Price adjustment for inflation (used only with Options A, B, C and D)

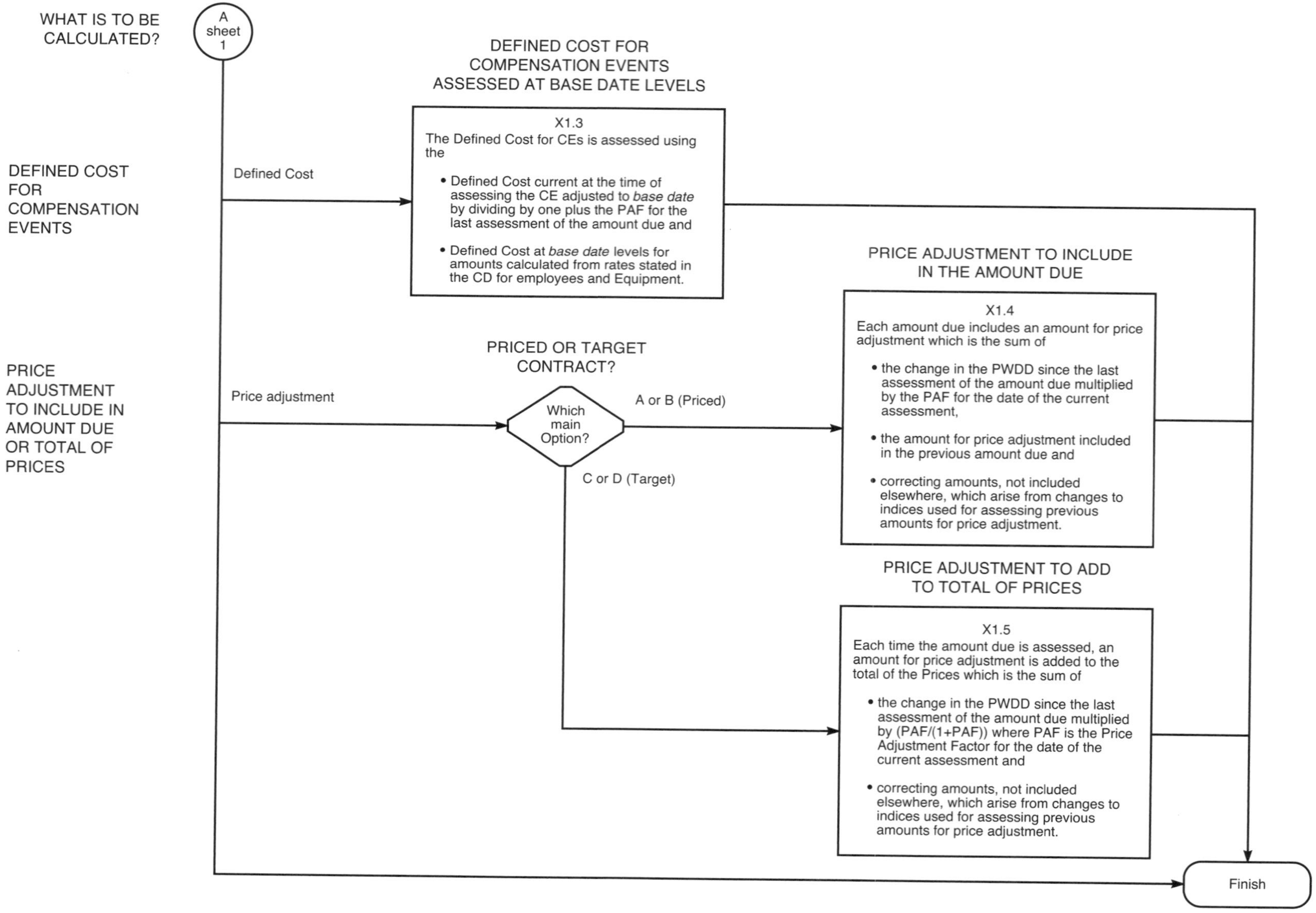

WHAT IS TO BE CALCULATED?

A sheet 1

DEFINED COST FOR COMPENSATION EVENTS

Defined Cost

DEFINED COST FOR COMPENSATION EVENTS ASSESSED AT BASE DATE LEVELS

X1.3
The Defined Cost for CEs is assessed using the

- Defined Cost current at the time of assessing the CE adjusted to *base date* by dividing by one plus the PAF for the last assessment of the amount due and
- Defined Cost at *base date* levels for amounts calculated from rates stated in the CD for employees and Equipment.

PRICE ADJUSTMENT TO INCLUDE IN AMOUNT DUE OR TOTAL OF PRICES

Price adjustment

PRICED OR TARGET CONTRACT?

Which main Option?

A or B (Priced)

C or D (Target)

PRICE ADJUSTMENT TO INCLUDE IN THE AMOUNT DUE

X1.4
Each amount due includes an amount for price adjustment which is the sum of

- the change in the PWDD since the last assessment of the amount due multiplied by the PAF for the date of the current assessment,
- the amount for price adjustment included in the previous amount due and
- correcting amounts, not included elsewhere, which arise from changes to indices used for assessing previous amounts for price adjustment.

PRICE ADJUSTMENT TO ADD TO TOTAL OF PRICES

X1.5
Each time the amount due is assessed, an amount for price adjustment is added to the total of the Prices which is the sum of

- the change in the PWDD since the last assessment of the amount due multiplied by (PAF/(1+PAF)) where PAF is the Price Adjustment Factor for the date of the current assessment and
- correcting amounts, not included elsewhere, which arise from changes to indices used for assessing previous amounts for price adjustment.

Finish

Flow chart X1 Sheet 2 of 2
Price adjustment for inflation (used only with Options A, B, C and D)

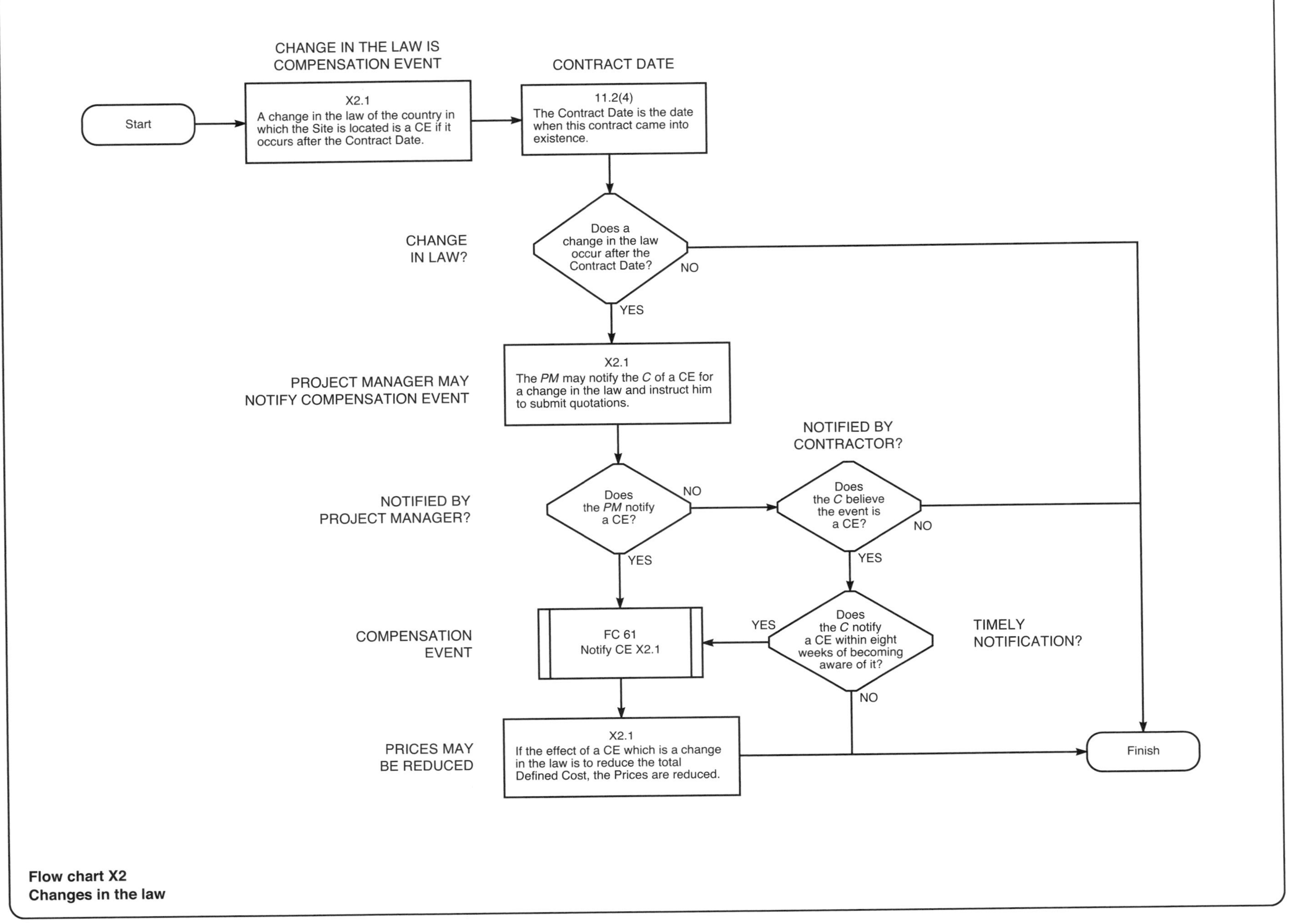
CHANGE IN THE LAW IS COMPENSATION EVENT
CONTRACT DATE
Start
X2.1
A change in the law of the country in which the Site is located is a CE if it occurs after the Contract Date.
11.2(4)
The Contract Date is the date when this contract came into existence.
CHANGE IN LAW?
Does a change in the law occur after the Contract Date?
NO
YES
PROJECT MANAGER MAY NOTIFY COMPENSATION EVENT
X2.1
The PM may notify the C of a CE for a change in the law and instruct him to submit quotations.
NOTIFIED BY CONTRACTOR?
NOTIFIED BY PROJECT MANAGER?
Does the PM notify a CE?
NO
Does the C believe the event is a CE?
NO
YES
YES
COMPENSATION EVENT
FC 61
Notify CE X2.1
YES
Does the C notify a CE within eight weeks of becoming aware of it?
TIMELY NOTIFICATION?
NO
PRICES MAY BE REDUCED
X2.1
If the effect of a CE which is a change in the law is to reduce the total Defined Cost, the Prices are reduced.
Finish
Flow chart X2
Changes in the law

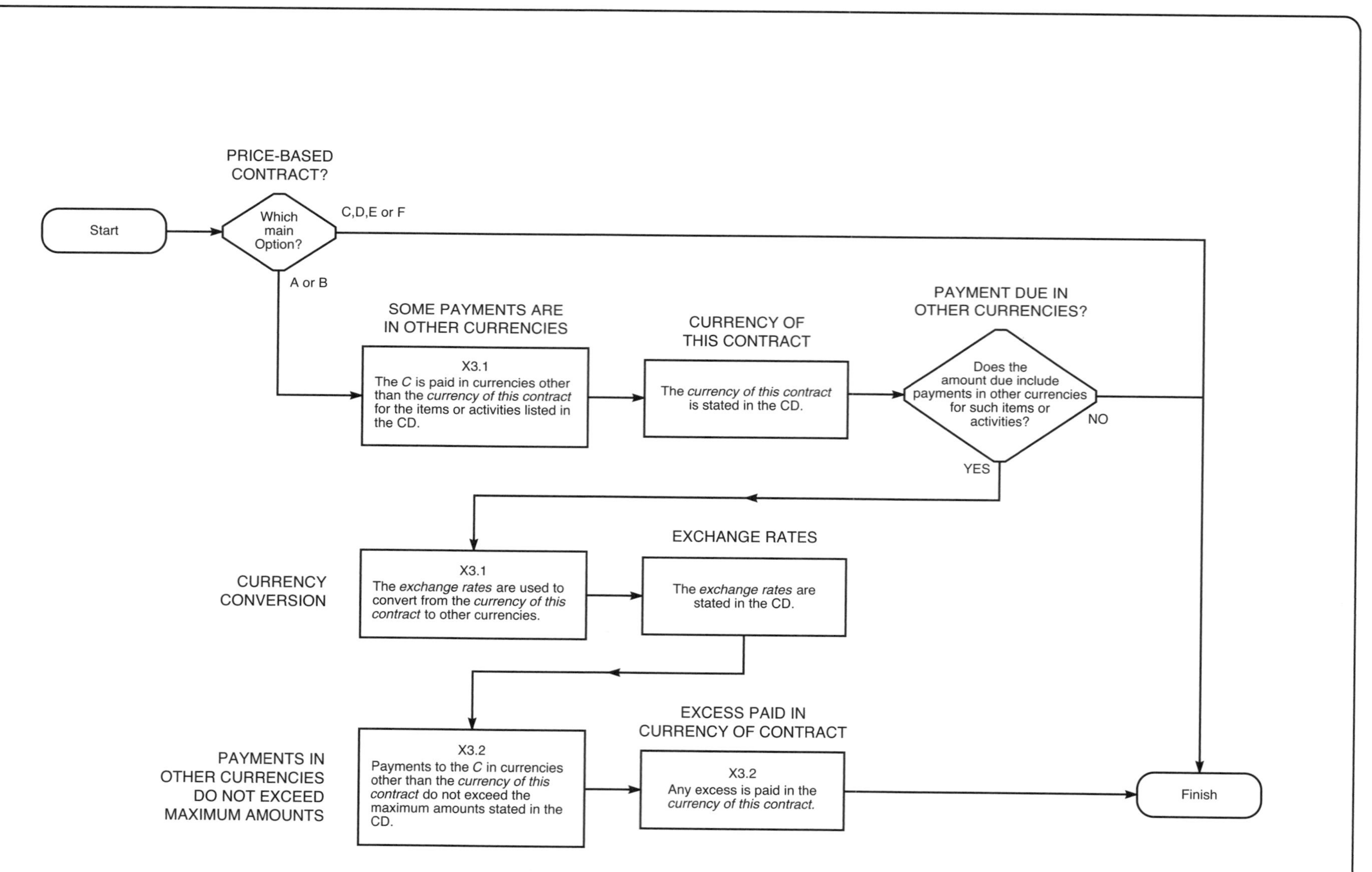
PRICE-BASED CONTRACT?
Start
Which main Option?
C,D,E or F
A or B
SOME PAYMENTS ARE IN OTHER CURRENCIES
X3.1
The C is paid in currencies other than the currency of this contract for the items or activities listed in the CD.
CURRENCY OF THIS CONTRACT
The currency of this contract is stated in the CD.
PAYMENT DUE IN OTHER CURRENCIES?
Does the amount due include payments in other currencies for such items or activities?
NO
YES
CURRENCY CONVERSION
X3.1
The exchange rates are used to convert from the currency of this contract to other currencies.
EXCHANGE RATES
The exchange rates are stated in the CD.
PAYMENTS IN OTHER CURRENCIES DO NOT EXCEED MAXIMUM AMOUNTS
X3.2
Payments to the C in currencies other than the currency of this contract do not exceed the maximum amounts stated in the CD.
EXCESS PAID IN CURRENCY OF CONTRACT
X3.2
Any excess is paid in the currency of this contract.
Finish

Flow chart X3
Multiple currencies (used only with Options A and B)

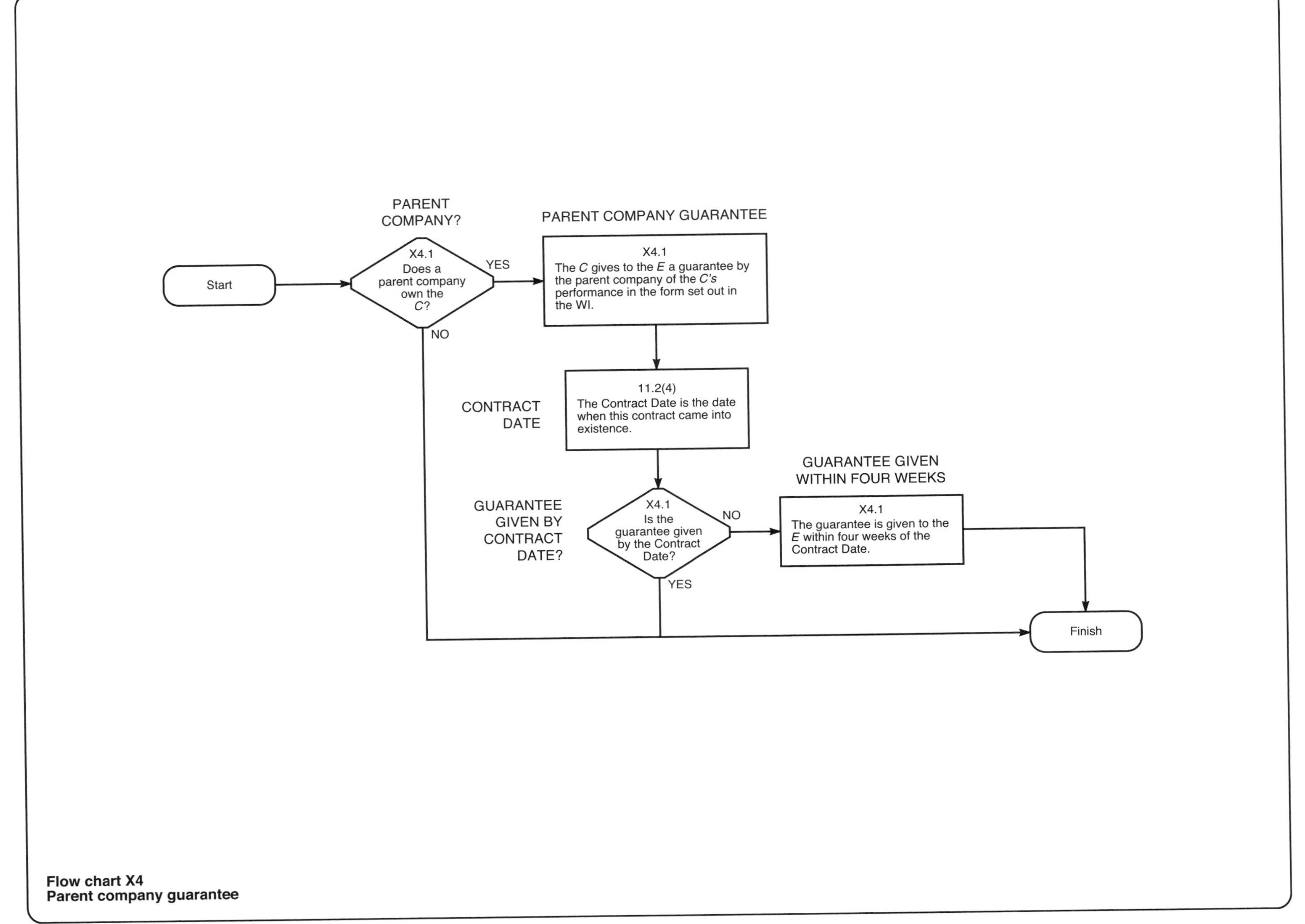
Start
PARENT COMPANY?
X4.1
Does a parent company own the *C*?
YES
NO
PARENT COMPANY GUARANTEE
X4.1
The *C* gives to the *E* a guarantee by the parent company of the *C's* performance in the form set out in the WI.
CONTRACT DATE
11.2(4)
The Contract Date is the date when this contract came into existence.
GUARANTEE GIVEN BY CONTRACT DATE?
X4.1
Is the guarantee given by the Contract Date?
NO
YES
GUARANTEE GIVEN WITHIN FOUR WEEKS
X4.1
The guarantee is given to the *E* within four weeks of the Contract Date.
Finish

Flow chart X4
Parent company guarantee

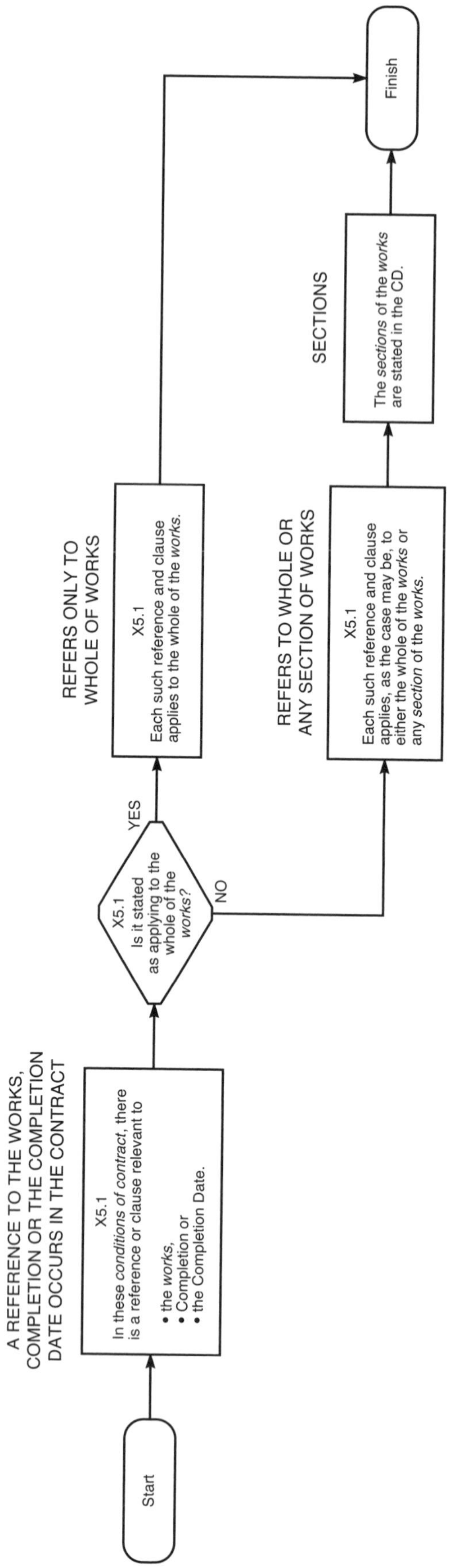

Start

A REFERENCE TO THE WORKS, COMPLETION OR THE COMPLETION DATE OCCURS IN THE CONTRACT

X5.1
In these *conditions of contract*, there is a reference or clause relevant to

- the *works*,
- Completion or
- the Completion Date.

X5.1
Is it stated as applying to the whole of the *works?*

YES

REFERS ONLY TO WHOLE OF WORKS

X5.1
Each such reference and clause applies to the whole of the *works*.

NO

REFERS TO WHOLE OR ANY SECTION OF WORKS

X5.1
Each such reference and clause applies, as the case may be, to either the whole of the *works* or any *section* of the *works*.

SECTIONS

The *sections* of the *works* are stated in the CD.

Finish

Flow chart X5
Sectional Completion

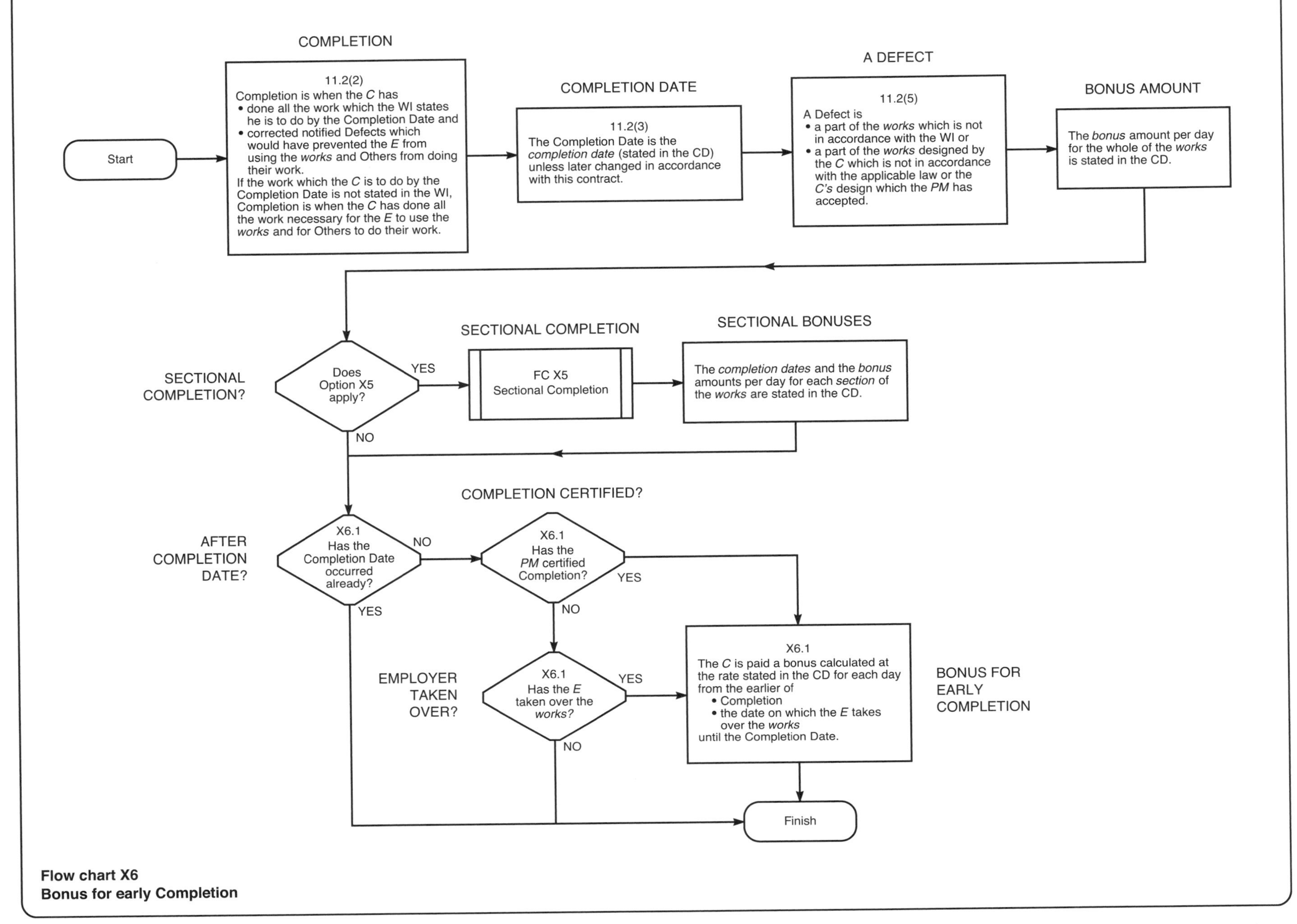
COMPLETION
11.2(2)
Completion is when the *C* has
• done all the work which the WI states he is to do by the Completion Date and
• corrected notified Defects which would have prevented the *E* from using the *works* and Others from doing their work.
If the work which the *C* is to do by the Completion Date is not stated in the WI, Completion is when the *C* has done all the work necessary for the *E* to use the *works* and for Others to do their work.
Start
COMPLETION DATE
11.2(3)
The Completion Date is the *completion date* (stated in the CD) unless later changed in accordance with this contract.
A DEFECT
11.2(5)
A Defect is
• a part of the *works* which is not in accordance with the WI or
• a part of the *works* designed by the *C* which is not in accordance with the applicable law or the *C's* design which the *PM* has accepted.
BONUS AMOUNT
The *bonus* amount per day for the whole of the *works* is stated in the CD.
SECTIONAL COMPLETION?
Does Option X5 apply?
YES
NO
SECTIONAL COMPLETION
FC X5 Sectional Completion
SECTIONAL BONUSES
The *completion dates* and the *bonus* amounts per day for each *section* of the *works* are stated in the CD.
COMPLETION CERTIFIED?
AFTER COMPLETION DATE?
X6.1 Has the Completion Date occurred already?
NO
YES
X6.1 Has the *PM* certified Completion?
YES
NO
EMPLOYER TAKEN OVER?
X6.1 Has the *E* taken over the *works*?
YES
NO
X6.1
The *C* is paid a bonus calculated at the rate stated in the CD for each day from the earlier of
• Completion
• the date on which the *E* takes over the *works*
until the Completion Date.
BONUS FOR EARLY COMPLETION
Finish

Flow chart X6
Bonus for early Completion

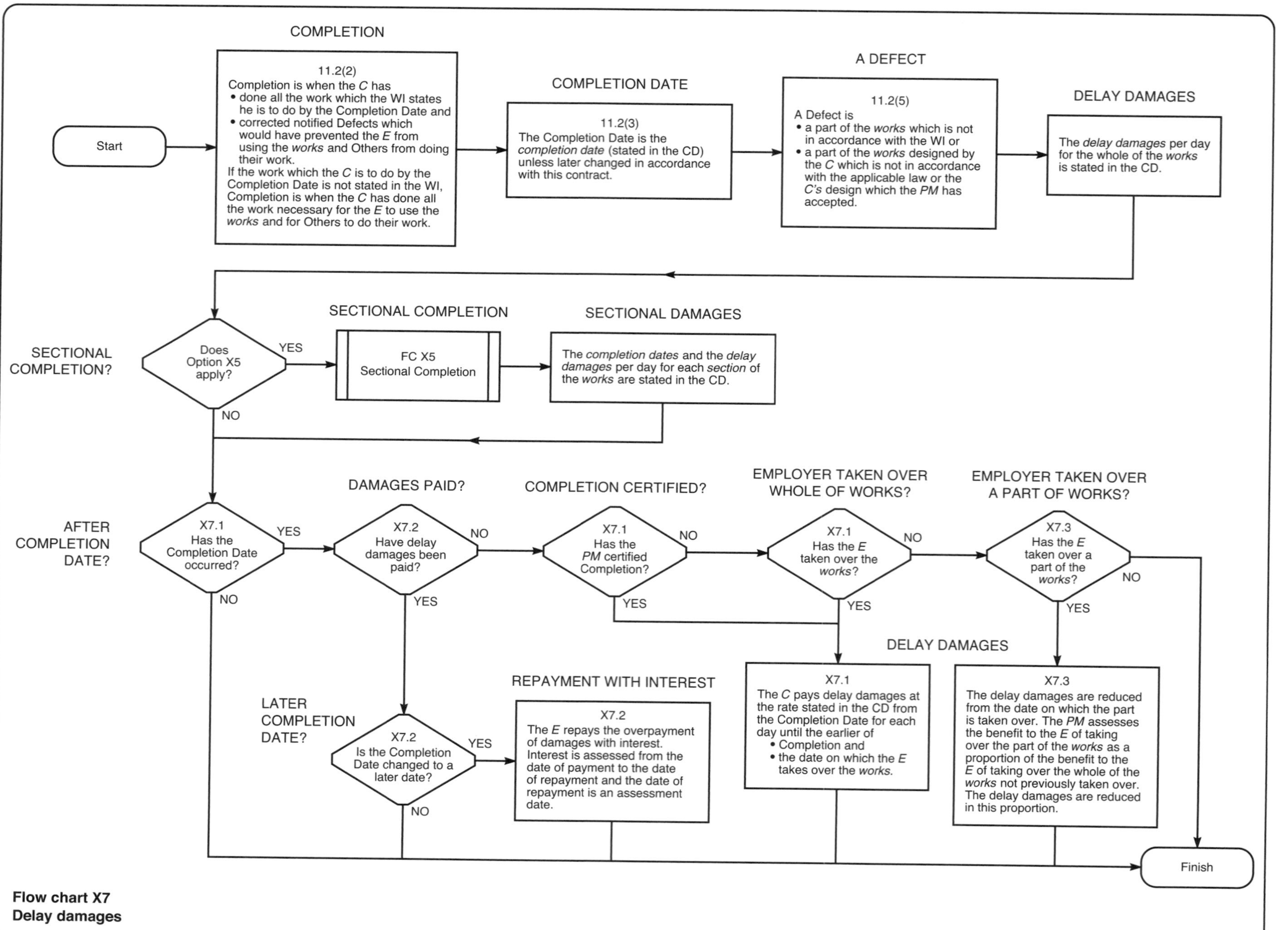
COMPLETION
Start
11.2(2)
Completion is when the C has
• done all the work which the WI states he is to do by the Completion Date and
• corrected notified Defects which would have prevented the E from using the works and Others from doing their work.
If the work which the C is to do by the Completion Date is not stated in the WI, Completion is when the C has done all the work necessary for the E to use the works and for Others to do their work.
COMPLETION DATE
11.2(3)
The Completion Date is the completion date (stated in the CD) unless later changed in accordance with this contract.
A DEFECT
11.2(5)
A Defect is
• a part of the works which is not in accordance with the WI or
• a part of the works designed by the C which is not in accordance with the applicable law or the C's design which the PM has accepted.
DELAY DAMAGES
The delay damages per day for the whole of the works is stated in the CD.
SECTIONAL COMPLETION?
Does Option X5 apply?
YES
NO
SECTIONAL COMPLETION
FC X5
Sectional Completion
SECTIONAL DAMAGES
The completion dates and the delay damages per day for each section of the works are stated in the CD.
AFTER COMPLETION DATE?
X7.1
Has the Completion Date occurred?
YES
NO
DAMAGES PAID?
X7.2
Have delay damages been paid?
NO
YES
COMPLETION CERTIFIED?
X7.1
Has the PM certified Completion?
NO
YES
EMPLOYER TAKEN OVER WHOLE OF WORKS?
X7.1
Has the E taken over the works?
NO
YES
EMPLOYER TAKEN OVER A PART OF WORKS?
X7.3
Has the E taken over a part of the works?
NO
YES
DELAY DAMAGES
LATER COMPLETION DATE?
X7.2
Is the Completion Date changed to a later date?
YES
NO
REPAYMENT WITH INTEREST
X7.2
The E repays the overpayment of damages with interest. Interest is assessed from the date of payment to the date of repayment and the date of repayment is an assessment date.
X7.1
The C pays delay damages at the rate stated in the CD from the Completion Date for each day until the earlier of
• Completion and
• the date on which the E takes over the works.
X7.3
The delay damages are reduced from the date on which the part is taken over. The PM assesses the benefit to the E of taking over the part of the works as a proportion of the benefit to the E of taking over the whole of the works not previously taken over. The delay damages are reduced in this proportion.
Finish

Flow chart X7
Delay damages

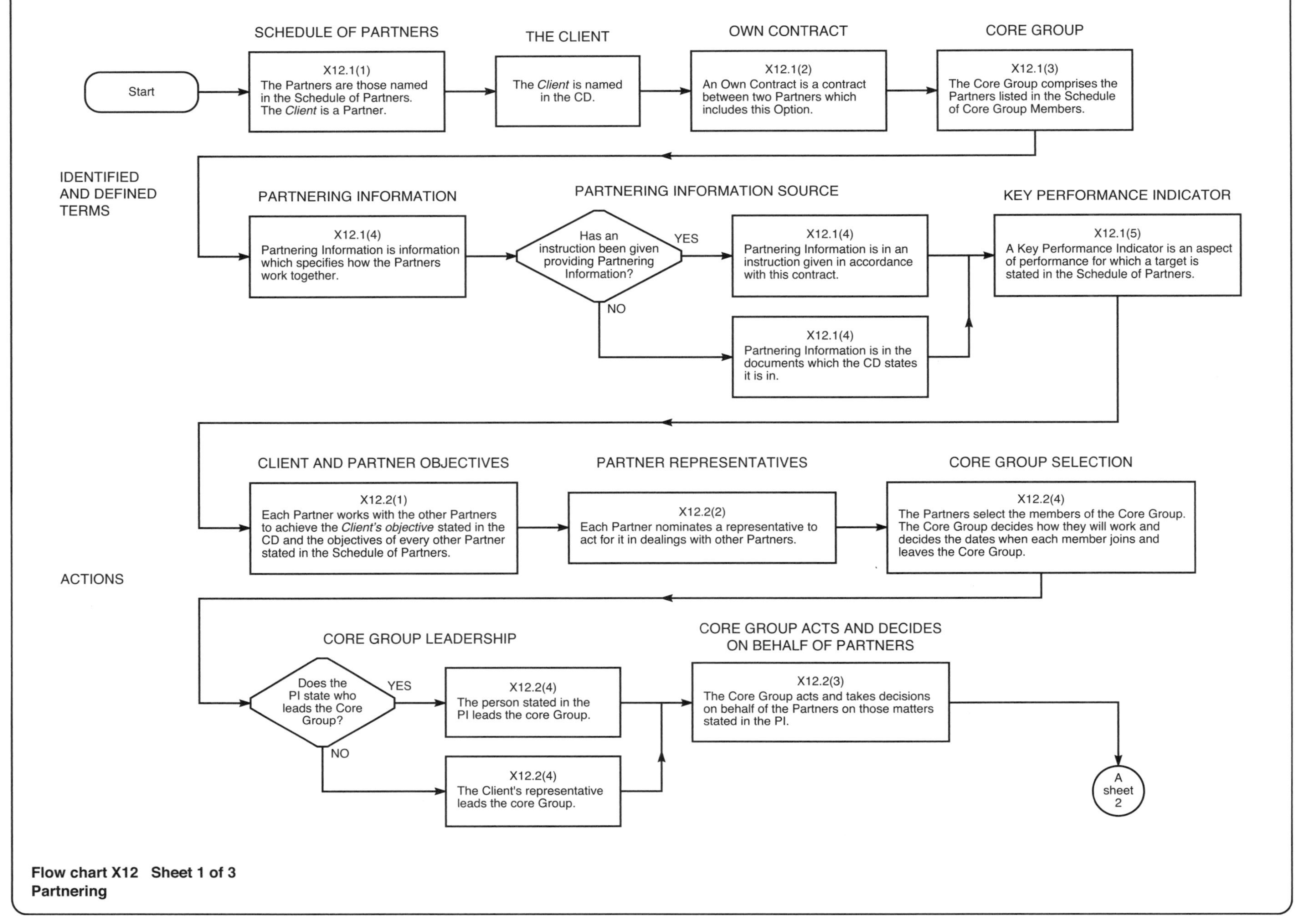
Start
SCHEDULE OF PARTNERS
X12.1(1)
The Partners are those named in the Schedule of Partners. The *Client* is a Partner.
THE CLIENT
The *Client* is named in the CD.
OWN CONTRACT
X12.1(2)
An Own Contract is a contract between two Partners which includes this Option.
CORE GROUP
X12.1(3)
The Core Group comprises the Partners listed in the Schedule of Core Group Members.
IDENTIFIED AND DEFINED TERMS
PARTNERING INFORMATION
X12.1(4)
Partnering Information is information which specifies how the Partners work together.
PARTNERING INFORMATION SOURCE
Has an instruction been given providing Partnering Information?
YES
NO
X12.1(4)
Partnering Information is in an instruction given in accordance with this contract.
X12.1(4)
Partnering Information is in the documents which the CD states it is in.
KEY PERFORMANCE INDICATOR
X12.1(5)
A Key Performance Indicator is an aspect of performance for which a target is stated in the Schedule of Partners.
ACTIONS
CLIENT AND PARTNER OBJECTIVES
X12.2(1)
Each Partner works with the other Partners to achieve the *Client's objective* stated in the CD and the objectives of every other Partner stated in the Schedule of Partners.
PARTNER REPRESENTATIVES
X12.2(2)
Each Partner nominates a representative to act for it in dealings with other Partners.
CORE GROUP SELECTION
X12.2(4)
The Partners select the members of the Core Group. The Core Group decides how they will work and decides the dates when each member joins and leaves the Core Group.
CORE GROUP LEADERSHIP
Does the PI state who leads the Core Group?
YES
NO
X12.2(4)
The person stated in the PI leads the core Group.
X12.2(4)
The Client's representative leads the core Group.
CORE GROUP ACTS AND DECIDES ON BEHALF OF PARTNERS
X12.2(3)
The Core Group acts and takes decisions on behalf of the Partners on those matters stated in the PI.
A sheet 2

Flow chart X12 Sheet 1 of 3
Partnering

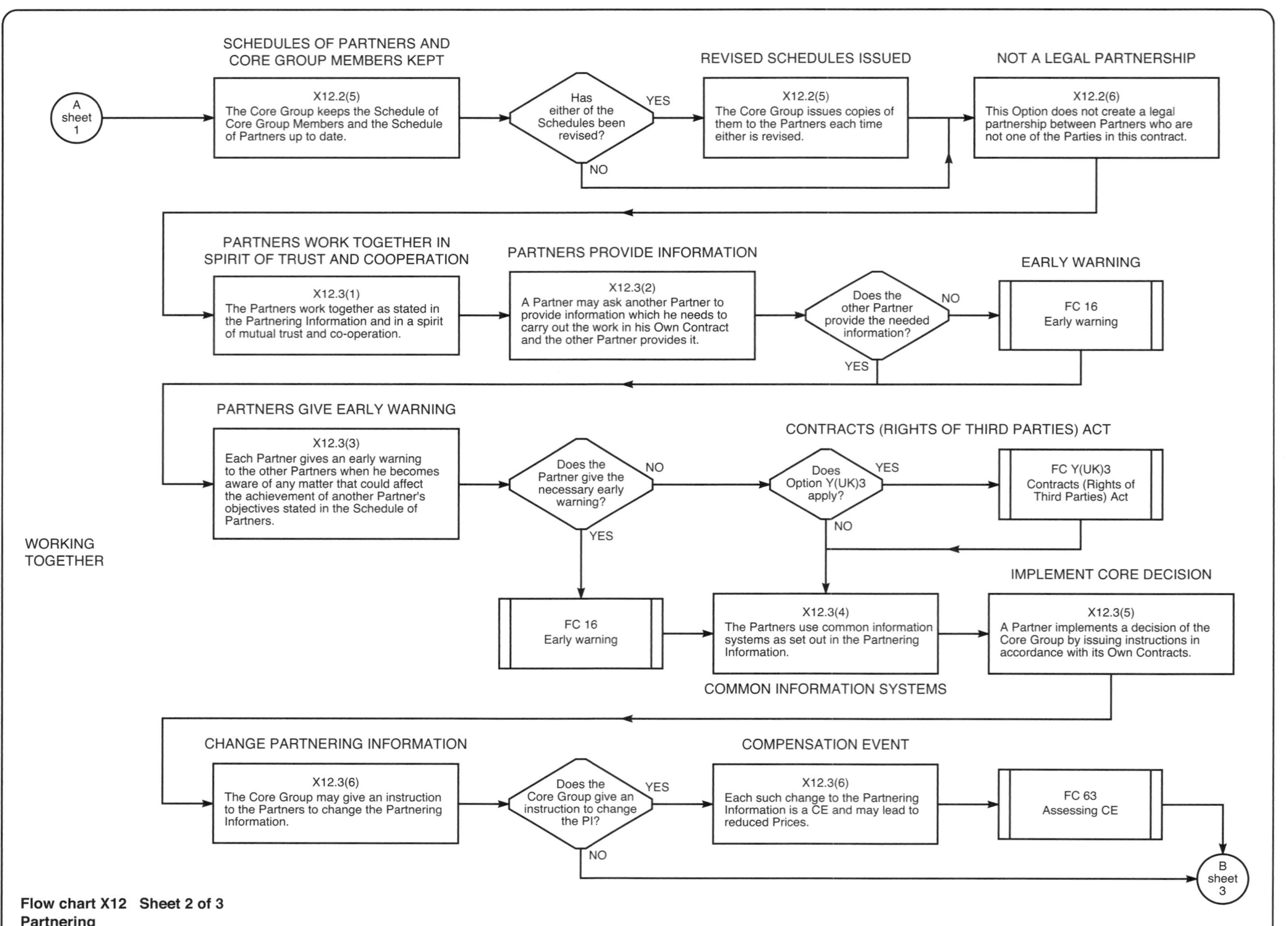

A sheet 1
SCHEDULES OF PARTNERS AND CORE GROUP MEMBERS KEPT
X12.2(5) The Core Group keeps the Schedule of Core Group Members and the Schedule of Partners up to date.
Has either of the Schedules been revised?
YES
NO
REVISED SCHEDULES ISSUED
X12.2(5) The Core Group issues copies of them to the Partners each time either is revised.
NOT A LEGAL PARTNERSHIP
X12.2(6) This Option does not create a legal partnership between Partners who are not one of the Parties in this contract.
PARTNERS WORK TOGETHER IN SPIRIT OF TRUST AND COOPERATION
X12.3(1) The Partners work together as stated in the Partnering Information and in a spirit of mutual trust and co-operation.
PARTNERS PROVIDE INFORMATION
X12.3(2) A Partner may ask another Partner to provide information which he needs to carry out the work in his Own Contract and the other Partner provides it.
Does the other Partner provide the needed information?
NO
YES
EARLY WARNING
FC 16 Early warning
PARTNERS GIVE EARLY WARNING
X12.3(3) Each Partner gives an early warning to the other Partners when he becomes aware of any matter that could affect the achievement of another Partner's objectives stated in the Schedule of Partners.
Does the Partner give the necessary early warning?
YES
NO
FC 16 Early warning
Does Option Y(UK)3 apply?
YES
NO
CONTRACTS (RIGHTS OF THIRD PARTIES) ACT
FC Y(UK)3 Contracts (Rights of Third Parties) Act
COMMON INFORMATION SYSTEMS
X12.3(4) The Partners use common information systems as set out in the Partnering Information.
IMPLEMENT CORE DECISION
X12.3(5) A Partner implements a decision of the Core Group by issuing instructions in accordance with its Own Contracts.
WORKING TOGETHER
CHANGE PARTNERING INFORMATION
X12.3(6) The Core Group may give an instruction to the Partners to change the Partnering Information.
Does the Core Group give an instruction to change the PI?
YES
NO
COMPENSATION EVENT
X12.3(6) Each such change to the Partnering Information is a CE and may lead to reduced Prices.
FC 63 Assessing CE
B sheet 3

Flow chart X12 Sheet 2 of 3
Partnering

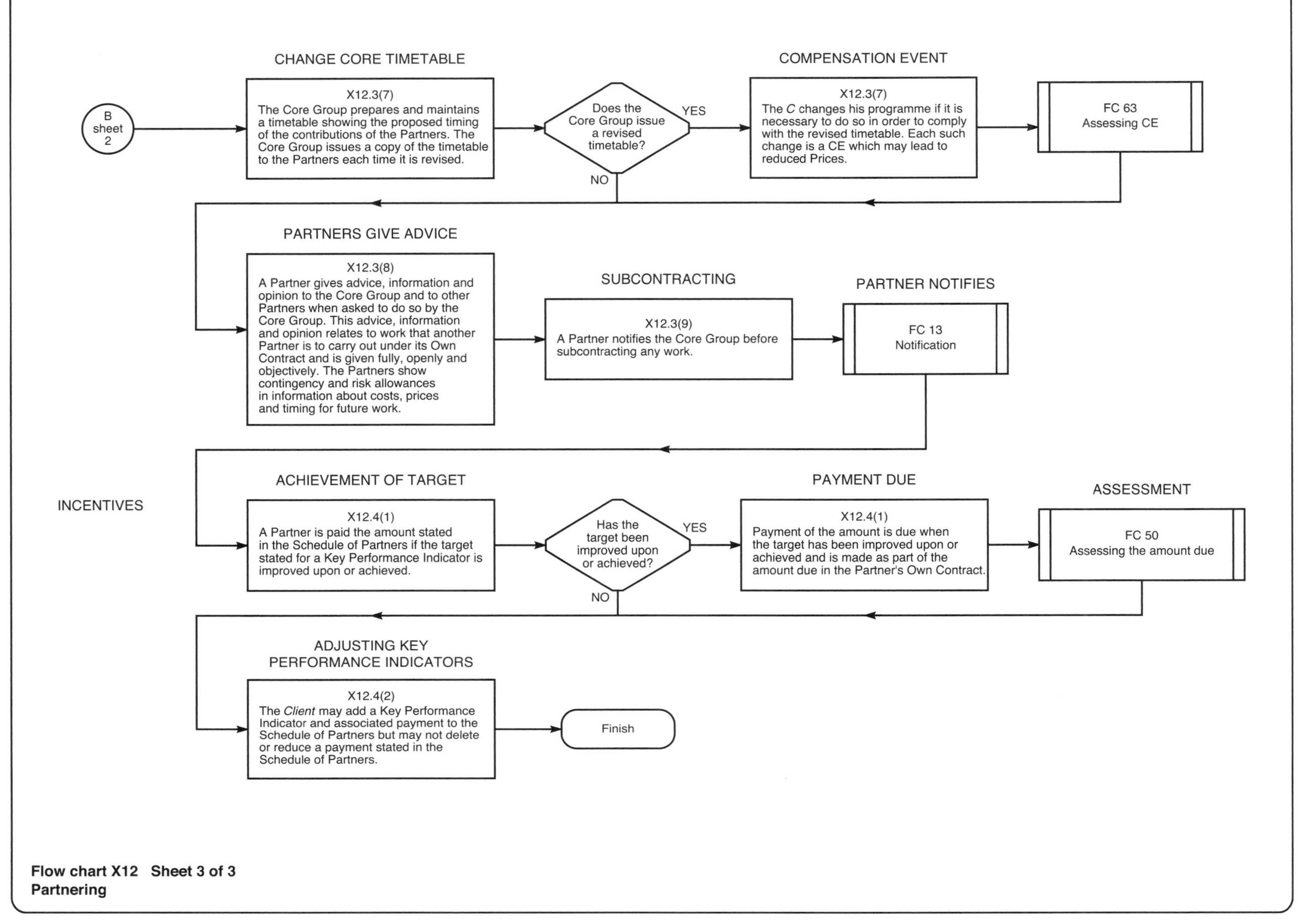
CHANGE CORE TIMETABLE
B sheet 2
X12.3(7)
The Core Group prepares and maintains a timetable showing the proposed timing of the contributions of the Partners. The Core Group issues a copy of the timetable to the Partners each time it is revised.
Does the Core Group issue a revised timetable?
YES
NO
COMPENSATION EVENT
X12.3(7)
The C changes his programme if it is necessary to do so in order to comply with the revised timetable. Each such change is a CE which may lead to reduced Prices.
FC 63
Assessing CE
PARTNERS GIVE ADVICE
X12.3(8)
A Partner gives advice, information and opinion to the Core Group and to other Partners when asked to do so by the Core Group. This advice, information and opinion relates to work that another Partner is to carry out under its Own Contract and is given fully, openly and objectively. The Partners show contingency and risk allowances in information about costs, prices and timing for future work.
SUBCONTRACTING
X12.3(9)
A Partner notifies the Core Group before subcontracting any work.
PARTNER NOTIFIES
FC 13
Notification
INCENTIVES
ACHIEVEMENT OF TARGET
X12.4(1)
A Partner is paid the amount stated in the Schedule of Partners if the target stated for a Key Performance Indicator is improved upon or achieved.
Has the target been improved upon or achieved?
YES
NO
PAYMENT DUE
X12.4(1)
Payment of the amount is due when the target has been improved upon or achieved and is made as part of the amount due in the Partner's Own Contract.
ASSESSMENT
FC 50
Assessing the amount due
ADJUSTING KEY PERFORMANCE INDICATORS
X12.4(2)
The Client may add a Key Performance Indicator and associated payment to the Schedule of Partners but may not delete or reduce a payment stated in the Schedule of Partners.
Finish

Flow chart X12 Sheet 3 of 3
Partnering

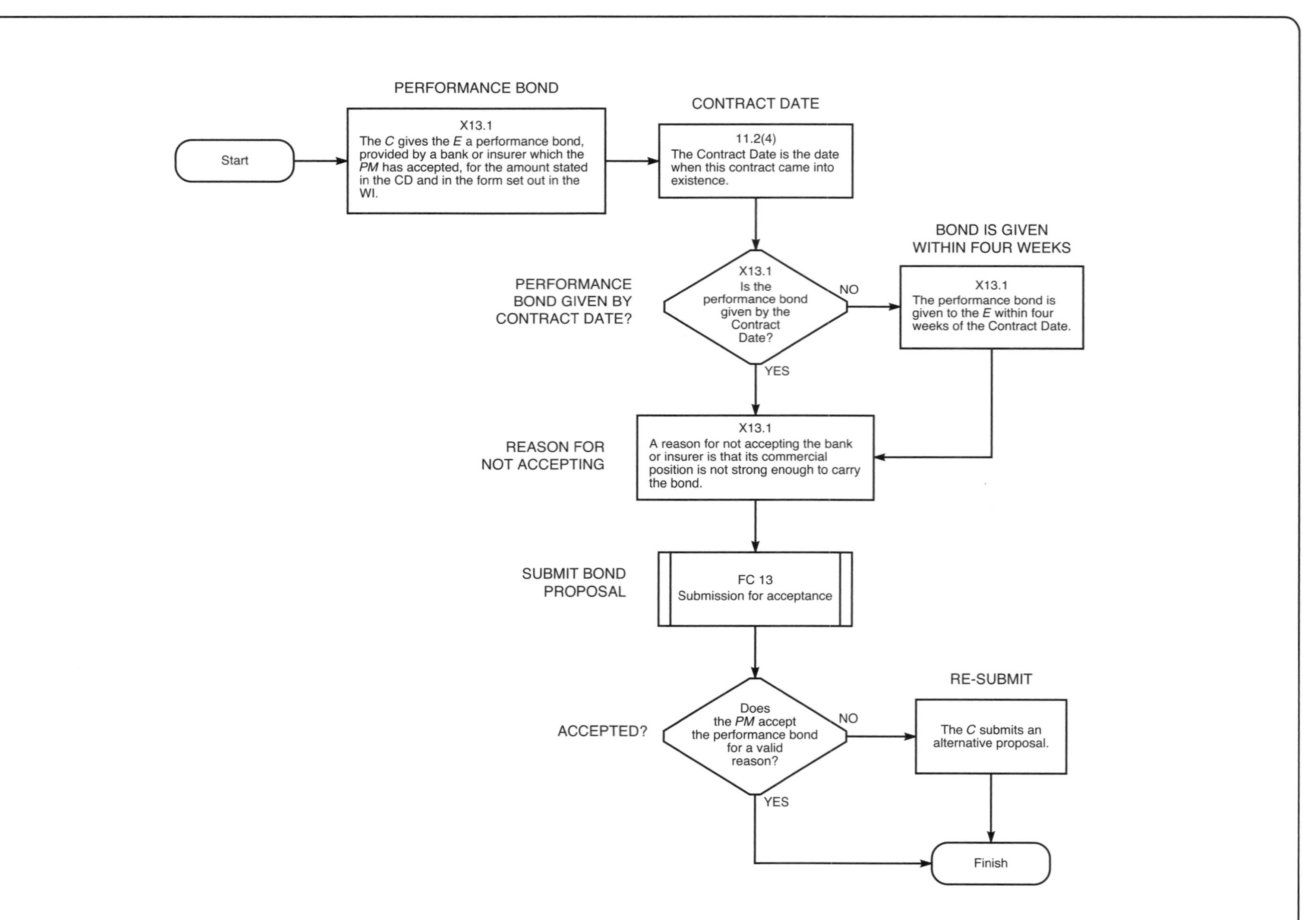
PERFORMANCE BOND
Start
X13.1
The C gives the E a performance bond, provided by a bank or insurer which the PM has accepted, for the amount stated in the CD and in the form set out in the WI.
CONTRACT DATE
11.2(4)
The Contract Date is the date when this contract came into existence.
PERFORMANCE BOND GIVEN BY CONTRACT DATE?
X13.1
Is the performance bond given by the Contract Date?
NO
YES
BOND IS GIVEN WITHIN FOUR WEEKS
X13.1
The performance bond is given to the E within four weeks of the Contract Date.
REASON FOR NOT ACCEPTING
X13.1
A reason for not accepting the bank or insurer is that its commercial position is not strong enough to carry the bond.
SUBMIT BOND PROPOSAL
FC 13
Submission for acceptance
ACCEPTED?
Does the PM accept the performance bond for a valid reason?
NO
YES
RE-SUBMIT
The C submits an alternative proposal.
Finish

Flow chart X13
Performance bond

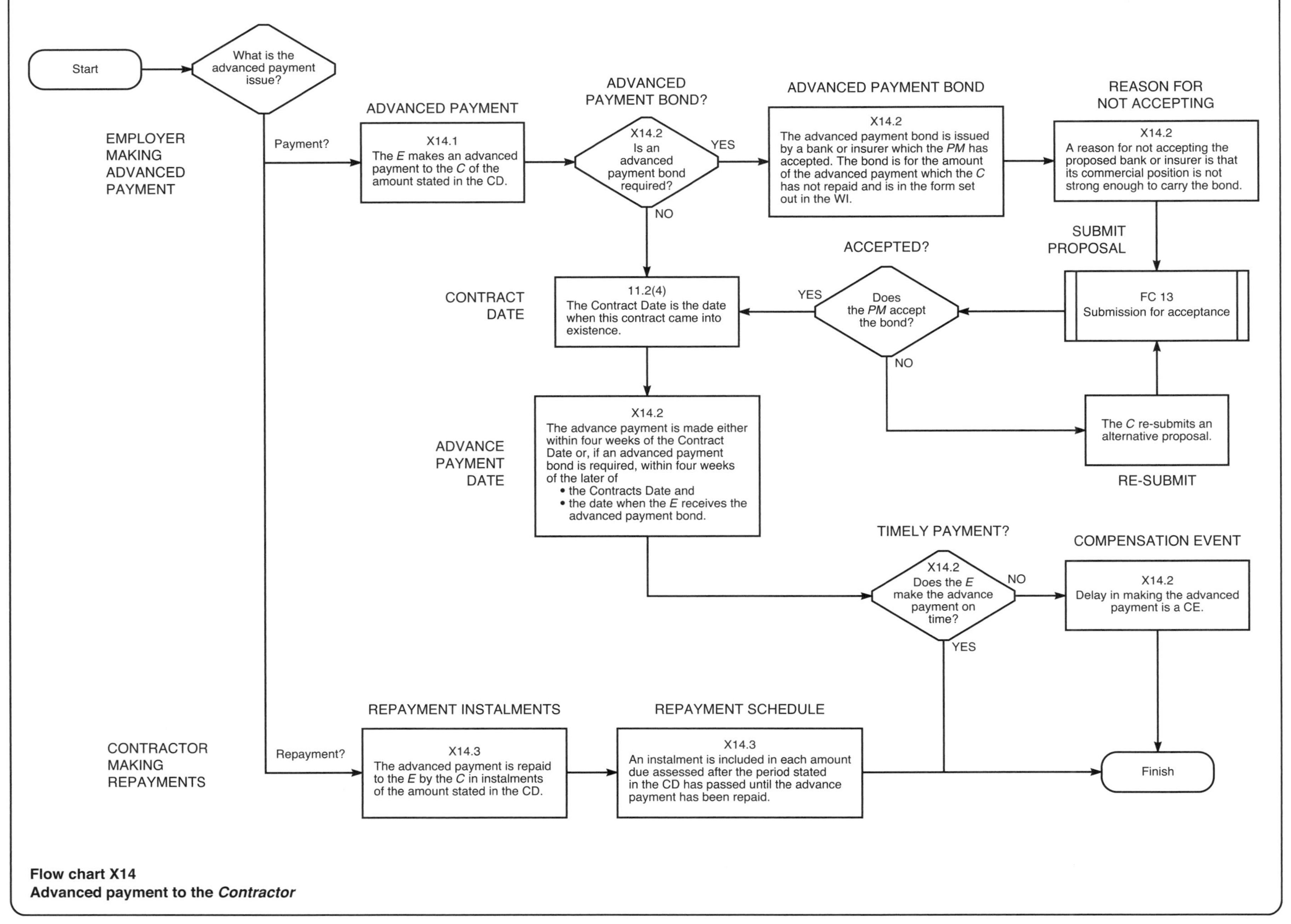
Start
What is the advanced payment issue?
EMPLOYER MAKING ADVANCED PAYMENT
Payment?
ADVANCED PAYMENT
X14.1
The E makes an advanced payment to the C of the amount stated in the CD.
ADVANCED PAYMENT BOND?
X14.2
Is an advanced payment bond required?
YES
NO
ADVANCED PAYMENT BOND
X14.2
The advanced payment bond is issued by a bank or insurer which the PM has accepted. The bond is for the amount of the advanced payment which the C has not repaid and is in the form set out in the WI.
REASON FOR NOT ACCEPTING
X14.2
A reason for not accepting the proposed bank or insurer is that its commercial position is not strong enough to carry the bond.
SUBMIT PROPOSAL
FC 13
Submission for acceptance
ACCEPTED?
Does the PM accept the bond?
YES
NO
The C re-submits an alternative proposal.
RE-SUBMIT
CONTRACT DATE
11.2(4)
The Contract Date is the date when this contract came into existence.
ADVANCE PAYMENT DATE
X14.2
The advance payment is made either within four weeks of the Contract Date or, if an advanced payment bond is required, within four weeks of the later of
• the Contracts Date and
• the date when the E receives the advanced payment bond.
TIMELY PAYMENT?
X14.2
Does the E make the advance payment on time?
NO
YES
COMPENSATION EVENT
X14.2
Delay in making the advanced payment is a CE.
Finish
CONTRACTOR MAKING REPAYMENTS
Repayment?
REPAYMENT INSTALMENTS
X14.3
The advanced payment is repaid to the E by the C in instalments of the amount stated in the CD.
REPAYMENT SCHEDULE
X14.3
An instalment is included in each amount due assessed after the period stated in the CD has passed until the advance payment has been repaid.

Flow chart X14
Advanced payment to the *Contractor*

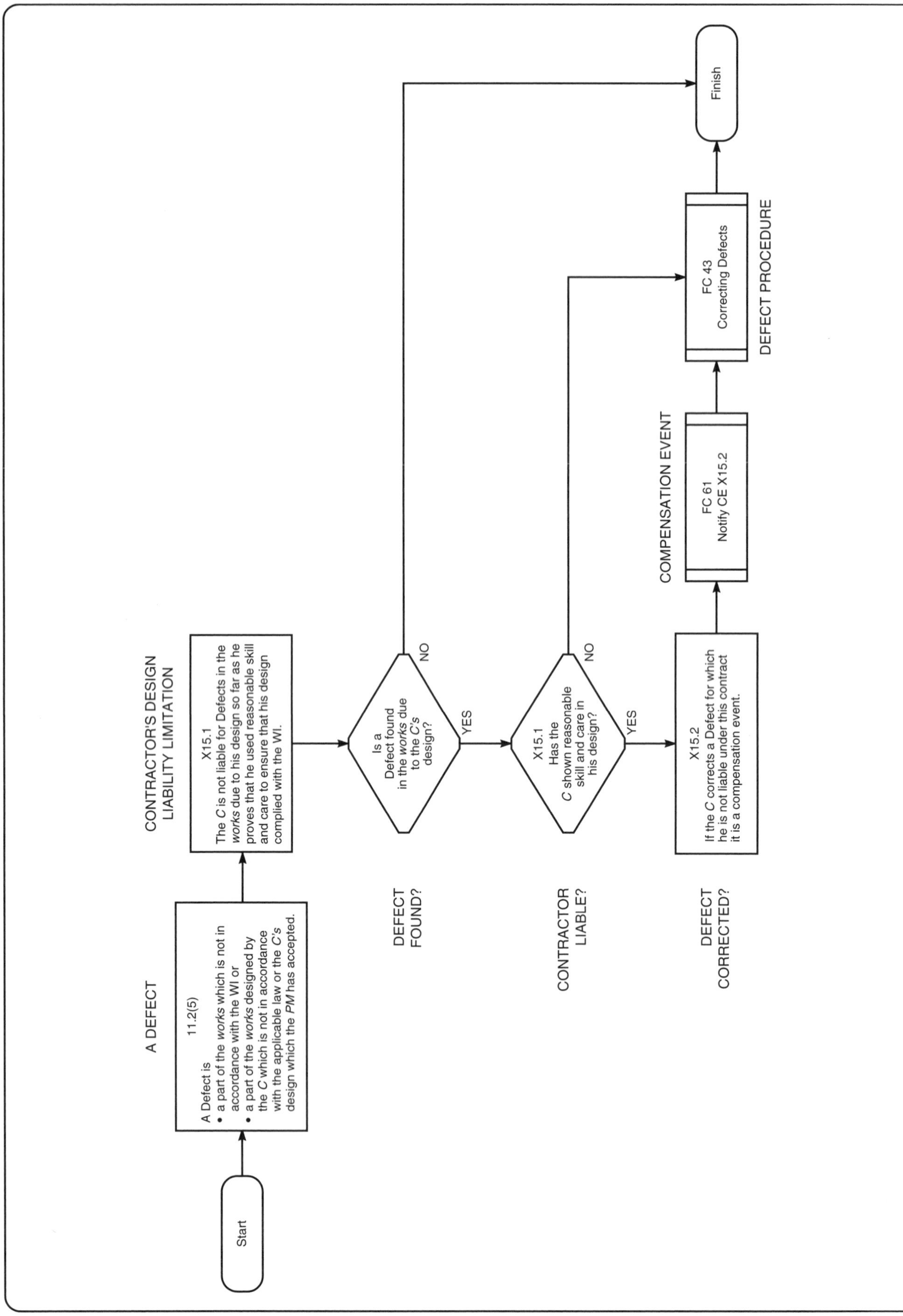

A DEFECT

Start

11.2(5)
A Defect is
- a part of the *works* which is not in accordance with the WI or
- a part of the *works* designed by the *C* which is not in accordance with the applicable law or the *C's* design which the *PM* has accepted.

CONTRACTOR'S DESIGN LIABILITY LIMITATION

X15.1
The *C* is not liable for Defects in the *works* due to his design so far as he proves that he used reasonable skill and care to ensure that his design complied with the WI.

DEFECT FOUND?

Is a Defect found in the *works* due to the *C's* design?

NO → Finish

YES

CONTRACTOR LIABLE?

X15.1
Has the *C* shown reasonable skill and care in his design?

NO → FC 43 Correcting Defects

YES

DEFECT CORRECTED?

X15.2
If the *C* corrects a Defect for which he is not liable under this contract it is a compensation event.

COMPENSATION EVENT

FC 61
Notify CE X15.2

FC 43
Correcting Defects

DEFECT PROCEDURE

Finish

Flow chart X15
Limitation of the *Contractor*'s liability for his design to reasonable skill and care

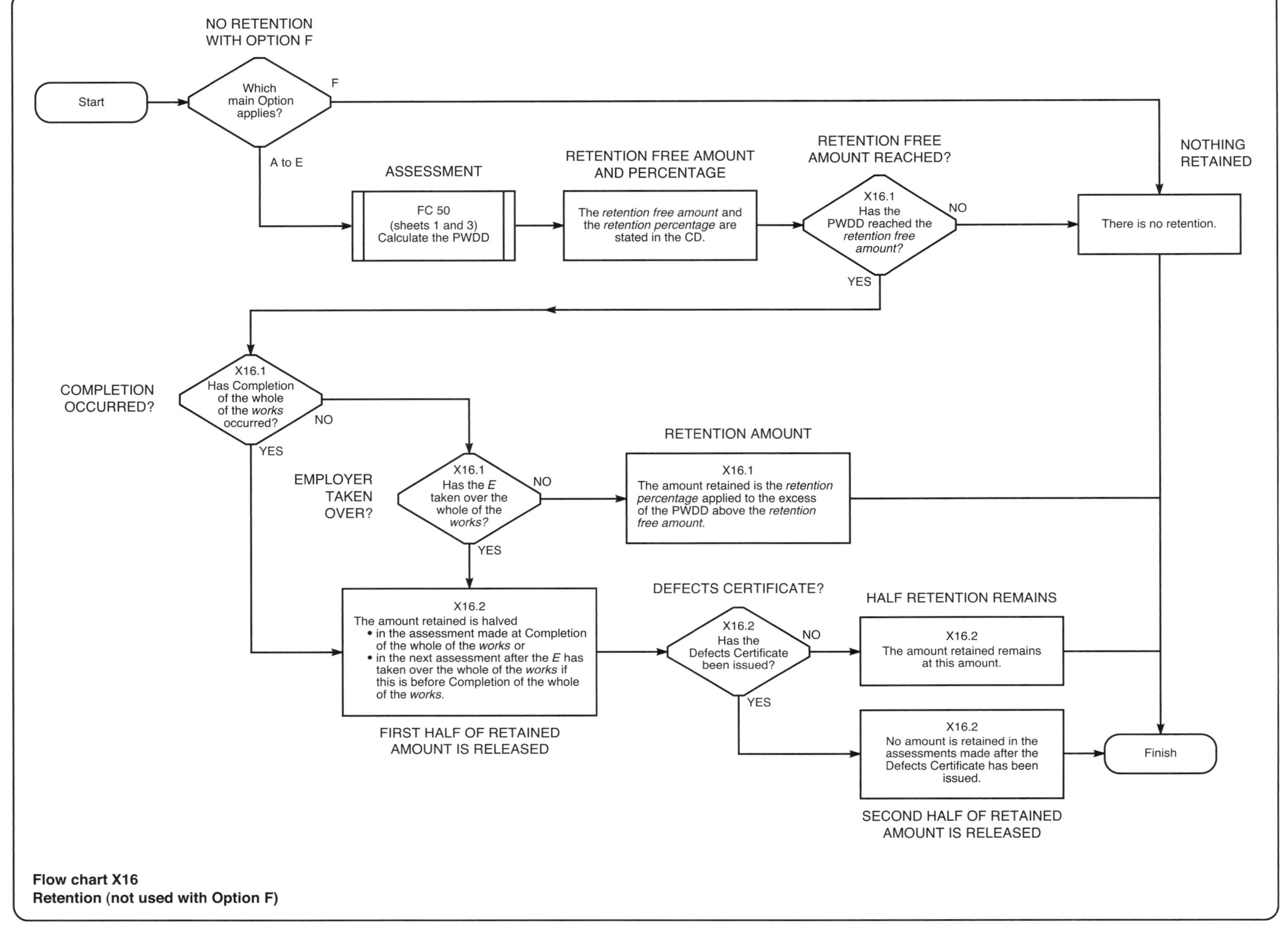
Start
NO RETENTION WITH OPTION F
Which main Option applies?
F
A to E
ASSESSMENT
FC 50 (sheets 1 and 3) Calculate the PWDD
RETENTION FREE AMOUNT AND PERCENTAGE
The *retention free amount* and the *retention percentage* are stated in the CD.
RETENTION FREE AMOUNT REACHED?
X16.1 Has the PWDD reached the *retention free amount?*
NO
YES
NOTHING RETAINED
There is no retention.
COMPLETION OCCURRED?
X16.1 Has Completion of the whole of the *works* occurred?
NO
YES
EMPLOYER TAKEN OVER?
X16.1 Has the *E* taken over the whole of the *works?*
NO
YES
RETENTION AMOUNT
X16.1 The amount retained is the *retention percentage* applied to the excess of the PWDD above the *retention free amount.*
X16.2 The amount retained is halved
• in the assessment made at Completion of the whole of the *works* or
• in the next assessment after the *E* has taken over the whole of the *works* if this is before Completion of the whole of the *works.*
FIRST HALF OF RETAINED AMOUNT IS RELEASED
DEFECTS CERTIFICATE?
X16.2 Has the Defects Certificate been issued?
NO
YES
HALF RETENTION REMAINS
X16.2 The amount retained remains at this amount.
X16.2 No amount is retained in the assessments made after the Defects Certificate has been issued.
SECOND HALF OF RETAINED AMOUNT IS RELEASED
Finish

Flow chart X16
Retention (not used with Option F)

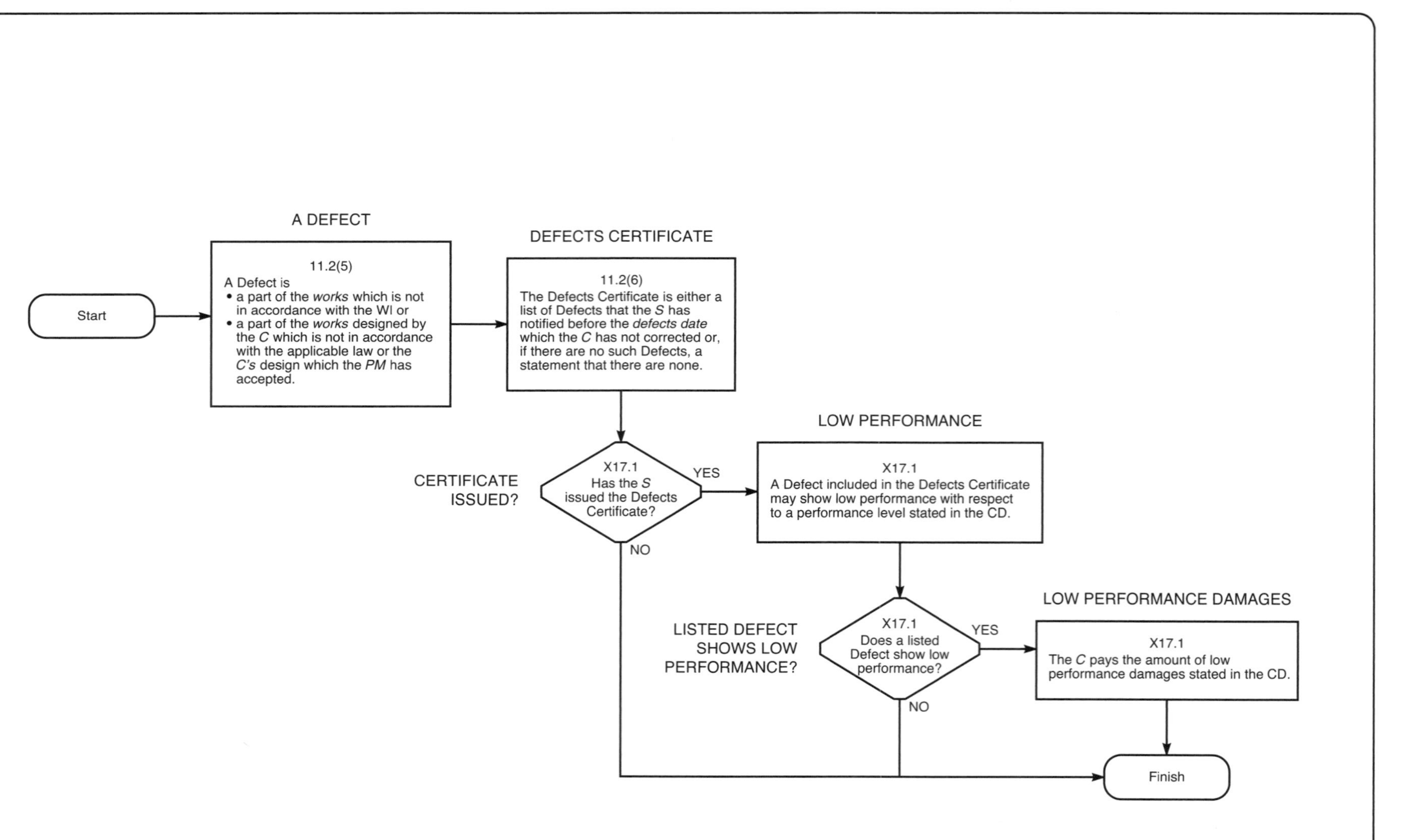
Start
A DEFECT
11.2(5)
A Defect is
• a part of the works which is not in accordance with the WI or
• a part of the works designed by the C which is not in accordance with the applicable law or the C's design which the PM has accepted.
DEFECTS CERTIFICATE
11.2(6)
The Defects Certificate is either a list of Defects that the S has notified before the defects date which the C has not corrected or, if there are no such Defects, a statement that there are none.
CERTIFICATE ISSUED?
X17.1
Has the S issued the Defects Certificate?
YES
NO
LOW PERFORMANCE
X17.1
A Defect included in the Defects Certificate may show low performance with respect to a performance level stated in the CD.
LISTED DEFECT SHOWS LOW PERFORMANCE?
X17.1
Does a listed Defect show low performance?
YES
NO
LOW PERFORMANCE DAMAGES
X17.1
The C pays the amount of low performance damages stated in the CD.
Finish

Flow chart X17
Low performance damages

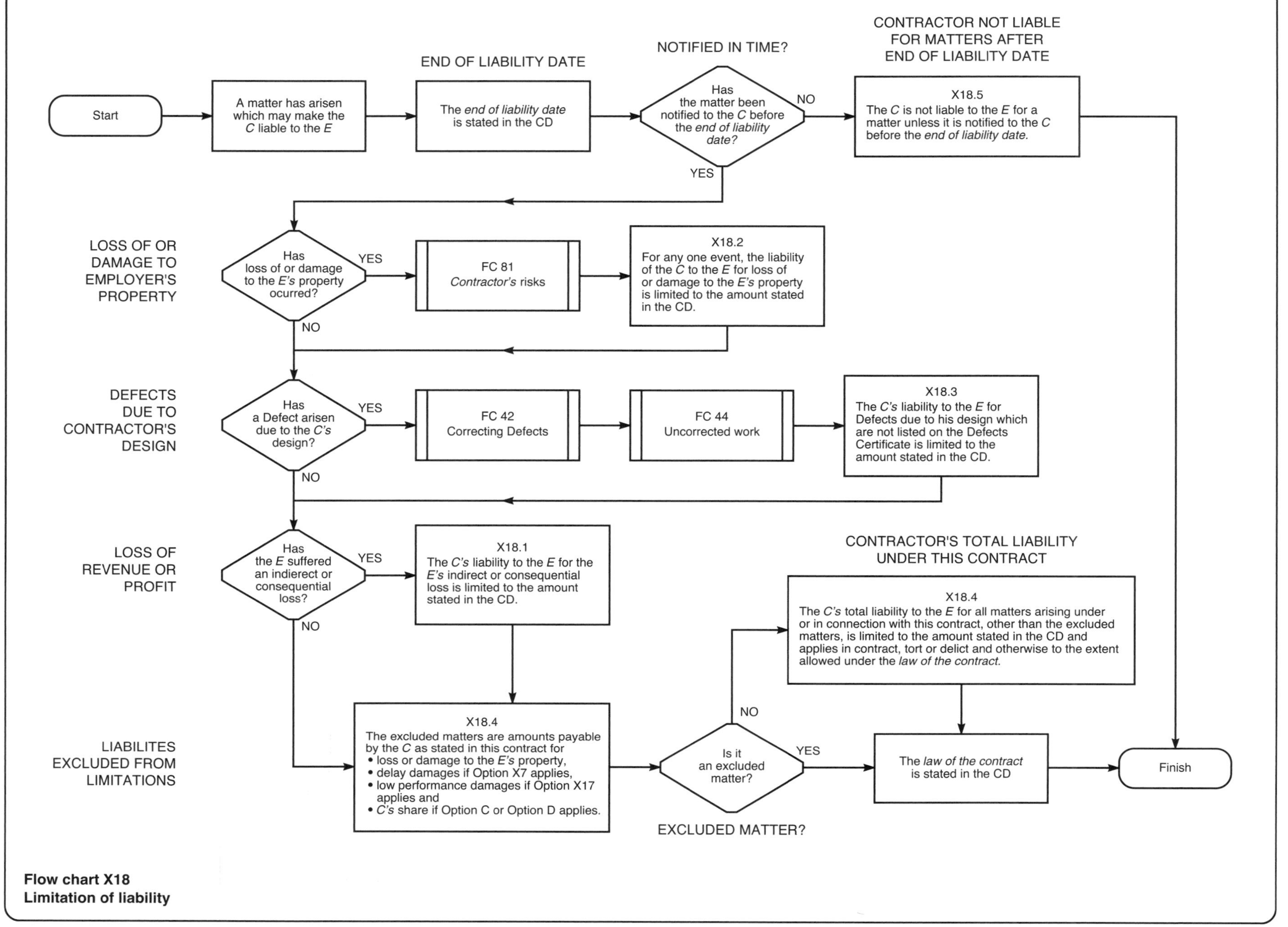
Start
A matter has arisen which may make the C liable to the E
END OF LIABILITY DATE
The end of liability date is stated in the CD
NOTIFIED IN TIME?
Has the matter been notified to the C before the end of liability date?
NO
YES
CONTRACTOR NOT LIABLE FOR MATTERS AFTER END OF LIABILITY DATE
X18.5 The C is not liable to the E for a matter unless it is notified to the C before the end of liability date.
LOSS OF OR DAMAGE TO EMPLOYER'S PROPERTY
Has loss of or damage to the E's property ocurred?
YES
NO
FC 81 Contractor's risks
X18.2 For any one event, the liability of the C to the E for loss of or damage to the E's property is limited to the amount stated in the CD.
DEFECTS DUE TO CONTRACTOR'S DESIGN
Has a Defect arisen due to the C's design?
YES
NO
FC 42 Correcting Defects
FC 44 Uncorrected work
X18.3 The C's liability to the E for Defects due to his design which are not listed on the Defects Certificate is limited to the amount stated in the CD.
LOSS OF REVENUE OR PROFIT
Has the E suffered an indierect or consequential loss?
YES
NO
X18.1 The C's liability to the E for the E's indirect or consequential loss is limited to the amount stated in the CD.
CONTRACTOR'S TOTAL LIABILITY UNDER THIS CONTRACT
X18.4 The C's total liability to the E for all matters arising under or in connection with this contract, other than the excluded matters, is limited to the amount stated in the CD and applies in contract, tort or delict and otherwise to the extent allowed under the law of the contract.
LIABILITES EXCLUDED FROM LIMITATIONS
X18.4 The excluded matters are amounts payable by the C as stated in this contract for
• loss or damage to the E's property,
• delay damages if Option X7 applies,
• low performance damages if Option X17 applies and
• C's share if Option C or Option D applies.
Is it an excluded matter?
NO
YES
EXCLUDED MATTER?
The law of the contract is stated in the CD
Finish
Flow chart X18
Limitation of liability

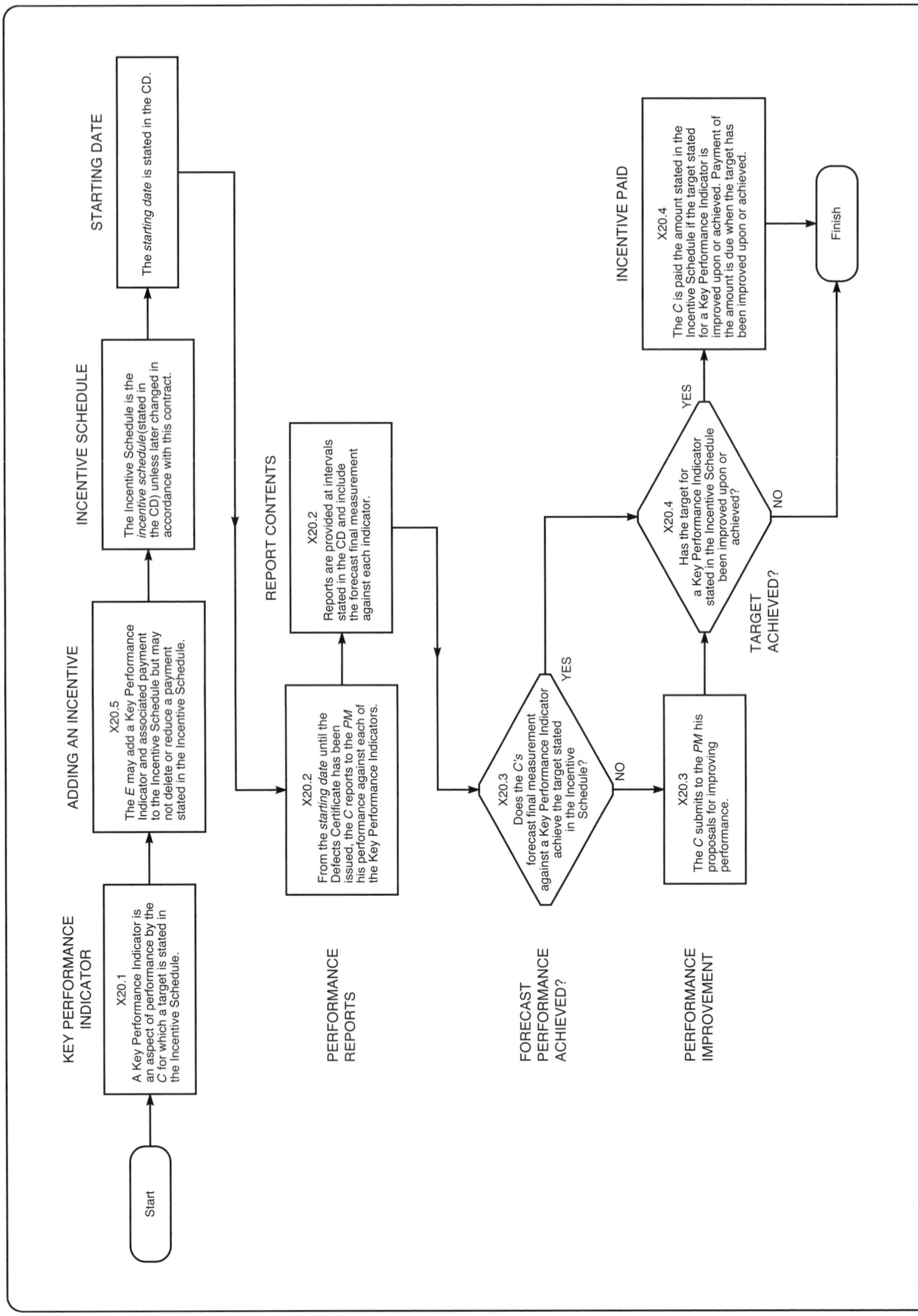

Start

KEY PERFORMANCE INDICATOR

X20.1
A Key Performance Indicator is an aspect of performance by the *C* for which a target is stated in the Incentive Schedule.

ADDING AN INCENTIVE

X20.5
The *E* may add a Key Performance Indicator and associated payment to the Incentive Schedule but may not delete or reduce a payment stated in the Incentive Schedule.

INCENTIVE SCHEDULE

The Incentive Schedule is the *incentive schedule*(stated in the CD) unless later changed in accordance with this contract.

STARTING DATE

The *starting date* is stated in the CD.

PERFORMANCE REPORTS

X20.2
From the *starting date* until the Defects Certificate has been issued, the *C* reports to the *PM* his performance against each of the Key Performance Indicators.

REPORT CONTENTS

X20.2
Reports are provided at intervals stated in the CD and include the forecast final measurement against each indicator.

FORECAST PERFORMANCE ACHIEVED?

X20.3
Does the *C's* forecast final measurement against a Key Performance Indicator achieve the target stated in the Incentive Schedule?

YES

NO

PERFORMANCE IMPROVEMENT

X20.3
The *C* submits to the *PM* his proposals for improving performance.

TARGET ACHIEVED?

X20.4
Has the target for a Key Performance Indicator stated in the Incentive Schedule been improved upon or achieved?

YES

NO

INCENTIVE PAID

X20.4
The *C* is paid the amount stated in the Incentive Schedule if the target stated for a Key Performance Indicator is improved upon or achieved. Payment of the amount is due when the target has been improved upon or achieved.

Finish

Flow chart X20
Key Performance Indicators (not used with Option X12)

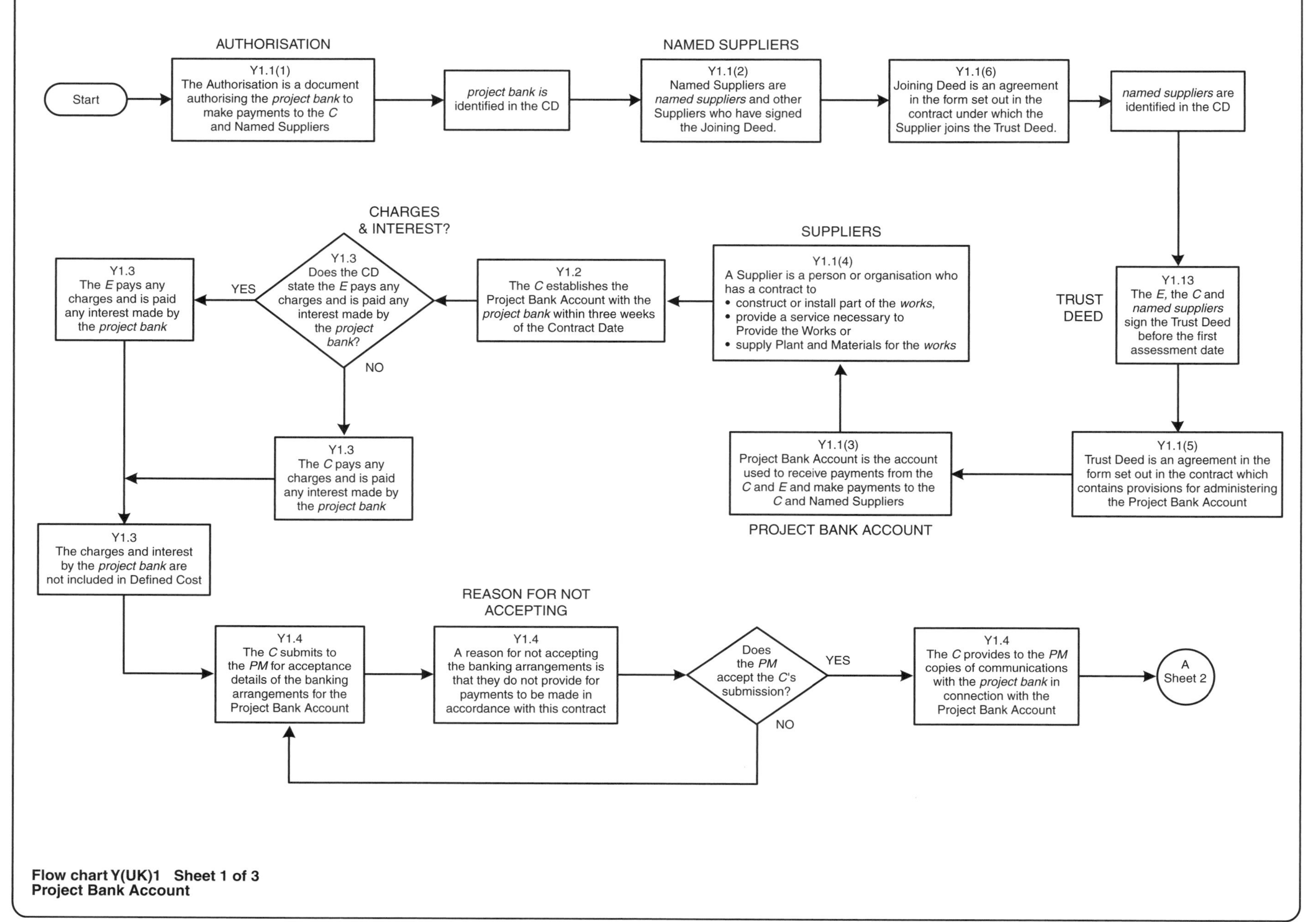
AUTHORISATION
Start
Y1.1(1)
The Authorisation is a document authorising the *project bank* to make payments to the *C* and Named Suppliers
project bank is identified in the CD
NAMED SUPPLIERS
Y1.1(2)
Named Suppliers are *named suppliers* and other Suppliers who have signed the Joining Deed.
Y1.1(6)
Joining Deed is an agreement in the form set out in the contract under which the Supplier joins the Trust Deed.
named suppliers are identified in the CD
CHARGES & INTEREST?
Y1.3
The *E* pays any charges and is paid any interest made by the *project bank*
YES
Y1.3
Does the CD state the *E* pays any charges and is paid any interest made by the *project bank*?
NO
Y1.2
The *C* establishes the Project Bank Account with the *project bank* within three weeks of the Contract Date
SUPPLIERS
Y1.1(4)
A Supplier is a person or organisation who has a contract to
• construct or install part of the *works*,
• provide a service necessary to Provide the Works or
• supply Plant and Materials for the *works*
TRUST DEED
Y1.13
The *E*, the *C* and *named suppliers* sign the Trust Deed before the first assessment date
Y1.3
The *C* pays any charges and is paid any interest made by the *project bank*
Y1.1(3)
Project Bank Account is the account used to receive payments from the *C* and *E* and make payments to the *C* and Named Suppliers
PROJECT BANK ACCOUNT
Y1.1(5)
Trust Deed is an agreement in the form set out in the contract which contains provisions for administering the Project Bank Account
Y1.3
The charges and interest by the *project bank* are not included in Defined Cost
REASON FOR NOT ACCEPTING
Y1.4
The *C* submits to the *PM* for acceptance details of the banking arrangements for the Project Bank Account
Y1.4
A reason for not accepting the banking arrangements is that they do not provide for payments to be made in accordance with this contract
Does the *PM* accept the *C*'s submission?
YES
NO
Y1.4
The *C* provides to the *PM* copies of communications with the *project bank* in connection with the Project Bank Account
A Sheet 2
Flow chart Y(UK)1 Sheet 1 of 3
Project Bank Account

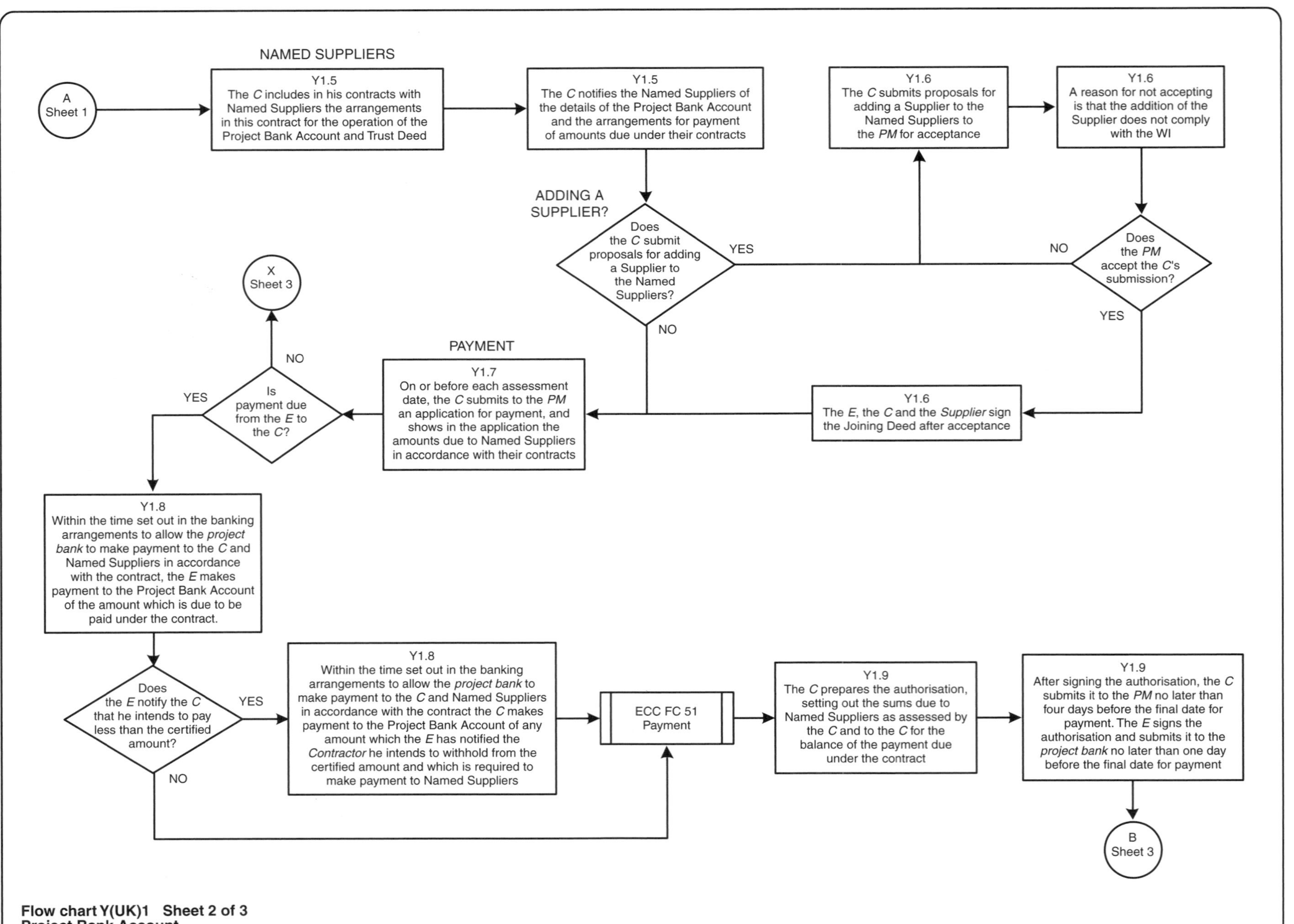
NAMED SUPPLIERS
A Sheet 1
Y1.5 The *C* includes in his contracts with Named Suppliers the arrangements in this contract for the operation of the Project Bank Account and Trust Deed
Y1.5 The *C* notifies the Named Suppliers of the details of the Project Bank Account and the arrangements for payment of amounts due under their contracts
ADDING A SUPPLIER?
Does the *C* submit proposals for adding a Supplier to the Named Suppliers?
YES
NO
Y1.6 The *C* submits proposals for adding a Supplier to the Named Suppliers to the *PM* for acceptance
Y1.6 A reason for not accepting is that the addition of the Supplier does not comply with the WI
Does the *PM* accept the *C*'s submission?
NO
YES
Y1.6 The *E*, the *C* and the *Supplier* sign the Joining Deed after acceptance
PAYMENT
Y1.7 On or before each assessment date, the *C* submits to the *PM* an application for payment, and shows in the application the amounts due to Named Suppliers in accordance with their contracts
Is payment due from the *E* to the *C*?
NO
X Sheet 3
YES
Y1.8 Within the time set out in the banking arrangements to allow the *project bank* to make payment to the *C* and Named Suppliers in accordance with the contract, the *E* makes payment to the Project Bank Account of the amount which is due to be paid under the contract.
Does the *E* notify the *C* that he intends to pay less than the certified amount?
YES
NO
Y1.8 Within the time set out in the banking arrangements to allow the *project bank* to make payment to the *C* and Named Suppliers in accordance with the contract the *C* makes payment to the Project Bank Account of any amount which the *E* has notified the *Contractor* he intends to withhold from the certified amount and which is required to make payment to Named Suppliers
ECC FC 51 Payment
Y1.9 The *C* prepares the authorisation, setting out the sums due to Named Suppliers as assessed by the *C* and to the *C* for the balance of the payment due under the contract
Y1.9 After signing the authorisation, the *C* submits it to the *PM* no later than four days before the final date for payment. The *E* signs the authorisation and submits it to the *project bank* no later than one day before the final date for payment
B Sheet 3

Flow chart Y(UK)1 Sheet 2 of 3
Project Bank Account

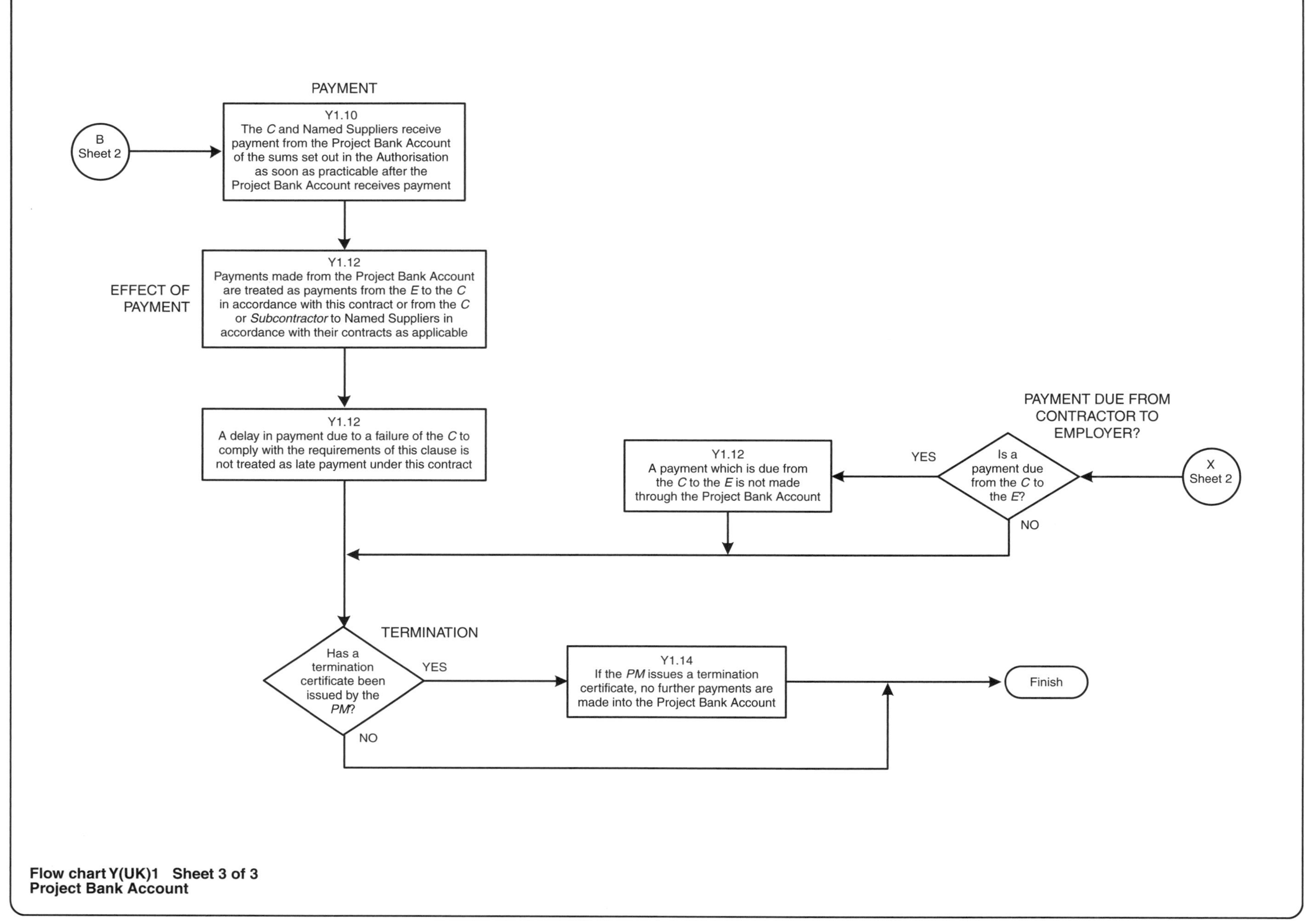
PAYMENT
B
Sheet 2
Y1.10
The *C* and Named Suppliers receive payment from the Project Bank Account of the sums set out in the Authorisation as soon as practicable after the Project Bank Account receives payment
EFFECT OF PAYMENT
Y1.12
Payments made from the Project Bank Account are treated as payments from the *E* to the *C* in accordance with this contract or from the *C* or *Subcontractor* to Named Suppliers in accordance with their contracts as applicable
Y1.12
A delay in payment due to a failure of the *C* to comply with the requirements of this clause is not treated as late payment under this contract
PAYMENT DUE FROM CONTRACTOR TO EMPLOYER?
X
Sheet 2
Is a payment due from the *C* to the *E*?
YES
NO
Y1.12
A payment which is due from the *C* to the *E* is not made through the Project Bank Account
TERMINATION
Has a termination certificate been issued by the *PM*?
YES
NO
Y1.14
If the *PM* issues a termination certificate, no further payments are made into the Project Bank Account
Finish
Flow chart Y(UK)1 Sheet 3 of 3
Project Bank Account

Flow chart Y(UK)2
The Housing Grants, Construction and Regeneration Act 1996

Start

DEFINITIONS

THE ACT

Y2.1(1)
The Act is the Housing Grants, Construction and Regeneration Act 1996 as amended by the Local Democracy, Economic Development and Construction Act 2009.

DAY TIME PERIOD

Y2.1(2)
A period of time stated in days is a period calculated in accordance with Section 116 of the Act.

DATES FOR PAYMENT

Y2.2
The date on which a payment becomes due is seven days after the assessment date. (The latest date for certification under clause 51.1)

DUE DATE FOR PAYMENT

FINAL DATE FOR PAYMENT

Y2.2
The final date for payment is fourteen days or a different period for payment if stated in the CD after the date on which payment becomes due. (The latest date for payment under clause 51.2)

PROJECT MANAGER'S CERTIFICATE

Y2.2
The *PM's* certificate is the notice of payment to the *Contractor* specifying the amount due at the payment due date (the notified sum) and stating the basis on which the amount was calculated.

NOTICE OF INTENTION TO PAY LESS

Y2.3
If either Party intends to pay less than the notified sum, he notifies the other Party not later than seven days (the prescribed period) before the final date for payment by stating the amount considered to be due and the basis on which that sum is calculated.

PAY LESS NOTICE

Y2.3
A Party does not withhold payment of an amount due under this contract unless he has notified his intention to pay less than the notified sum as required by this contract.

SUSPENSION OF PERFORMANCE

Y2.4
If the *C* excercises his right under the Act to suspend performance, it is a CE.

COMPENSATION EVENT

Finish

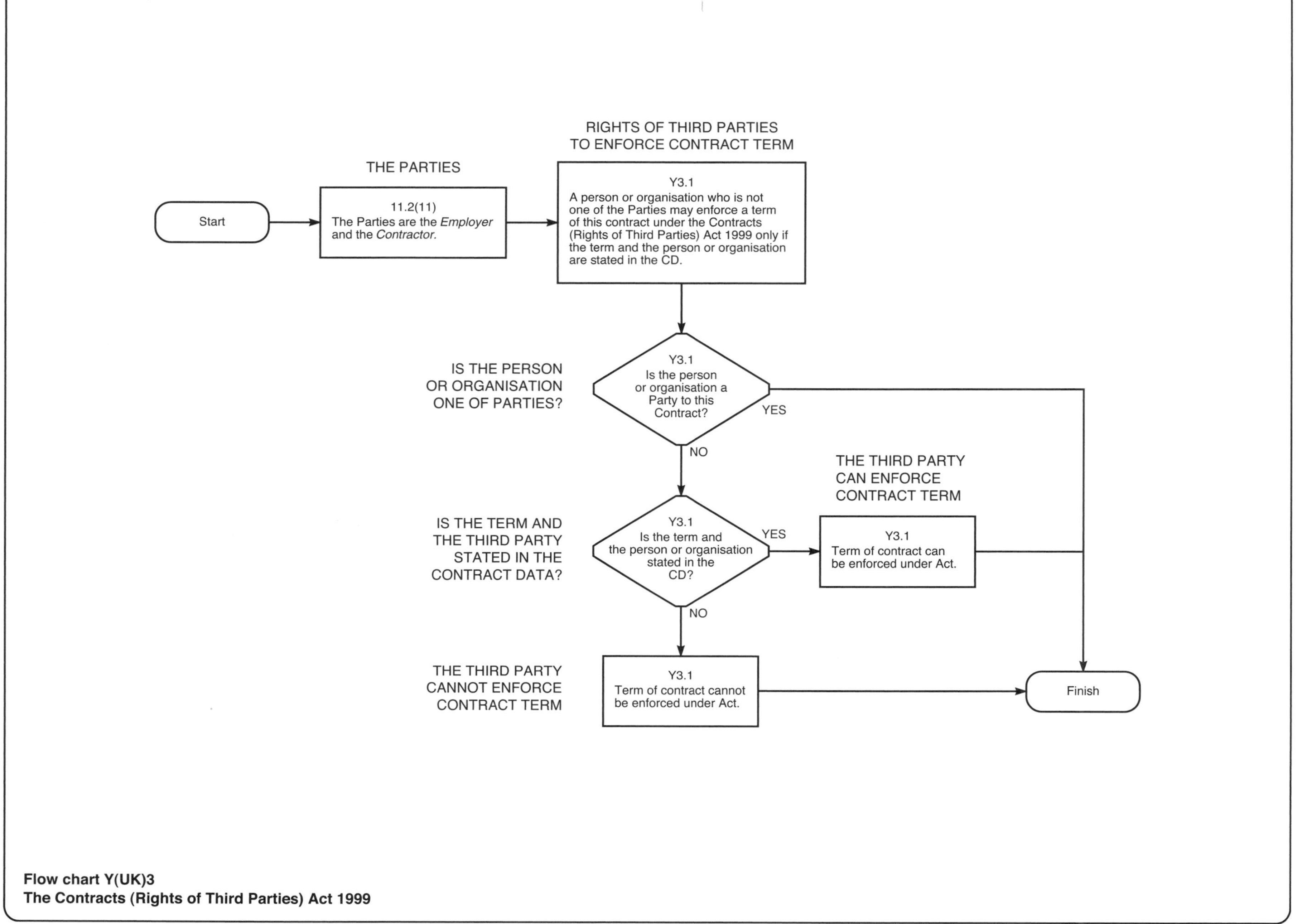
Start
THE PARTIES
11.2(11)
The Parties are the *Employer* and the *Contractor*.
RIGHTS OF THIRD PARTIES TO ENFORCE CONTRACT TERM
Y3.1
A person or organisation who is not one of the Parties may enforce a term of this contract under the Contracts (Rights of Third Parties) Act 1999 only if the term and the person or organisation are stated in the CD.
IS THE PERSON OR ORGANISATION ONE OF PARTIES?
Y3.1
Is the person or organisation a Party to this Contract?
YES
NO
IS THE TERM AND THE THIRD PARTY STATED IN THE CONTRACT DATA?
Y3.1
Is the term and the person or organisation stated in the CD?
YES
NO
THE THIRD PARTY CAN ENFORCE CONTRACT TERM
Y3.1
Term of contract can be enforced under Act.
THE THIRD PARTY CANNOT ENFORCE CONTRACT TERM
Y3.1
Term of contract cannot be enforced under Act.
Finish

Flow chart Y(UK)3
The Contracts (Rights of Third Parties) Act 1999